FOUNDATIONS OF THE THERMODYNAMIC THEORY OF GENERALIZED FIELDS

ESSAYS IN NATURAL PHILOSOPHY

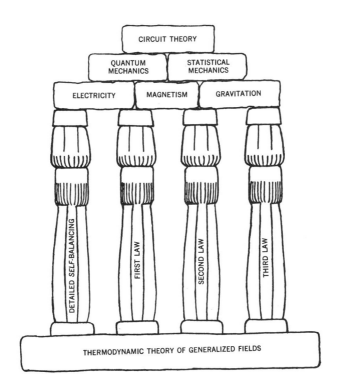

*We are to admit no more causes of natural things than such as are
both true and sufficient to explain their appearances.* To
this purpose the philosophers say that Nature does
nothing in vain, and more is in vain when less
will serve; for Nature is pleased with
simplicity, and affects not the
pomp of superfluous causes.

Isaac Newton
(1642–1727)

(COURTESY OF NIELS BOHR LIBRARY)

The only justification for our concepts and system of
concepts is that they serve to represent the
complex of our experiences; beyond this
they have no legitimacy . . . .

Albert Einstein
(1879–1955)

Foundations of the Thermodynamic Theory of Generalized Fields

Essays in Natural Philosophy

Mahmoud A. Melehy

The University of Connecticut

1973

Mono Book Corp. ⌒ *Baltimore*

Copyright © 1973 by Mahmoud A. Melehy

MONO BOOK CORP.
6747 Whitestone Road
Baltimore, Maryland 21207

Library of Congress Catalog Number 72-91417

PRINTED IN THE UNITED STATES OF AMERICA

To

Catharina, Omar, Hassan and Essam

and

to the memory of my parents

PREFACE

The nineteenth century has witnessed the evolution of one of the most important branches of natural philosophy: thermodynamics. By the end of that century, it was believed that this general macroscopic theory would lead to a unified understanding of nearly all properties of matter. This view is evidenced in the preface of the 1892 Henri Poincaré's book, "Thermodynamique." Specifically, Poincaré has stated:

"The role of the two laws of thermodynamics becomes from day to day more important in all branches of natural philosophy. Abandoning the ambitious theories of 40 years ago, which were cluttered up by molecular hypotheses, we attempt today to build the entire structure of mathematical physics on thermodynamics. Will the two principles of Mayer and Clausius provide a sufficiently solid foundation for some time to come? No one has any doubt about this; but what is the origin of this confidence?"

The twentieth century, however, has brought about some disappointment in these seemingly optimistic expectations. Indeed, the advent of the quantum theory, and the development of quantum statistical mechanics have given thermodynamics new capabilities to solve specific problems. Despite this needed revitalization, classical thermodynamics, with its simple but general principles, has fallen somewhat short of providing complete answers for a vast number of problems. Consequently, while the established general thermodynamic results have remained highly venerable, the scientific thought has inevitably been left with one choice: to proceed with hypothesizing the existence of mechanisms and models to explain most phenomena that are under investigation. In the meantime, the primary incentives for keeping thermodynamics a major area of fundamental research have almost completely disappeared. This situation is well described by Max Born in his 1949 book, "Natural Philosophy of Cause and Chance," which states:

"Therefore one can rightly say that with ordinary thermodynamics the descriptive method of physics has come to its natural end. Something new had to appear."

It is rather absurd that the confidence in thermodynamics, and its powers to provide theoretical unification, would change so drastically in only a few decades. Could it be that such conclusions had been arrived at too soon, and without exhaustive considerations? Some significant comments have been made by Laszlo Tisza on this matter at the Pittsburgh 1969 International Symposium on Thermodynamics. Specifically, Tisza has remarked on the same statements of Poincaré and Born, quoted above, by saying:

"It would be easy enough to smile at this relegation of the kinetic theory to limbo, and this description of thermodynamics as a venerable, but somewhat dusty museum piece. However, this is not the response I wish to evoke in you; not only because this would be unfair to the authorities quoted, who incidentally, had made fundamental contributions to the disciplines of their second choice, but mainly because I believe that we are badly in need of a more responsible and searching attitude for our own good. Could it not be that we still share some of the methodological prejudices that were at the root of the quoted forecasts? And, maybe in another sense, we merely shifted from one extreme to another, going off along another tangent? I submit that the answer to both questions is in the affirmative, and that a careful scrutiny of these problems is relevant to our contemporary concerns."

For many years, I have been reflecting on whether there could exist a general thermodynamic theory fundamentally different from the classical one. While searching for new premises relevant to such a theory, let it be called *theory X*, I have often asked myself the following questions:

(1) Can the mechanism of detailed balancing, which characterizes thermal equilibrium, be *more detailed* in reality than it has been postulated in classical thermodynamics? Prompting this question is that, in the Gibbsian framework, the balancing is detailed only on the basis of constituents, but not processes, or driving forces, such as diffusion and drift of electrons in any interface between two different metals, or semiconductors.

(2) If a new mechanism of thermal equilibrium underlies theory X, can this theory be so formulated as to rest on three additional pillars: the first, second and third law of thermodynamics, with *all four pillars being equally indispensable?*

(3) Can theory X lead to general theoretical unification which cannot be achieved through classical thermodynamics?

Searching for answers, to the three preceding questions, would be motivated by some crucial reasons. If there were a positive answer to the first question, then this would point concretely to the existence of a new thermodynamic theory, or framework, which should be explored. If the second question had a positive answer, it would then mean that a relatively complete formulation of theory X had become possible; with the three laws playing a role quite different from that in classical thermodynamics. For in the latter case—as historically evident from, for example, Poincaré's statements cited above—the formulation was completed well before the end of the nineteenth century; several decades before the third law was recognized by W. Nernst in 1912. Whereas in theory X, even the third law would be indispensable, and without it the theory would be significantly incomplete.

If, additionally, the third question were to be answered affirmatively, then, not only the hopes of the nineteenth century in thermodynamics would be rightly revived, but also a primary objective of all scientific foundations would be fulfilled. Such a success, if achieved, would have revolutionary philosophical implications relevant to the contemporary scientific thought.

For more than a decade, I have searched for, and carefully pondered, some answers for the three questions stated above. The interesting results, which have gradually emerged, constitute the primary reason for the existence of this book. Chapter 1 summarizes these results, together with other material presented in various chapters.

The new general thermodynamic theory has been applied in this volume to a number of problems which are of current interest in Physics and/or Electrical Engineering. The problems pertain to what is generally described as the electron transport theory. They have been chosen to fulfill three important objectives. First, to provide illustrative examples to help understand the general thermodynamic theory. Second, to provide means for checking theory directly by experiment. Third, to test whether the new thermodynamic theory is capable of generating new fundamental consequences.

Traditionally, the formulation and application of classical equilibrium and/or nonequilibrium thermodynamics have been taught in numerous academic disciplines. To make this book understandable to more readers, I have included some background material. It is only assumed that the reader is familiar with some advanced calculus, the simple laws of electric circuit theory and the elementary aspects of classical thermodynamics. Familiarity with vector calculus, electricity and magnetism, and quantum and statistical mechanics will be very helpful, but not essential; since all the needed results are introduced in Chapters 2, 3 and 5. Readers majoring in physics and electrical engineering ordinarily have this background. However, some parts of these chapters will provide helpful background for readers majoring in disciplines such as mechanical, chemical and metallurgical engineering, chemistry, and biophysics, who wish to develop a deep understanding of the new thermodynamic theory. Researchwise, it would be particularly interesting in such disciplines to solve problems involving, for example, interfacial transport phenomena by applying the new thermodynamic results; either in an original way, or in a manner analogous to those solutions of problems treated already in this volume.

Rarely one writes a research-oriented book which is also pedagogical. It so happens that the material presented in this book lies in this category. I have, therefore, added a number of problems in nearly every chapter. Some of these problems are relatively simple; others are not so, and could well have been incorporated as part of the text. To make the book suitable for self-teaching, answers are given in many cases.

Since 1963, I have presented—in steadily increasing amounts—the core material of this book to graduate students majoring in electrical engineering, and sometimes in physics, at the University of Connecticut. The content of Chapters 6 and 7 has been taught since 1967. Recently, the material presented in Chapters 4, and subsequent chapters has occupied the major part of two graduate courses I have taught on the transport theory.

Some basic results presented in Chapter 4, and all of the material of Chapters 6 and 7 have been published in scattered articles during a period approaching a decade. Chapters 8, 9, 10, and Appendix A, however, have never before been published; although, in the period March–May, 1971, I discussed their content together with other basic material of this book in six campus-wide lectures, which were attended occasionally by outside guests. During these lectures, a number of stimulating questions were asked by many persons, of whom I would particularly like to mention: Professor O. F. Devereux (Metallurgy), Professor F. E. Steigert (Physics), and Professor J. H. Tripp (Physics) of the University of Connecticut; and Dr. Gary Derbenwick of the Bell Telephone Laboratories.

The relief from teaching duties by an invitation to spend a sabbatic leave in 1970 in the Division of Engineering and Applied Physics, Harvard University, provided the stimulus and the opportunity for me to concentrate deeply on my theoretical research work. At Harvard, I wrote the first version of Chapter 8, considered the ideas now discussed in Chapter 10, and gave serious thought in planning the contents of this book. I had further the opportunity for valuable discussions with Professor William Paul, and Professor N. F. Ramsey, of Harvard University; and Professor Laszlo Tisza of the Massachusetts Institute of Technology.

I am greatly indebted to a number of my present and former graduate students. In particular, I would like to thank Faquir C. Jain and Gobind H. Atmaram for checking tirelessly the whole manuscript in its various stages; and Dr. William R. Smith, III and Clement V. Valerio, Jr., for their careful reading of the proofs.

Mahmoud A. Melehy
Scotland, Connecticut

September 9, 1971

CONTENTS

Chapter 4

FOUNDATION OF THE THEORY OF GENERALIZED FIELDS IN RELATION TO CLASSICAL THERMODYNAMICS

Chapter 5

CLASSICAL AND DEGENERATE GASES
Electrons and Holes in Semiconductors and Electrons in Metals

Chapter 6

REAL-SPACE FORMULATION OF THE THERMODYNAMIC THEORY OF GENERALIZED FIELDS

Chapter 7

UNIFIED THEORY OF ELECTRICAL CONDUCTION IN p-n JUNCTIONS, HETEROJUNCTIONS AND SCHOTTKY DIODES

Chapter 8

CONSERVATION OF TRANSPORT ENERGY IN THE TEMPERATURE-POSITION HYPERSPACE

Chapter 9

HYPERSPACE EQUATION AND ITS FUNDAMENTAL SOLUTIONS APPLIED TO THE SEEBECK AND PELTIER EFFECTS

Chapter 10

SUPERCONDUCTIVITY AND SUPERFLUIDITY AND THE TEMPERATURE-POSITION HYPERSPACE

PARTIAL LIST OF SYMBOLS

The list to follow contains definitions of symbols which have been used in more than one section, or subsection. Whenever possible, standard symbols have been used.

A	cross-sectional area of a junction diode (Chapter 7 only)
$\mathbf{a}$	a unit vector
$\mathbf{a}_r, \mathbf{a}_\theta, \mathbf{a}_\phi$	unit vectors in the spherical coordinate system
$\mathbf{a}_\rho, \mathbf{a}_\phi, \mathbf{k}$	unit vectors in the cylindrical coordinate system
B	Bose–Einstein distribution function
$\mathbf{B}$	magnetic flux density
c	specific heat per unit volume
$\mathbf{D}$	electric flux density
$\mathbf{D}_g$	gravitational flux density
D_n, D_p	diffusion constants for electrons, and for holes, respectively
dl	infinitesimal increment of length
dQ	increment of heat added reversibly to a system
$d\mathbf{s}$	differential surface area. Direction of this vector is perpendicular to the area
dv	differential volume
$\mathbf{E}$	electric field intensity with the active and passive properties unspecified
$\mathbf{E}_g$	gravitational field intensity
e	instantaneous value of electric voltage
F	Fermi–Dirac distribution function
$\mathbf{f}_d\dagger$	diffusion (force) field (per particle) with the active or passive property unspecified
$\mathbf{f}_{da}\dagger$	active diffusion (force) field (per particle)
$\mathbf{f}_{ds}\dagger$	passive diffusion (force) field (per particle)
$\mathbf{f}_e\dagger$	electrostatic force field (per particle), with the active or passive property unspecified
$\mathbf{f}_{ea}\dagger$	active electrostatic force field (per particle)
$\mathbf{f}_{es}\dagger$	passive electrostatic force field (per particle)
$\mathbf{f}_f$	impeding force field, invariably associated with heat dissipation
$\mathbf{f}_g$	force per particle associated with gravity
$\mathbf{f}_{iaj}$	force field (per particle) of constituent j associated with process i. This force field is active as designated by the middle sub-

† Adding n or p here, as a third subscript, signifies pertinence to electrons or holes, respectively.

xix

	script. The first subscript i may be replaced, for example, by d, e, or g to signify pertinence of the field to diffusion, an electric or a gravitational effect, respectively. The subscript j may be replaced by, for example, n to signify that the particles acted on by the field are electrons
$\mathbf{f}_{isj}$	force field per particle of constituent j associated with process i. This force field is passive as designated by the middle subscript s. For further explanation of the subscripts i and j, see $\mathbf{f}_{iaj}$
$\mathbf{f}_{la}$	Lorentz (electromagnetic) force per particle, which is invariably active
$\mathbf{f}_0$	total nonresidual force field; that is, the resultant of all force fields which do not contain (∇T)
$\mathbf{f}_T$	thermomotive field
$\mathbf{f}_{ta}, \mathbf{f}_{ts}$†	total active and passive force fields (per particle) associated with all processes
$\mathbf{f}_{taR}$	total residual, active force field; that is, the resultant of all active force fields which contain (∇T)
G	gravitational constant
GECE	generalized equation of conservation of energy as defined in the TTGF
$\mathbf{g}$	gravitational acceleration, and as subscript signifies nature of field to be gravitational
$g(\epsilon)$	volume energy density of quantum states at an energy ϵ
$\mathbf{H}$	magnetic field intensity
h	Planck's constant
I	electric current (dc)
I^*	junction-diode reverse saturation current computed according to the TTGF (Chapter 7)
i	instantaneous value of electric current
$\mathbf{i}$	unit vector along the Cartesian coordinate x
$\mathbf{J}_d$†	diffusion current density
$\mathbf{J}_e$†	electron drift current density; that is, the current associated with an electric field entirely
$\mathcal{J}$	particle flux density, that is, number of particles crossing a small area, per unit area, per unit time
$\mathcal{J}_{ij}$	particle flux density associated with a process i and carried by constituent j
$\mathbf{j}$	unit vector along the Cartesian coordinate y
k	Boltzmann's constant
$\mathbf{k}$	unit vector along the Cartesian coordinate z
L_n, L_p	diffusion length for electrons and for holes, respectively

† Adding n or p here, as a third subscript, signifies pertinence to electrons or holes, respectively.

m	mass per particle
m_e	electron effective mass
m_h	hole effective mass
N	number of particles within a small volume V
N_a, N_d	concentration of acceptor and donor atoms, respectively, in a semiconductor crystal
n_a, n_d	concentration of ionized acceptor and donor atoms, respectively, in a semiconductor crystal
n	concentration of electrons, and as subscript signifies the constituent to be electrons
n_i	electron concentration in a pure semiconductor crystal
n_j	number of particles of constituent j per unit volume
n_n	concentration of majority electrons in an n-type semiconductor
P_j	internal pressure of constituent j
P_v	vapor pressure of a liquid
p	pressure as defined in classical thermodynamics (use confined to Chapter 4 and Appendix A)
p	concentration of holes, and as subscript signifies the constituent to be holes
p_e	boundary value of the concentration of minority holes injected into the n region of a $p-n$ junction
p_i	hole concentration in a pure semiconductor crystal
p_n	thermal-equilibrium value of the concentration of minority holes in a semiconductor crystal
p_p	concentration of majority holes in a p-type semiconductor
Q	electric charge
Q_{taj}	$(\partial Q_{taj}/\partial t)$: time rate of increase of internal energy of the non-transported particles, per unit volume, associated with a particle flux density of constituent j and a total intrinsic active field $\mathbf{f}_{taj}$
Q_{isj}	$(\partial Q_{isj}/\partial t)$: time rate of heat evolution per unit volume associated with a passive force field $\mathbf{f}_{isj}$, of nature i, generated by flux density pertaining to constituent j
q	magnitude of the electron charge
R_b	ohmic resistance of the bulk regions in a junction diode
S	entropy as defined in the TTGF for a system of particles
s	closed surface, or surface bounded by a closed loop. Also, thermoelectric power
s_j	entropy per particle (of constituent j) as defined in the TTGF
T	absolute temperature
$\tilde{T}$	independent temperature axis of the thermodynamic hyperspace as defined in the TTGF. The derivative $(d/d\tilde{T})$ signifies differentiation with respect to temperature holding the three position coordinates constant

TTGF	thermodynamic theory of generalized fields
t	time
U	internal energy of a system of particles
u	internal energy per particle
V	an appropriately small volume. Also, (limited use) electric voltage between two points, and in Chapter 7, the forward dc voltage applied to a junction diode. In the sense indicated here, V frequently has subscripts
υ	volume bounded by a closed surface
v	flow velocity of electrons, or any other fluid
W_{dab}(eV)	average work done on a composite carrier‡ by the active diffusion field acting on majority electrons as the composite carrier is transported through the entire n region in a p-n junction (Chapter 7)
W_{dsb}(eV)	average work done on a composite carrier‡ by the passive diffusion field acting on minority holes as the composite carrier is transported through the entire n region in a p-n junction (Chapter 7)
W_{esb}(eV)	line integral through the bulk of the passive electrostatic force per majority carrier introduced into the bulk regions in a p-n junction (Chapter 7)
W_{daj}(eV)	line integral of $\mathbf{f}_{da}$ through the transition region in a p-n junction (Chapter 7)
W_{esj}(eV)	line integral of the passive electrostatic force per particle in the transition region of a p-n junction
W_{eaj}(eV)	line integral of $\mathbf{f}_{ea}$ through the transition region of a p-n junction
W_{ta}, W_{ts}	work done on a composite carrier‡ associated with all the active and all the passive fields acting on both electrons and holes
W_{tan}, W_{tsn}	work done on a composite carrier‡ associated, respectively, with the active and passive fields acting on electrons only
W_{tap}, W_{tsp}	work done on a composite carrier‡ associated, respectively, with the active and passive fields acting on holes only
w	width of the transition region in a p-n junction
x	distance between any point in the p region and the junction (in a p-n junction)
y	distance between any point within the transition region and the p-region boundary in a p-n junction
y'	distance between any point within the transition region and the n-region boundary in a p-n junction
α	I/I^* (use limited to Chapter 7)
α_T	linear thermal expansivity of a metal
ϵ	difference between an energy level associated with any quantum state and the bottom of the conduction band

‡ For a definition of composite carrier, see Section 3 [Chapter 7].

$\langle \epsilon \rangle$	average thermal kinetic energy per particle
ϵ_b	Bose energy (at any temperature) measured from the bottom of the quantum-mechanical energy band
ϵ_f	Fermi energy (at any temperature) measured from the bottom of the quantum-mechanical energy band
$\epsilon_f(n_e)$	energy difference between the electron quasi Fermi level and the bottom of the conduction band, evaluated at the p-region boundary in a forward-biased p-n junction
$\epsilon_f(n_n)$	value of ϵ_f for majority electrons in a p-n junction
$\epsilon_f(n_p)$	thermal-equilibrium value of $\epsilon_f(n_e)$
ϵ_{f0}	value of ϵ_f at 0°K
ϵ_g	magnitude of the energy gap in a semiconductor
ζ	intrinsic transport energy coefficient as defined in the TTGF
η	entropy as defined in classical thermodynamics
κ	dielectric constant of any medium
κ_0	dielectric constant of free space
μ	magnetic permeability (use limited to Chapters 3 and 10), and with a subscript 0 designates pertinence to free space
μ_n, μ_p	mobility of electrons and of holes, respectively
$\tilde{\mu}$	chemical potential as used in classical thermodynamics
$\tilde{\mu}_t$	generalized potential as used in classical thermodynamics
ν	intrinsic transport energy function as defined in the TTGF
ν_t	generalized transport energy function as defined in the TTGF
Π_{AB}	Peltier coefficient for two metals, A and B
ρ	volume charge density
ρ_m	mass per unit volume
σ	electrical conductivity
τ	$\delta\tau$: small displacement on the independent temperature axis of the thermodynamic hyperspace
Υ	the Seebeck active voltage (emf) of a thermocouple
Φ	total magnetic flux lines
$\phi_0(\text{eV})$	the line integral of the active diffusion field through the transition region in a p-n junction at thermal equilibrium
$\phi_c(\text{eV})$	line integral of the active diffusion field through both ohmic contacts of a p-n junction
Ψ	total electric flux lines
Ψ_g	total gravitational flux lines
$\psi(\text{eV})$	line integral of the active electrostatic force field (per particle) through the transition region of a forward-biased p-n junction
ψ_0	value of ψ at thermal equilibrium
$\psi_c(\text{eV})$	line integral of the active electrostatic force field through both ohmic contacts of a p-n junction.

FOUNDATIONS OF THE THERMODYNAMIC THEORY OF GENERALIZED FIELDS

ESSAYS IN NATURAL PHILOSOPHY

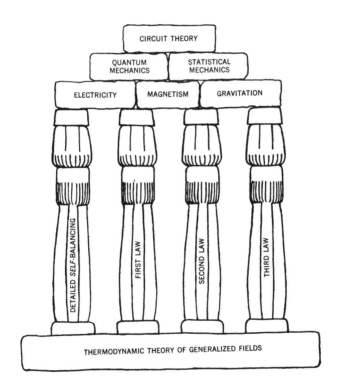

Chapter 1

SOME ASPECTS OF NATURAL PHILOSOPHY, AND THE SCOPE OF THIS VOLUME

The central objective in this volume is to present a treatment of a newly-proposed thermodynamic framework, to be called the *thermodynamic theory of generalized fields*. The subject of thermodynamics, regardless of how it is formulated, seeks, in the broadest sense, the fundamental laws, which govern how any system attains a state of thermal equilibrium, and how the system departs from such a state to one of nonequilibrium. The latter state may be manifested by the flow of an electric current, chemical reactions, biological and biochemical processes, radiation, etc.; or more generally the change of microscopic particles and/or energy from one kind to another, and/or from one location to another.

It is understandable that one would immediately raise the following fundamental question. Why should we look for any new general framework, while there has existed another one, such as that of presently-known thermodynamics? In particular this century-old framework underlies an extensive amount of the present understanding in the various branches of science.

In attempting to answer this rather philosophical question, one cannot evade citing the fundamental rules pertaining to the formulation of any framework. Those rules have been developed through the centuries by the foremost of natural philosophers.

In this chapter, we shall attempt to discuss these rules generally, and as they relate to the basic formulation of classical thermodynamics and of the thermodynamic theory of generalized fields. We shall further summarize other relevant material presented in this volume.

1. NATURAL PHILOSOPHY AND THE EVOLUTION OF SCIENTIFIC FOUNDATIONS

The main objectives of natural philosophy are twofold. First, the constant evaluation of existing foundations of scientific theories. Second, the continued search for new foundations. In attempting to fulfill these objectives, there are at least three fundamental rules, which are somewhat inter-related, and must be observed.

Rule I. Any foundation, new or established, should not be inconsistent within its own framework.

1

Violation of this rule will mean that the foundation is at least over-extended, if it is not totally without validity, or nearly so. Consequently, there should exist an entire unknown foundation to be searched for.

An example of this situation is the observation by Maxwell (1864) that Kirchhoff's current law (1847) breaks down in the case of a capacitor. For within the framework of circuit theory, as established by Ohm (1825, 1826a, b) and Kirchhoff, there exists no other than conduction current, which is strictly carried by the migration of electrically charged particles. For a capacitor being charged, there will be a conduction current flowing toward, or out of, only one side of any one plate; but not both sides.

To remove this serious inconsistency, Maxwell has postulated the existence of what is called a *displacement* current. Introducing this crucial concept made it possible for Maxwell to formulate a beautiful and completely self-consistent foundation for electromagnetism. This topic will be dealt with at length in Chapter 3.

Rule II. Any foundation should lead to many fundamental consequences without the continued introduction of hypotheses ad hoc. Such consequences must be further verifiable by experiment. The sequence of discovering the experimental facts and the foundation is, of course, immaterial.

For example, Newton's laws (Newton, 1687) of classical mechanics have resulted in complete predictability of the motion of macroscopic particles with speeds much less than the speed of light. Consequently, at any instant, the location of many celestial bodies can be determined well in advance and with the utmost accuracy. Maxwell's formulation of electromagnetism (1864) has led to predicting the possibility of propagation of radio waves long before their detection by Hertz (1887, 1888). Einstein's theory of relativity (Einstein 1905, 1916) has established the equivalence of mass and energy, and has predicted the bending of a light beam in a transverse gravitational field. The two theoretical conclusions and many others had preceded the experimental observations by a few years. The quantum theory has explained much of the behavior of microscopic particles including the emission and absorption in atoms of electromagnetic spectra, the structure of the periodic table (Mendeléeff, 1902), etc. These two particular topics happen to have been substantially known for a few decades, on the basis of experiment entirely.

Rule III. Last but not least, we discuss the third rule, which is, by no means, completely unrelated to the previous two. *The existence of a new foundation is totally justifiable, if it leads to a unification of theories explaining phenomena which otherwise have to be explained by the continued introduction of hypotheses ad hoc.*

Outside the realm of natural philosophy, Rule III is perhaps the most difficult one to understand, particularly when first encountered. There are considerations which cannot be divorced from the human nature. What is old becomes familiar and traditional, and can be passed without questioning or scrutiny. The older it gets, the more sanctity it acquires, even if it was ignored, or even rejected at its birth. As related by Angrist (1968), an account of the first law of thermodynamics was submitted in an article by J. R. von Mayer in about 1842 to the foremost scientific journal of his time, *Annalen der Physik und Chemie*. The paper was considered unworthy of publication, and, therefore, rejected. Fortunately, it was published in an inconspicuous journal. Nearly five years later, Hermann von Helmholtz submitted in an article, again to *Annalen der Physik und Chemie*, a more complete and more substantiated account of the first law of thermodynamics. Like Mayer, Helmholtz too was rejected.

Nevertheless, through the centuries, to natural philosophers the prospect of achieving theoretical unification has provided a strong incentive to search for new foundations. As stated by d'Abro* (1950),

"Although in the course of the last three centuries scientific theories have been subject to all manner of vicissitude and change, the governing motive that has inspired scientists has been ever the same—a search for unity in diversity, a desire to bring harmony and order into what might at first sight appear to be a hopeless chaos of experimental facts."

Nearly three centuries ago, in defining the first of his four "rules of reasoning in (natural) philosophy," Newton (1687), has said,

"*We are to admit no more causes of natural things than such as are both true and sufficient to explain their appearances.* To this purpose the philosophers say that Nature does nothing in vain, and more is in vain when less will serve; for Nature is pleased with simplicity, and affects not the pomp of superfluous causes."

This philosophy has been reaffirmed by Einstein, who once remarked (d'Abro* 1950, p. xvi) in his Princeton lectures,

"The only justification for our concepts and system of concepts is that they serve to represent the complex of our experiences; beyond this they have no legitimacy...."

Rule III and the question of uniqueness of a foundation. In natural philosophy, Rule III further provides a fundamental criterion for dealing with the question of validity arising in situations for which there exist a multiplicity of foundations of one subject. This aspect has been most lucidly described by d'Abro* (1950, pp. xiv–xv) as follows:

"... This procedure of ascribing discrepancies in our mathematical anticipations to the presence of contingent influences rather than to the falsity of our theory is only human. There is no inclination, merely because the hundredth case turns out to be an exception, to abandon a theory which has led to accurate anticipations in 99 cases

* All excerpts from d'Abro's book have been reprinted through permission of Dover Publications, Inc.

out of 100. But we must realise that this procedure of appealing to foreign influences, while perfectly legitimate in a tentative way, must be applied with a certain amount of caution; in every particular case it must be justified by *a posteriori* determination of fact. Thus Leverrier was also the first to discover certain irregularities in the motion of the planet Mercury. As in the case of Uranus, he attempted to ascribe these discrepancies to the presence of an interior planet which he called Vulcan and which he assumed to be moving between the orbit of Mercury and the sun. Astronomers have, however, failed to find the slightest trace of Vulcan, and a belief in its existence has been abandoned. If contingent influences are to be invoked for Mercury's anomalies, we must search for them in some other direction.

In this particular case all other suggestions were equally unsatisfactory. Hence even before the advent of Einstein's theory, doubts had been raised as to the accuracy of Newton's law of gravitation. The procedure of patching up a mistaken theoretical anticipation with hypotheses *ad hoc* has not much to commend it. Yet when, as was the case with Vulcan and Neptune, the influence we appeal to is of a category susceptible of being observed directly, the method is legitimate. *But when our hypothesis ad hoc transcends observation by its very nature, and when, added to this, its utility is merely local, accounting for one definite fact and for no other, it becomes worse than useless.*

This abhorrence of science for the unverifiable type of hypothesis *ad hoc* so frequently encountered in the speculations of the metaphysicians is not due to a mere phenomenalistic desire to eliminate all that cannot be seen or sensed. It arises from a deeper motive entailing the entire *raison d'être* of a scientific theory. Suppose, for instance, that our theory had led us to anticipate a certain result, and that experiment or observation should prove that in reality a different result was realised. We could always adjust matters by arbitrarily postulating some local invisible and unverifiable influence, which we might ascribe to the presence of a mysterious medium—say, the ether A. We should thus have added a new influence to our scheme of nature.

If we should now take this new influence into consideration, the first numerical result would, of course, be explained automatically, since our ether A was devised with this express purpose in view. But we should now be led to anticipate a different numerical result for some other phenomenon. If this second anticipation were to be disproved by experiment we could invoke some second unverifiable disturbing influence to account for the discrepancy, while leaving the first result unchanged. Let us call this new influence the ether B. We might go on in this way indefinitely.

But it is obvious that our theory of mathematical physics whose object it was to allow us to foresee and to foretell would now be useless. No new phenomenon could be anticipated, since past experience would have shown us that unforeseen influences must constantly be called into play if theory were to be verified by experiment. Under these circumstances we might just as well abandon all attempts to construct a mathematical model of the universe.

Suppose now that by modifying once and for all our initial premises we are led to a theory which allows us to foresee and foretell numerical results that are invariably verified with the utmost precision by experiment, without our having to call to our assistance a number of foreign hypotheses. In this case we may assume that the new theory is correct, since it is fruitful; and that our former theory was incorrect, because it led us nowhere.''

2. CLASSICAL THERMODYNAMICS AND THE THERMODYNAMIC THEORY OF GENERALIZED FIELDS

In the previous section, we have reviewed in general terms the primary objectives and rules of natural philosophy. We shall next briefly discuss,

on the basis of these rules, some basic aspects pertaining to classical thermodynamics, and the thermodynamic theory of generalized fields.

2.1. *The Classical Thermodynamic Formulation*

We begin with raising the inevitable question as to whether there exist
any inconsistencies in classical thermodynamics, within its own framework.
The existence of such problems in classical thermodynamics has been
the concern of a number of eminent thinkers, past and present. As recent
as the 1969 International Symposium on Thermodynamics, this conern
was conspicuous and significant. The preface of the Proceedings (Stuart,
Gal-Or and Brainard 1970) of this Symposium states,

"A growing number of scientists believe today that the very foundations of present-
day thermodynamic theories should be reexamined and perhaps modified. The constant
search towards better thermodynamic theories is not merely a logical necessity, but is
mainly due to the failure of classical, statistical and relativistic thermodynamics to
solve and eliminate the existing problems, inconsistencies and paradoxes inherent in
present-day thermodynamic theories . . ."

The question whether there are inconsistencies in classical thermodynamics within its own framework, is a matter to be discussed in detail
in Chapter 4. At the moment, however, we mention briefly that entropy,
as classically defined, seems to lack uniqueness, and thus possible mathematical existence, for a state attained during an irreversible process. This
basic criticism has been raised by a number of prominent thermodynamicists, including Mayer (1955), and Meixner (1970).* Without resolving
this important matter, one cannot hope that the second law will be interpreted satisfactorily. Neither will the first Rule of natural philosophy be
properly satisfied.

2.2. *Real-Space Formulation of the Thermodynamic Theory of Generalized Fields*

In Chapter 4, it will be shown that certain fundamental limitations inherent in the classical thermodynamic formulation can be traced to the
internal energy equation. It will be further shown that all these limitations
can be completely removed by reinterpreting every one of the existing
terms in the classical internal energy equation. In addition, new fundamental terms are introduced. These terms involve forces per particle, to
be called *force fields*, which are statistical, or otherwise, and can be defined
at every point in the *real* (three-dimensional position) *space* occupied by
the system. For each constituent in a multicomponent system, there exist
generally five distinguishable force fields which can be electric in nature,

* A quotation of Meixner's important statement concerning the nonexistence of entropy, for a state attained during an irreversible process, may be found on p. 61–62.

magnetic (or electromagnetic), gravitational and what are defined as the thermomotive field, f_T, and the diffusion field, f_d. The force field, f_T, is associated with a temperature gradient and the entropy per particle which is strictly defined through *Clausius equality*, rather than inequality. The diffusion field, f_d, is associated with the particle concentration and the gradient of what is defined as the internal pressure. In Chapter 6, a number of fundamental properties of these force fields will be explored from the point of view of the real space for systems generally in nonequilibrium.

In the thermodynamic theory of generalized fields (TTGF), it is a crucial matter that a distinction is made between what is defined as *passive* (dissipative) and *active* (emf-like) force fields. This important distinction between two such types of force fields has created the necessity and provided the opportunity to invoke two independent generalized relations. The first describes how each passive force field is related to the corresponding particle flux density. This relation leads to Ohm's, Fick's, Stokes's and other *dissipative* laws. The second relation expresses the conservation of transport energy in the real space. This novel interpretation of the first law prescribes how active and passive force fields in a system shall interact.

At thermal equilibrium, this scheme crucially leads to a state of detailed *self*-balancing. Specifically, in the framework of the TTGF, passive force fields vanish individually and each active force field becomes conservative. Thus, each active force field leads to a vanishing amount of transport energy around every closed loop in the system, and, consequently, becomes in self-balance. By contrast, in the framework of classical thermodynamics, if expressed in force fields, then thermal equilibrium is necessarily established by the balancing of all the force fields combined.

Accordingly, in the framework of the TTGF, thermal equilibrium is generally a state for which the balancing occurs in the most detailed possible manner—which is indeed far more detailed than prescribed in the framework of classical thermodynamics.

2.3. *Conservation of Transport Energy in the Temperature-Position Hyperspace*

A careful consideration of the mechanism of detailed *self*-balancing leads to the conclusion that for an observer, only conscious of the real space, it will seem that in any system every identifiable force field is completely decoupled from all other force fields at thermal equilibrium. Since nature cannot be so chaotic as to allow total decoupling between force fields in every system at thermal equilibrium, it follows that the real space cannot be the most general space in which active and passive force fields interact. Rather, there must exist some hyperspace in which active and passive force fields remain invariably coupled, even at thermal equilibrium. In that particular state, passive fields vanish individually, but active fields do not vanish necessarily and will have to remain coupled.

It will be shown in Chapter 8 that this hyperspace consists of the three position coordinates of the real space and a fourth *independent axis of temperature*. In this hyperspace, the conservation of transport energy leads to a fundamental relation to be called the *hyperspace equation*.

To solve the hyperspace equation, it is necessary that the boundary conditions of the hyperspace be specified at all points of the real space in a system at the absolute zero. These boundary conditions will be determined for all systems on the basis that no heat can be extracted from a system at the absolute zero and other considerations relevant to the third law of thermodynamics.

In Chapter 9, the hyperspace equation, and its general solutions and boundary conditions will be discussed as applied to the Seebeck and Peltier effects.

The hyperspace equation and the laws of thermodynamics. The hyperspace equation expresses the first and second laws of thermodynamics in a general and novel manner for a system of particles involving interfaces and temperature gradients while subject to electric, magnetic and gravitational effects. The boundary conditions of this equation are relevant to the third law. The equation prescribes further that the coupling between the new and established force fields in a system would occur in such a way as to lead to a state of detailed *self*-balancing at thermal equilibrium.

Thus, in the framework of the TTGF, the use of the hyperspace equation automatically invokes all the four thermodynamic principles simultaneously. This result is not without philosophical implications. The simplest space—not accounting for relativistic effects—in which the interactions take place in any system is four-dimensional. In that hyperspace, the four thermodynamic principles are crucially relevant and none is superfluous even at thermal equilibrium.

By contrast, in classical thermodynamics, it is considered that the generalized potential is constant in any system at thermal equilibrium, thereby confining the interactions in a system simply to the real space. Therefore, no particular need arises for using the third law and its consequences, or the first law in a manner which corresponds to that used in the thermodynamic theory of generalized fields.

3. THE THERMODYNAMIC THEORY OF GENERALIZED FIELDS AND THE RULES OF NATURAL PHILOSOPHY

In this volume, we shall attempt to solve, on the basis of the TTGF a number of problems which lend themselves to experimental testing. We summarize in this section some of the results achieved, which have relevance to Rules II and III of natural philosophy.

3.1. *Theory of Forward Electrical Conduction in p-n Junctions, Heterojunctions, and Schottky Diodes*

In Chapter 7, we shall treat the problem of forward electrical conduction in what are called p-n junctions, heterojunctions and Schottky (metal-semiconductor) diodes. To explain, within the classical thermodynamic framework, the voltage-current characteristics in highly limited ranges of current, temperature, etc., it has been found necessary to resort to the continued introduction of hypotheses *ad hoc*. More than 25 different theories have been developed in the last four decades to explain (mostly semiquantitatively) only a small fraction of the massive data gathered by numerous experimenters, particularly in the last two decades.

Applying the thermodynamic theory of generalized fields to the three different types of diodes has led to a unified theory. Theoretical predictions have been found to be accurately in agreement with experimental measurements for 16 different p-n junctions, heterojunctions and Schottky diodes made of semiconductor materials with energy gaps ranging from 0.17 eV to 2.8 eV. In some experiments, the forward currents were varied over more than 10 orders of magnitude. In total, 65 experimentally measured voltage-current characteristics have been studied at temperatures ranging from 4.2°K to 800°K. The experiments have been conducted by 22 different authors between 1952 and 1968.

3.2. *The Hyperspace Equation and the Observed Phenomena of Superconductivity and Superfluidity*

In Chapter 10, we shall show that if the hyperspace boundary conditions are satisfied, in a continuous temperature range which includes 0°K, then in that range the system necessarily exhibits (nearly) all the observed phenomena of superconductivity or superfluidity; depending on whether the particles of the system are electrically charged or neutral, respectively. The condition required for freezing these boundary conditions will be determined for a large number of cases.

4. THE SCOPE OF THIS VOLUME

Although a fairly general account of the thermodynamic theory of generalized fields is to be presented in this volume, the treatment will be mostly confined to systems which contain no other than solenoidal particle flux densities. The cases of interest involve driving forces which have no variation in time. Under such conditions there is no accumulation of particles anywhere and generally there is no generation or destruction of constituents in a multicomponent system. Only in one special case, to be treated in Chapter 7, shall we consider the problem of recombination of electrons and holes.

There are a number of fundamental areas which are of concern to the development of the thermodynamic theory of generalized fields. In an effort to make a coherent presentation of the main topic, a brief review has been included of those areas of relevance. Chapter 2 presents a brief development of vector calculus. The classical theories of electromagnetism and gravitation are treated in Chapter 3. Finally, in Chapter 5, we present a review of the fundamental aspects of the quantum theory and statistical mechanics. The results of both are applied mainly to electrons in metals and electrons and holes in semiconductors.

REFERENCES

d'Abro, A. 1950, The Evolution of Scientific Thought from Newton to Einstein, Dover. The excerpts from this reference have been reprinted through permission of the publisher.

Angrist, S. W. 1968, "Perpetual Motion Machines," Scientific American, January, pp. 114–122.

Einstein, A. 1905, Ann. Physik **18**, pp. 639–644.

——— 1916, Ann. Physik **49**, pp. 769–822.

Hertz, H. R. 1887, Berlin Akad. Sber., pp. 885–896.

——— 1888, Ann. Phys. Chem. **34**, pp. 273–285.

Kirchhoff, G. 1847, Pogg. Ann. Phys. **72**, 497.

Maxwell, J. C. 1864, Roy. Soc. Proc. **3**, pp. 531–536.

Mayer, J. E. 1955, "Two Unresolved Problems of Statistical Mechanics," Comm. Pure Appl. Math. **8**, pp. 73–83.

Meixner, J. 1970, Proc. of the Pittsburgh, Pennsylvania 1969 International Symposium on "A Critical Review of Thermodynamics," pp. 37–47, Mono Book Corp.

Mendeléeff, D. 1902, The Principles of Chemistry, seventh edition, Translated from Russian by G. Kemensky, and edited by T. H. Pope, 1905, two volumes, Longmans, Green and Co., London. Reprinted 1969 by Kraus Reprint Co., New York.

Newton, I. 1687, Philosophiae Naturalis Principia Mathematica (London: Jessu Societatis Regiae ac Typis Josephi Streater), English Translation by Andrew Motte 1729. Revised by Florian Cajori, 1934 (Berkeley; University of California).

Ohm, G. S. 1825, Pogg. Ann. **4**, 79.

——— 1826a, Ibid. **6**, 459.

——— 1826b, Ibid. **7**, 45.

Stuart, E. B., Gal-Or B., and Brainard, A. J. 1970, Proceedings of the Pittsburgh, Pennsylvania 1969 International Symposium on: A Critical Review of Thermodynamics, pp. xi–xii, Mono Book Corp.

Chapter 2

ELEMENTS OF VECTOR ANALYSIS

Classical field theories can be presented concisely and elegantly by means of vector calculus. This mathematical tool happens to provide particularly useful advantages in treating the thermodynamic theory of generalized fields to be presented in this volume. In this chapter, we shall summarize some basic relevant aspects of this branch of mathematics.

Applications of vector calculus, which are of concern in this volume, will strictly be to physical problems. For such problems, the questions of mathematical existence do not usually arise. Thus, in developing the various theorems, we shall omit stating the conditions of continuity, differentiability and other aspects pertinent to mathematical existence.

1. SCALAR AND VECTOR QUANTITIES

1.1. *Definitions*

Scalars. A quantity is said to be a *scalar* if it is totally defined by a magnitude and an algebraic sign. Energy, temperature and height are examples of scalars. Such quantities will be usually designated by italic letters such as A, B, C, a, b, c.

Vectors. Quantities which cannot be specified completely without a magnitude and a direction are called *vectors*. Forces, velocities and accelerations are examples of vectors. Such quantities will always be denoted by bold-faced letters such as **A, B, C, a, b, c**.

1.2. *Summation and Subtraction of Vectors*

Scalars can be added and subtracted in the usual algebraic way. Addition and subtraction of vectors, however, can be performed geometrically as illustrated in Fig. 1. It is also possible to carry out these operations analytically by making reference to some coordinate system.

In this volume, we shall mostly use the Cartesian coordinate system. The three mutually perpendicular axes of this system will be always designated by x, y, and z. In this coordinate system, a vector **A** may be represented in terms of its components A_x, A_y, A_z along the axes x, y, and z, respectively, by

$$\mathbf{A} = \mathbf{i}A_x + \mathbf{j}A_y + \mathbf{k}A_z. \tag{1}$$

Here, the quantities **i**, **j**, and **k** are *unit vectors* along the axes x, y, and z, respectively. A unit vector, by definition, has a magnitude of unity.

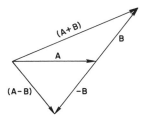

Fig. 1. Vector summation and subtraction.

The scalar quantities A_x, A_y, and A_z are the projections of the vector **A** on the x, y, and z axes, respectively, as may be observed in Fig. 2.

Suppose now that we have another vector **B** with components B_x, B_y, and B_z along the axes x, y, and z, respectively. We may, therefore, write

$$\mathbf{B} = iB_x + jB_y + kB_z. \tag{2}$$

The summation **C** of the vectors **A** and **B** can then be expressed as

$$\mathbf{C} = \mathbf{A} + \mathbf{B} = i(A_x + B_x) + j(A_y + B_y) + k(A_z + B_z). \tag{3}$$

From the geometry of Fig. 2, it follows that the magnitude A of vector **A** will be

$$A = (A_x^2 + A_y^2 + A_z^2)^{1/2}. \tag{4}$$

Similarly,

$$B = (B_x^2 + B_y^2 + B_z^2)^{1/2}, \tag{5}$$

$$C = |\mathbf{A} + \mathbf{B}| = [(A_x + B_x)^2 + (A_y + B_y)^2 + (A_z + B_z)^2]^{1/2}. \tag{6}$$

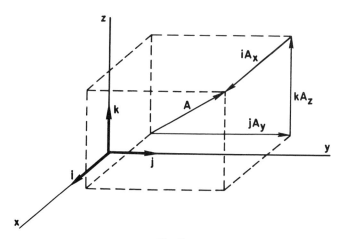

Fig. 2.

1.3. *Scalar and Vector Multiplication of Two Vectors*

Scalar Multiplication. The *scalar product* of two vectors **A** and **B** is a scalar quantity designated as (**A·B**), and defined as follows:

$$\mathbf{A \cdot B} = AB \cos\alpha. \tag{7}$$

Here α is the angle between the two vectors **A** and **B** (Fig. 3). The quantity (**A·B**) represents the product of the magnitude of one vector and the projection of the other on it. Sometimes (**A·B**) is called the *dot product* of **A** and **B**.

From Eq. (7), it follows that

$$\mathbf{i \cdot i = j \cdot j = k \cdot k} = 1, \tag{8-a}$$

$$\mathbf{i \cdot j = j \cdot k = k \cdot i} = 0. \tag{8-b}$$

From Eq. (7), it also follows that

$$\mathbf{A \cdot B = B \cdot A}. \tag{9}$$

When the order of any operation does not affect the answer, it is said that the operation obeys the *commutative law.* Thus, according to Eq. (9), it can be concluded that the dot product of two vectors obeys the commutative law.

Problem 1. Show that $\mathbf{A \cdot B} = A_x B_x + A_y B_y + A_z B_z$.

Vector Multiplication. The *vector product* of **A** and **B** is a vector quantity designated by (**A ✕ B**), and defined as

$$\mathbf{A \times B} = \mathbf{a} AB \sin\alpha. \tag{10}$$

The unit vector **a** is perpendicular to both **A** and **B**. The sense of the direction of **a** is specified by the axial direction in which a right-hand screw moves when rotated from **A** to **B**, through the smaller angle α included. In Fig. 3, the direction of **a** should be perpendicular to the plane of the paper and should further point inwardly.

The vector product of two vectors is sometimes called the *cross product.* From Eq. (10), it is apparent that the cross product of any vector and itself must vanish. Thus, for example,

$$\mathbf{i \times i = j \times j = k \times k} = 0. \tag{11}$$

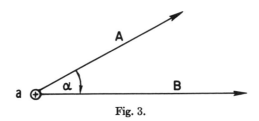

Fig. 3.

From Eq. (10), it follows that

$$\mathbf{A} \times \mathbf{B} = -\mathbf{B} \times \mathbf{A}. \tag{12}$$

Hence, the cross product of any two vectors does not obey the commutative law.

If the directions of positive increase are chosen for, say, the x and y Cartesian axes (Fig. 4), then the direction of positive increase along the z axis is chosen such that

$$\mathbf{i} \times \mathbf{j} = \mathbf{k} = -\mathbf{j} \times \mathbf{i}. \tag{13-a}$$

Accordingly,

$$\mathbf{j} \times \mathbf{k} = \mathbf{i} = -\mathbf{k} \times \mathbf{j}, \tag{13-b}$$

$$\mathbf{k} \times \mathbf{i} = \mathbf{j} = -\mathbf{i} \times \mathbf{k}. \tag{13-c}$$

The reader may verify Eqs. (13) using Eq. (10).

Problem 2. Given two vectors **A** and **B**, as expressed by Eqs. (1) and (2), respectively; using Eqs. (10), (11) and (13), show that

$$\mathbf{A} \times \mathbf{B} = \begin{vmatrix} \mathbf{i} & \mathbf{j} & \mathbf{k} \\ A_x & A_y & A_z \\ B_x & B_y & B_z \end{vmatrix}. \tag{14}$$

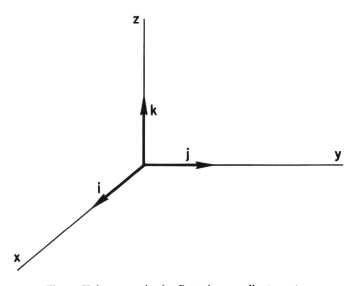

Fig. 4. Unit vectors in the Cartesian coordinate system.

2. THE GRADIENT OF A SCALAR FUNCTION

2.1. *The Del Operator*

The vector differential operator, ∇, called *del*, or *nabla*, is defined as

$$\nabla = \mathbf{i}\, \partial/\partial x + \mathbf{j}\, \partial/\partial y + \mathbf{k}\, \partial/\partial z. \tag{15}$$

The term operator is used here in the same sense as that for the operator $D = \partial/\partial x$ in ordinary calculus. For example, Dy means $(\partial y/\partial x)$.

2.2. *Definition of the Gradient*

If V is a scalar function of the Cartesian coordinates x, y, and z, then the *gradient* of V, or *grad V*, is defined as ∇V. Thus, in view of Eq. (15), we may write

$$\text{grad } V = \nabla V = \mathbf{i}\, \partial V/\partial x + \mathbf{j}\, \partial V/\partial y + \mathbf{k}\, \partial V/\partial z. \tag{16}$$

Clearly, ∇V is a vector quantity, even though V is a scalar.

2.3. *A Mathematical Property of ∇V*

Consider an infinitesimal increment $d\mathbf{l}$ of length such that

$$d\mathbf{l} = \mathbf{i}\, dx + \mathbf{j}\, dy + \mathbf{k}\, dz. \tag{17}$$

Let us now evaluate the scalar product $(\nabla V \cdot d\mathbf{l})$, which may be written as

$$\nabla V \cdot d\mathbf{l} = (\partial V/\partial x)\, dx + (\partial V/\partial y)\, dy + (\partial V/\partial z)\, dz. \tag{18}$$

Since, by definition,

$$V = V(x, y, z), \tag{19}$$

it follows, from the well-known rules of differential calculus, that

$$dV = (\partial V/\partial x)\, dx + (\partial V/\partial y)\, dy + (\partial V/\partial z)\, dz. \tag{20}$$

Comparison of Eqs. (18) and (20) leads to the following identity:

$$\nabla V \cdot d\mathbf{l} = dV. \tag{21}$$

Equation (21) represents an important general mathematical relationship, from which we shall deduce the two consequences to follow.

2.4. *Two Physical Properties of ∇V*

Consider the infinitesimal increment of length $d\mathbf{l}$. Let the vector $d\mathbf{l}$ be chosen such that it has a constant magnitude. Let the angle θ between

$d\mathbf{l}$ and ∇V be allowed to change. Equation (21), therefore, leads to

$$dV = |\nabla V| \, |dl| \, \cos\theta. \tag{22}$$

From Eq. (22), it follows that

$$dV = 0, \text{ i.e., } V = \text{constant}, \quad \text{when } \theta = 90°, \tag{23}$$

and

$$|dV|, \text{ and } |dV/dl|, \text{ each one attains a maximum,} \quad \text{when } \theta = 0. \tag{24}$$

The implication of Eqs. (23) and (24) are that when $d\mathbf{l}$ is chosen perpendicular to ∇V, then inevitably $d\mathbf{l}$ will be along the surface of constant V, for which $dV = 0$. However, if $d\mathbf{l}$ is chosen along ∇V, then dV will attain a maximum value, and so will $|dV/dl|$. In other words, ∇V is always perpendicular to the surfaces of constant V.

2.5. *Summary*

The gradient of a scalar function V is a vector which is perpendicular, at all points, to the surfaces of constant V, and which represents the maximum value of the spatial derivative of V at any given point.

An example of a scalar function is the temperature T in a nonisothermal system. In this case, ∇T represents the rate of change of T with respect to distance. It is evident that although T is a scalar quantity, its spatial rate of change is a vector. The direction of that vector is that in which the temperature changes most rapidly.

Problem 3. Assuming that the temperature T, between two concentric spheres, whose center lies at the origin, is given by

$$T = T_0(x^2 + y^2 + z^2)$$

where T_0 is a constant. Determine ∇T and sketch a few isothermal surfaces and lines parallel to the direction of ∇T.

Identities. The following are three useful identities. They can be verified by (a) direct expansions, or (b) by dotting the left-hand sides by $d\mathbf{l}$, using Eq. (21) and the elementary rules of differentials.

$$\nabla(A+B) = \nabla(B+A) = \nabla A + \nabla B \tag{25}$$

$$\nabla(AB) = \nabla(BA) = A\nabla B + B\nabla A \tag{26}$$

$$\nabla(A^2) = 2A\nabla A \tag{27}$$

Identity (25) implies that the gradient of two scalar quantities obeys the commutative law.

3. DIVERGENCE OF A VECTOR FUNCTION

3.1. *Definition*

If **A** is a vector, which is a function of the Cartesian coordinates x, y, and z, then the *divergence* of **A**, or *div* **A**, is defined to be $\nabla \cdot \mathbf{A}$. Hence, we may write

$$\nabla \cdot \mathbf{A} = (\mathbf{i}\, \partial/\partial x + \mathbf{j}\, \partial/\partial y + \mathbf{k}\, \partial/\partial z) \cdot (\mathbf{i}\, A_x + \mathbf{j}\, A_y + \mathbf{k}\, A_z). \tag{28}$$

The right-hand side of Eq. (28), when expanded, consists of nine terms. Six of these terms vanish because $\mathbf{i} \cdot \mathbf{j} = \mathbf{j} \cdot \mathbf{k} = \mathbf{k} \cdot \mathbf{i} = 0$ [see Eq. (8–b)]. Consequently, Eq. (28) reduces to

$$\nabla \cdot \mathbf{A} = \partial A_x/\partial x + \partial A_y/\partial y + \partial A_z/\partial z. \tag{29}$$

Problem 4. Given $\mathbf{A} = \mathbf{i}\, x^2 yz + \mathbf{j}\, xy^2 z + \mathbf{k}\, xyz^2$, show that $\nabla(\nabla \cdot \mathbf{A}) = \mathbf{i}\, 6yz + \mathbf{j}\, 6xz + \mathbf{k}\, 6xy$.

Problem 5. Given $\mathbf{A} = \mathbf{i}\, x^2 y + \mathbf{j}\, xyz + \mathbf{k}\, xyz^2$, evaluate $\nabla \cdot \mathbf{A}$ at the point $(1, 1, 2)$. [Ans. $\nabla \cdot \mathbf{A} = 8$.]

The following are useful identities which can be verified by direct expansion.

$$\nabla \cdot (\mathbf{A} + \mathbf{B}) = \nabla \cdot (\mathbf{B} + \mathbf{A}) = \nabla \cdot \mathbf{A} + \nabla \cdot \mathbf{B} \tag{30}$$

$$\nabla \cdot (A\mathbf{B}) = A\, \nabla \cdot \mathbf{B} + \mathbf{B} \cdot (\nabla A) \tag{31}$$

$$\nabla \cdot (\mathbf{A} \times \mathbf{B}) = \mathbf{B} \cdot (\nabla \times \mathbf{A}) - \mathbf{A} \cdot (\nabla \times \mathbf{B}) \tag{32}$$

3.2. *Physical Interpretation of the Divergence of a Vector*

Suppose that in a given three-dimensional region, we have a large number of geometric lines (we shall call *flux lines*) for which we wish to express how close they are to each other at any point Q in the region. To do so, imagine a small area Δs which contains point Q and which is transverse to the flux lines at Q. Let the number of lines crossing Δs at point Q be Δn. We may now define the magnitude of the density D of flux lines at Q by

$$D = \lim_{\Delta s \to 0} (\Delta n/\Delta s). \tag{33}$$

The direction of **D** is, of course, that of the lines at Q.

To determine the physical meaning of $(\nabla \cdot \mathbf{D})$, consider Fig. 5 which represents a small volume $\Delta V = \Delta x\, \Delta y\, \Delta z$. If **D** is a function of position, so will its component D_x along x. Thus, the total number of flux lines $[D_x(x_0)\, \Delta y\, \Delta z]$ entering the volume along x at x_0 will be different from the number $[D_x(x_0 + \Delta x)\, \Delta y\, \Delta z]$ of those flux lines leaving the volume at $(x_0 + \Delta x)$. The net num-

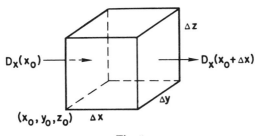

Fig. 5.

ber of lines crossing the volume outwardly along x will be

$$[(D_x)_{x_0+\Delta x} - (D_x)_{x_0}] \, \Delta y \, \Delta z = \{[(D_x)_{x_0+\Delta x} - (D_x)_{x_0}]/\Delta x\} \, \Delta x \, \Delta y \, \Delta z.$$

From the definition of a derivative, we may rewrite the preceding equation as

$$\lim_{\Delta x \to 0, \Delta y \to 0, \Delta z \to 0}[(D_x)_{x_0+\Delta x} - (D_x)_{x_0}] \, \Delta y \Delta z = (\partial D_x/\partial x) \, \Delta x \Delta y \Delta z.$$

Similar results may be obtained for the y and z directions, using the components D_y and D_z of $\mathbf{D}$.

Thus, we may state that as Δx, Δy, and Δz tend to zero, the limit of the net number of lines flowing out of the volume in all three directions will be

$$[\partial D_x/\partial x + \partial D_y/\partial y + \partial D_z/\partial z](dx \, dy \, dz) = (\nabla \cdot \mathbf{D}) \, dx \, dy \, dz. \qquad (34)$$

We may summarize the preceding result by stating:

Theorem A. If $\mathbf{D}$ *is a vector function expressing the density of flux lines at every point in a region, then* $(\nabla \cdot \mathbf{D})$ *represents the net number of flux lines flowing outwardly per unit volume at any point.*

Theorem A will be used to arrive at a number of fundamental consequences to be treated in this and the next chapter.

3.3. *The Divergence, or Gauss's Theorem*

Physical vectors are not necessarily actual (flux) lines. Hence, Theorem A may seem, at first glance, to be inapplicable in a general sense. Applying Theorem A, however, to any vector may be accomplished by considering that associated with any vector $\mathbf{A}$, there exists a density $\mathbf{D}_a$ of (fictitious) flux lines of $\mathbf{A}$ such that

$$\mathbf{D}_a = \kappa_a \mathbf{A}, \qquad (35)$$

where κ_a is a scalar arbitrary constant parameter which does not depend on position and which has the proper dimension to make Eq. (35) consistent.

Suppose now that we have a vector **A** and its associated density $\mathbf{D}_a$ of flux lines defined at every point of a volume $\mathcal{V}$. Let $\mathcal{V}$ be bounded by a closed surface $\mathcal{S}$. The net flux lines $\mathcal{F}$ crossing $\mathcal{S}$ outwardly may be calculated in two independent ways as follows.

Let $d\mathbf{s}$ be a vector such that its magnitude is a differential increment of surface area, and its direction is perpendicular to the surface. Let $d\mathbf{s}$ be considered positive whenever it is pointing outwardly with reference to $\mathcal{S}$. We may recognize at once that $(\mathbf{D} \cdot d\mathbf{s})$ represents the number of flux lines crossing the surface area $d\mathbf{s}$ outwardly. Thus, $\mathcal{F}$ can simply be expressed by

$$\mathcal{F} = \oiint_{\mathcal{S}} \mathbf{D}_a \cdot d\mathbf{s}. \tag{36}$$

The flux lines $\mathcal{F}$ can also be calculated using Theorem A. The net number of flux lines flowing outwardly of the differential volume $dv = dx\,dy\,dz$ is equal to $[\nabla \cdot \mathbf{D}_a\,dv]$. Hence, for the volume $\mathcal{V}$, we may write

$$\mathcal{F} = \int_{\mathcal{V}} \nabla \cdot \mathbf{D}_a\,dv. \tag{37}$$

From Eqs. (36) and (37), it follows that

$$\int_{\mathcal{V}} \nabla \cdot \mathbf{D}_a\,dv = \oiint_{\mathcal{S}} \mathbf{D}_a \cdot d\mathbf{s}. \tag{38}$$

Substituting Eq. (35) into Eq. (38) and dividing both sides of the resulting equation by the constant parameter κ_a, we get

$$\int_{\mathcal{V}} \nabla \cdot \mathbf{A}\,dv = \oiint_{\mathcal{S}} \mathbf{A} \cdot d\mathbf{s}. \tag{39}$$

Equation (39) expresses what is known as the *divergence* or *Gauss's theorem*, which is applicable to vectors regardless of whether or not they represent density of flux lines.

Problem 6. Given $\mathbf{A} = \mathbf{i}\,x + \mathbf{j}\,y + \mathbf{k}\,z$, using Gauss's theorem, evaluate the volume integral of $\nabla \cdot \mathbf{A}$ for a volume bounded by a sphere whose radius is R, and whose center is the origin. *Hint:* Notice first that **A** on the surface of the sphere is constant. Show then that **A** is perpendicular to the surface and proceed to evaluate the surface integral. [Ans. $4\pi R^3$.]

4. CURL OF A VECTOR FUNCTION

4.1. *Definition*

If **A** is a vector, which is a function of the Cartesian coordinates x, y, and z, then the *curl* of **A**, or *curl* **A** is defined as

$$\text{curl } \mathbf{A} = \nabla \times \mathbf{A}. \tag{40}$$

From the definition of the del operator, it follows that

$$\nabla \times \mathbf{A} = (\mathbf{i}\,\partial/\partial x + \mathbf{j}\,\partial/\partial y + \mathbf{k}\,\partial/\partial z) \times (\mathbf{i}\,A_x + \mathbf{j}\,A_y + \mathbf{k}\,A_z). \tag{41}$$

By comparison with the cross multiplication of two vectors, expressed by Eq. (14), Eq. (41) may be written as

$$\nabla \times \mathbf{A} = \begin{vmatrix} \mathbf{i} & \mathbf{j} & \mathbf{k} \\ \partial/\partial x & \partial/\partial y & \partial/\partial z \\ A_x & A_y & A_z \end{vmatrix} = \mathbf{i}\,(\partial A_z/\partial y - \partial A_y/\partial z) + \mathbf{j}\,(\partial A_x/\partial z - \partial A_z/\partial x)$$

$$+ \mathbf{k}\,(\partial A_y/\partial x - \partial A_x/\partial y). \quad (42)$$

Problem 7. Given $\mathbf{A} = \mathbf{i}\,3x^2yz + \mathbf{j}\,xy^2z + \mathbf{k}\,x^2yz^2$, show that

$$\nabla \times \mathbf{A} = \mathbf{i}\,(x^2z^2 - xy^2) + \mathbf{j}\,(3x^2y - 2xyz^2) + \mathbf{k}\,(y^2z - 3x^2z).$$

Problem 8. Given $\mathbf{A} = \mathbf{i}\,x^2y + \mathbf{j}\,xyz + \mathbf{k}\,xyz^2$, evaluate $\nabla \times \mathbf{A}$, and $|\nabla \times \mathbf{A}|$ at the point $(1, 1, 2)$.
[Ans. $\nabla \times \mathbf{A} = \mathbf{i}\,3 - \mathbf{j}\,4 + \mathbf{k}$, $|\nabla \times \mathbf{A}| = (26)^{1/2}$.]

The following are useful identities which can be verified by direct expansion.

$$\nabla \times (\mathbf{A} + \mathbf{B}) = \nabla \times (\mathbf{B} + \mathbf{A}) = \nabla \times \mathbf{A} + \nabla \times \mathbf{B}. \quad (43)$$

$$\nabla \times \nabla \mathbf{A} = 0. \quad (44)$$

$$\nabla \cdot (\nabla \times \mathbf{A}) = 0. \quad (45)$$

$$\nabla \times (\nabla \times \mathbf{A}) = \nabla(\nabla \cdot \mathbf{A}) - \nabla^2 \mathbf{A}, \quad \text{where } \nabla^2 = \nabla \cdot \nabla. \quad (46)$$

$$\nabla \times (A\mathbf{B}) = (\nabla A) \times \mathbf{B} + A\,(\nabla \times \mathbf{B}). \quad (47)$$

Definitions. A vector, which has a vanishing curl, is called *irrotational.* Such vectors must be the gradients of some scalar functions, as indicated by Eq. (44). Hence, the line integral of irrotational vectors between any two points will not depend on the path. Accordingly, force fields which are irrotational are called conservative. A vector, whose divergence vanishes, is defined as *solenoidal.* Solenoidal vectors must be the curls of some other vectors, as follows from Eq. (45).

Irrotational and solenoidal vectors will be of significance in presenting the thermodynamic theory of generalized fields.

4.2. *Physical Interpretation of the Curl of a Vector*

The curl of a vector has a fundamental physical meaning which we shall investigate in this subsection.

Consider Fig. 6 which represents the Cartesian components of a vector **A** in the xy plane at and near a point Q; the coordinates of Q being $(x_0, y_0, 0)$. The x- and y-components of **A** at Q are A_x and A_y, respectively.

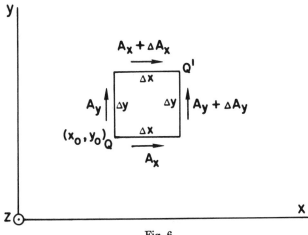

Fig. 6.

Q' is a second point, which also lies in the xy plane and is near point Q. The coordinates of point Q' are $(x_0+\Delta x, y_0+\Delta y, 0)$.

It is convenient to define the *circulation* of a vector **A** around a closed loop C to be the line integral of vector **A** around C. Let us now calculate the counterclockwise circulation of **A** around the perimeter of the small area $\Delta s = \Delta x \Delta y$, represented in Fig. 6. In terms of the infinitesimal increment of length dl on C, this circulation will be

$$\oint \mathbf{A} \cdot dl = A_x \Delta x + (A_y + \Delta A_y)\Delta y - (A_x + \Delta A_x)\Delta x - A_y \Delta y$$

$$= (\Delta A_y)\Delta y - (\Delta A_x)\Delta x. \tag{48}$$

As may be observed in Fig. 6, the increment ΔA_y in A_y results because of the change in x_0 by Δx. Likewise, the increment ΔA_x in A_x results because of the change in y_0 by Δy. Therefore, in view of Taylor's series, we may write

$$\Delta A_y = (\partial A_y/\partial x)_{x_0,y_0}\Delta x + \sum_{\nu=2}^{\infty} (\partial^\nu A_y/\partial x^\nu)_{x_0,y_0}[(\Delta x)^\nu/\nu!], \tag{49}$$

$$\Delta A_x = (\partial A_x/\partial y)_{x_0,y_0}\Delta y + \sum_{\nu=2}^{\infty} (\partial^\nu A_x/\partial y^\nu)_{x_0,y_0}[(\Delta y)^\nu/\nu!]. \tag{50}$$

Substituting Eqs. (49) and (50) into (48), we get

$$\oint \mathbf{A} \cdot dl = [(\partial A_y/\partial x)_{x_0,y_0} - (\partial A_x/\partial y)_{x_0,y_0}]\Delta x \Delta y$$

$$+ \sum_{\nu=2}^{\infty} \{ (\partial^\nu A_y/\partial x^\nu)_{x_0,y_0}[(\Delta x)^{\nu-1}/\nu!]$$

$$- (\partial^\nu A_y/\partial y^\nu)_{x_0,y_0}[(\Delta y)^{\nu-1}/\nu!]\} \Delta x \Delta y. \tag{51}$$

Therefore, in the xy plane

$$\lim_{\Delta x \to 0, \Delta y \to 0} \oint \mathbf{A} \cdot d\mathbf{l} = \left[\partial A_y / \partial x - \partial A_x / \partial_y \right] dx \, dy. \tag{52}$$

Notice that the coefficient of $(dx \, dy)$ in Eq. (52) is the magnitude of the z-component of curl $\mathbf{A}$, which is expressed by Eq. (42). Hence, we may state that in the xy plane,

$$\lim_{x \to 0, y \to 0} \oint \mathbf{A} \cdot d\mathbf{l} = \mathbf{k} \cdot (\nabla \times \mathbf{A}) \, ds. \tag{53}$$

Here, the direction of the differential vector $d\mathbf{s}$ is perpendicular to the area, and in our particular problem, it is the direction of increasing z. Notice that the direction of $d\mathbf{s}$ is determined, once the direction of the closed-loop integration is specified. In our case, the rule of a right-hand screw applies. Specifically, if the screw turns along the line of integration, then the direction of $d\mathbf{s}$ is along the axial movement of the screw.

Clearly, in deriving Eq. (53), the differential vector $d\mathbf{s}$ need not have been taken to be in the xy plane. Thus, Eq. (53) may be stated more generally as follows:

Theorem B. If $d\mathbf{s}$ is a differential vector, whose magnitude is the differential area ds, and whose direction is perpendicular to the area ds (Fig. 7), then the circulation of $\mathbf{A}$ around C

$$\oint_C \mathbf{A} \cdot d\mathbf{l} = (\nabla \times \mathbf{A}) \cdot d\mathbf{s}. \tag{54}$$

Here, C is a closed loop surrounding the area ds.

4.3 *Stokes's Theorem*

Equation (54) expresses the relation between the curl of a vector $\mathbf{A}$ at any point Q in terms of the circulation of $\mathbf{A}$ around the perimeter of an infinitesimal area in which Q is an interior point. It is often very useful to have a relationship corresponding to Eq. (54) when the surface area under consideration and its perimeter are finite.

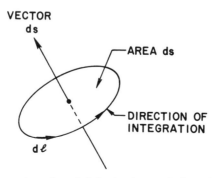

Fig. 7. Vector representation of an infinitesimal area ds bounded by a closed loop, the infinitesimal increment of which is $d\mathbf{l}$.

To arrive at such a relationship, consider the finite surface S, shown in Fig. 8. Let this surface be divided into a large number of rectangles, and approximate triangles and quadrangles. Let the area of each rectangle, triangle, or quadrangle be denoted by Δs_i, where i is any integer varying between 1 and the total number, n, of the small segments of areas Δs_i's.

Imagine now that a vector function $\mathbf{A}$ is defined at all points in some neighborhood of the surface S shown in Fig. 8. Thus, around the rectangle marked a, there will be generally a circulation as indicated by the arrows. As follows from Eq. (54), this circulation corresponds to curl $\mathbf{A}$ at a point interior to rectangle a. Similarly, around the adjacent rectangle marked b, in general, there will be a circulation of $\mathbf{A}$ around b. The rectangles a and b, however, have one side in common. Thus, the sum of curl $\mathbf{A}$ in rectangle a and curl $\mathbf{A}$ in rectangle b can be determined from the circulation of $\mathbf{A}$

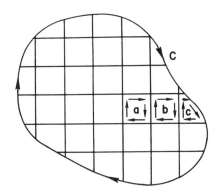

Fig. 8. A surface, S, bounded by a closed loop, C.

around the outer perimeter of the larger rectangle which consists of rectangles a and b combined. For, the components of the circulation along the common sides of the two rectangles a and b, being equal in magnitude and opposite in sign, exactly cancel.

It can now be readily seen that, for all the elements of areas, the summation,

$$\sum_{i=1}^{n} \nabla \times \mathbf{A} \cdot \Delta s_i,$$

can be found by summing the individual circulations around every one of the areas Δs_i. Always the contribution of common sides to the overall circulation of the outer perimeter of S can be disregarded, no matter what the shape of S and the perimeter may be, and no matter how large n may be.

Accordingly, in the limit as n tends to infinity (i.e., Δs_i tends to zero), we may write

$$\oint_C \mathbf{A} \cdot d\mathbf{l} = \int_S \nabla \times \mathbf{A} \cdot d\mathbf{s}. \tag{55}$$

Equation (55) expresses what is known as *Stokes's theorem*, which is of particular significance in vector calculus.

It should be pointed out that, from the derivation of Eq. (55), the surface S does not have to be in a plane. Generally, S can be of any geometric shape.

5. GRADIENT OF SCALARS INVOLVING MULTIPLE-FUNCTION DEPENDENCE

In some problems to be treated in this volume, it is desirable to determine the gradient of scalars which are functions of variables that depend directly, or indirectly on position. The object in this section is to treat a general problem of this kind.

Suppose that

$$\Theta = \Theta[\Phi, T], \tag{56}$$

$$\Phi = \Phi[\epsilon(T, x, y, z), \eta(T, x, y, z)], \tag{57}$$

$$T = T(x, y, z), \tag{58}$$

where x, y, z are the Cartesian position coordinates.

In order to determine grad Θ, we shall first evaluate $d\Theta$. From the basic principles of differential calculus and the functional dependence of Θ on the independent variables Φ and T, we may write

$$d\Theta = (\partial\Theta/\partial\Phi)_T \, d\Phi + (\partial\Theta/\partial T)_\Phi \, dT. \tag{59}$$

From Eq. (57) and (58), however, it follows that

$$d\Phi = (\partial\Phi/\partial\epsilon)_\eta \, d\epsilon + (\partial\Phi/\partial\eta)_\epsilon \, d\eta, \tag{60}$$

$$d\epsilon = (\partial\epsilon/\partial T)_{x,y,z} \, dT + (\partial\epsilon/\partial x)_{T,y,z} \, dx + (\partial\epsilon/\partial y)_{T,x,z} \, dy + (\partial\epsilon/\partial z)_{T,x,y} \, dz, \tag{61}$$

$$d\eta = (\partial\eta/\partial T)_{x,y,z} \, dT + (\partial\eta/\partial x)_{T,y,z} \, dx + (\partial\eta/\partial y)_{T,x,z} \, dy + (\partial\eta/\partial z)_{T,x,y} \, dz, \tag{62}$$

$$dT = (\partial T/\partial x) \, dx + (\partial T/\partial y) \, dy + (\partial T/\partial z) \, dz. \tag{63}$$

Consider the differential increment of length $d\mathbf{l}$, given by

$$d\mathbf{l} = \mathbf{i} \, dx + \mathbf{j} \, dy + \mathbf{k} \, dz. \tag{64}$$

In terms of $d\mathbf{l}$, the differential dT, expressed by Eq. (63), may be written as

$$dT = \nabla T \cdot d\mathbf{l}. \tag{65}$$

By virtue of the last two equations, and Eq. (21), Eqs. (61) and (62) will reduce to

$$d\epsilon = [(\partial\epsilon/\partial T)_{x,y,z} \nabla T + (\nabla\epsilon)_T] \cdot d\mathbf{l}, \tag{66}$$

$$d\eta = [(\partial\eta/\partial T)_{x,y,z} \nabla T + (\nabla\eta)_T] \cdot d\mathbf{l}. \tag{67}$$

It is now possible to calculate the differential of Θ. From Eqs. (59) and (60), it is evident that

$$d\Theta = (\partial\Theta/\partial\Phi)_T [(\partial\Phi/\partial\epsilon)_\eta \, d\epsilon + (\partial\Phi/\partial\eta)_\epsilon \, d\eta] + (\partial\Theta/\partial T)_\Phi \, dT. \tag{68}$$

Substituting Eqs. (65), (66) and (67) into Eq. (68), we get

$$d\Theta = [[(\partial\Theta/\partial\Phi)_T \{ (\partial\Phi/\partial\epsilon)_\eta [(\partial\epsilon/\partial T)_{x,y,z} \nabla T + (\nabla\epsilon)_T]$$
$$+ (\partial\Phi/\partial\eta)_\epsilon [(\partial\eta/\partial T)_{x,y,z} \nabla T + (\nabla\eta)_T] \} + (\partial\Theta/\partial T)_\Phi \nabla T]] \cdot d\mathbf{l}. \tag{69}$$

Equations (56), (57), and (58) specify that every variable, which Θ is a function of, is a function of position. Hence, Θ is essentially a function of position. As shown in Subsection 2.3, and by virtue of Eq. (21), we may, therefore, write

$$d\Theta = \nabla\Theta \cdot d\mathbf{l}. \tag{70}$$

Comparison of Eqs. (69) and (70) directly leads to

$$\nabla\Theta = (\partial\Theta/\partial\Phi)_T \{ (\partial\Phi/\partial\epsilon)_\eta [(\partial\epsilon/\partial T)_{x,y,z} \nabla T + (\nabla\epsilon)_T]$$
$$+ (\partial\Phi/\partial\eta)_\epsilon [(\partial\eta/\partial T)_{x,y,z} \nabla T + (\nabla\eta)_T] \} + (\partial\Theta/\partial T)_\Phi \nabla T. \tag{71}$$

The method followed to derive Eq. (71) can generally be used for determining the gradient of any scalar, no matter how its functional dependence on other variables may be.

6. DEL OPERATIONS IN THE CYLINDRICAL AND SPHERICAL COORDINATE SYSTEMS

For solving certain problems, there are significant advantages in using some coordinate systems, other than the Cartesian. The most common other types are the cylindrical and the spherical systems.

Figure 9 illustrates how the three cylindrical coordinates (ρ, ϕ, z) can be used to specify uniquely a point in space. As observed in the figure, ρ represents the radius of the cylinder passing through the point of interest. The angle ϕ is that between the xz plane, and the plane passing through the z axis and our point. The z coordinate is the same as it is in the Cartesian system.

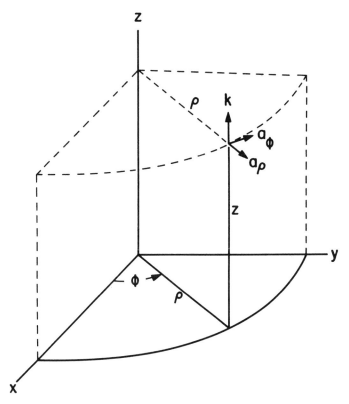

Fig. 9. Representation of the three unit vectors $\mathbf{a}_\rho$, $\mathbf{a}_\phi$ and $\mathbf{k}$ of the cylindrical-coordinate system.

The spherical coordinate system is illustrated in Fig. 10. The three co-ordinates are r, θ and ϕ. The first coordinate, r, is the shortest distance between the point of interest and the origin. The second, θ, is the angle between the z axis and the radial line joining the origin to our point. The third coordinate, ϕ, is the angle between the xz plane and the plane passing through the z axis and our point.

On the basis of the definitions, or general properties of the gradient, divergence and curl, it is possible to express these del operations in other than the Cartesian system. Transforming the gradient is fairly direct. Transforming the divergence and curl, however, can be done on the basis of Theorems A and B, respectively.

We shall state next, without proofs, transformations of the three del operations in the cylindrical and spherical coordinate systems. Readers interested in the proofs can find them in a number of excellent references, including Gibbs (1913), Kaplan (1952), and Phillips (1933).

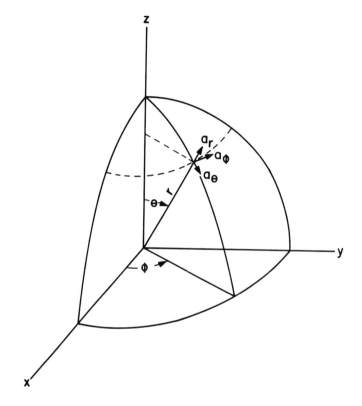

Fig. 10. Representation of the three unit vectors $\mathbf{a}_r$, $\mathbf{a}_\theta$ and $\mathbf{a}_\phi$ of the spherical-coordinate system.

6.1. *The Cylindrical Coordinate System*

Let V be a scalar function, and $\mathbf{A}$ be a vector function expressed in the cylindrical coordinates as

$$\mathbf{A} = \mathbf{a}_\rho A_\rho + \mathbf{a}_\phi A_\phi + \mathbf{k} A_z. \tag{72}$$

Here $\mathbf{a}_\rho$, $\mathbf{a}_\phi$, and $\mathbf{k}$ are unit vectors, as represented in Fig. 9, and A_ρ, A_ϕ, and A_z are the ρ-, ϕ-, and z-components of vector $\mathbf{A}$, respectively.

It can then be shown that

$$\nabla V = \mathbf{a}_\rho (\partial V/\partial \rho) + \mathbf{a}_\phi (1/\rho)(\partial V/\partial \phi) + \mathbf{k}(\partial V/\partial z), \tag{73}$$

$$\nabla \cdot \mathbf{A} = (1/\rho)\partial(\rho A\rho)/\partial\rho + (1/\rho)(\partial A_\phi/\partial\phi) + \partial A_z/\partial z, \tag{74}$$

$$\nabla \times \mathbf{A} = \mathbf{a}_\rho[(1/\rho)(\partial A_z/\partial\phi) - (\partial A_\phi/\partial z)] + \mathbf{a}_\phi[(\partial A_\rho/\partial z) - (\partial A_z/\partial\rho)]$$

$$+ \mathbf{k}(1/\rho)[\partial(\rho A_\phi)/\partial\rho - (\partial A_\rho/\partial\phi)]. \tag{75}$$

6.2. *The Spherical Coordinate System*

In the spherical coordinate system, a vector **A** will be expressed as

$$\mathbf{A} = \mathbf{a}_r A_r + \mathbf{a}_\theta A_\theta + \mathbf{a}_\phi A_\phi, \tag{76}$$

where A_r, A_θ, and A_ϕ are the r-, θ-, and ϕ-components of vector **A**, respectively, and $\mathbf{a}_r$, $\mathbf{a}_\theta$, and $\mathbf{a}_\phi$ are unit vectors, as represented in Fig. 10.
It can be shown that

$$\nabla V = \mathbf{a}_r (\partial V/\partial r) + \mathbf{a}_\theta (1/r)(\partial V/\partial \theta) + \mathbf{a}_\phi (1/r \sin\theta)(\partial V/\partial \phi), \tag{77}$$

$$\nabla \cdot \mathbf{A} = (1/r^2)\partial (r^2 A_r)/\partial r + (1/r \sin\theta)\partial (A_\theta \sin\theta)/\partial \theta + (1/r \sin\theta)(\partial A_\phi/\partial \phi), \tag{78}$$

$$\nabla \times \mathbf{A} = \mathbf{a}_r (1/r \sin\theta)[\partial (A_\phi \sin\theta)/\partial \theta - (\partial A_\theta/\partial \phi)] + \mathbf{a}_\theta [(1/r \sin\theta)(\partial A_r/\partial \phi)$$
$$- (1/r)\partial (rA_\phi)/\partial r] + \mathbf{a}_\phi (1/r)[\partial (rA_\theta)/\partial r - (\partial A_r/\partial \theta)]. \tag{79}$$

ADDITIONAL PROBLEMS

1. If a scalar function $V(x, y, z)$ is given by

$$V = (x^2 + y^2 + z^2)^{-1/2},$$

show that

$$|\nabla V| = (x^2 + y^2 + z^2)^{-1}.$$

2. Determine the components of a unit vector **a** which is perpendicular to both of the following vectors:

$$\mathbf{A} = \mathbf{i} + \mathbf{j} + \mathbf{k}, \quad \mathbf{B} = \mathbf{i} + \mathbf{j}\,2 + \mathbf{k}.$$

[Ans. $\mathbf{a} = \pm \mathbf{i}/\sqrt{2} \mp \mathbf{k}/\sqrt{2}$).]

3. Given $\mathbf{A} = \mathbf{i}\,x^2 + \mathbf{j}\,y^2 + \mathbf{k}\,z^2$, verify Gauss's theorem for a volume bounded by the surface of a sphere whose radius is R and whose center is the origin.

4. Show that if n is any number, then $\nabla (A^n) = nA^{n-1}\nabla A$.

5. If n is an integer, show that

$$\nabla \cdot (\mathbf{G}A^n) = nA^{n-1}\mathbf{G} \cdot \nabla A + A^n \nabla \cdot \mathbf{G}.$$

6. If the vector $\mathbf{A} = \mathbf{i}A_x$, and n is an integer, show that

$$\nabla \times (\mathbf{i}A_x^n) = n(A_x)^{n-1}[\mathbf{j}\,\partial A_x/\partial z - \mathbf{k}\,\partial A_x/\partial y].$$

7. Evaluate generally $\nabla \times (\mathbf{a}A^n)$, where **a** is a unit vector and n is an integer.

8. Show that:

$$\nabla \times [\mathbf{k}(x^2+y^2+z^2)^{-1/2}] = (x^2+y^2+z^2)^{-3/2}[-\mathbf{i}y+\mathbf{j}x].$$

9. Given $P = P[\epsilon_f(T, x, y, z)]$ and $T = T(x, y, z)$, show that

$$\nabla P = (\nabla P)_T + (dP/dT)_{x,y,z} \nabla T.$$

10. Given $V = (1/r)$, use the Cartesian coordinate system to show that $\nabla V = -\mathbf{a}_r(1/r^2)$. Verify this answer by using the cylindrical, then the spherical coordinate system.

11. If $\nabla^2 = \nabla \cdot \nabla$, show that in the cylindrical-coordinate system

$$\nabla^2 V = (1/\rho)(\partial/\partial\rho)[\rho\partial V/\partial\rho] + (1/\rho^2)\partial^2 V/\partial\phi^2 + \partial^2 V/\partial z^2.$$

12. Show that in the spherical-coordinate system

$$\nabla^2 V = (1/r^2)(\partial/\partial r)(r^2\partial V/\partial r) + (r^2\sin\theta)^{-1}(\partial/\partial\theta)[(\partial V/\partial\theta)\sin\theta]$$

$$+ (r\sin\theta)^{-2}\,\partial^2 V/\partial\phi^2.$$

13. Given $\mathbf{A} = \mathbf{k}/r$, use each one of the three coordinate systems to show that

$$\nabla \times \mathbf{A} = \mathbf{a}_\phi(\sin\theta)/r^2.$$

14. Verify identities (44) and (45) using the cylindrical, then the spherical coordinate systems.

REFERENCES

Gibbs, J. W. 1913, Vector Analysis, Yale University Press. Reproduced in 1960 by Dover Publications, Inc.
Kaplan, Wilfred 1952, Advanced Calculus, Addison-Wesley Press, Inc.
Phillips, H. B. 1933, Vector Analysis, John Wiley.

Chapter 3

ELECTRIC, MAGNETIC AND GRAVITATIONAL FIELDS

1. INTRODUCTION

Classically, there exist three fundamental forces involving action at-a-distance. The nature of these forces is either electric, magnetic or gravitational. A thermodynamic system may generally contain all of these force fields, which may originate inside, or outside the system. The central objective in this volume is to determine how such a system attains and departs from a state of thermal equilibrium, while its particles are subject to electric, magnetic and gravitational force fields.

In this chapter, we shall discuss the basic laws of electric, magnetic and gravitational fields. We shall further present a brief account of Maxwell's fundamental theory of electromagnetism.

2. THE ELECTRIC FIELD

2.1. *Coulomb's Law*

Based on experiment, it is found that any two electrically charged bodies either repel or attract each other, depending on whether the charges are alike, or dissimilar, respectively. It is further found that, if two spheres with charges Q_1 and Q_2 are separated by a distance r, which is much larger than their radii, then the mutual force F exerted between the two spheres will be proportional to both Q_1 and Q_2 and to $(1/r^2)$. That is

$$F = Q_1 Q_2 / A r^2, \tag{1}$$

where A is the constant of proportionality. The force $\mathbf{F}$ will be along the straight line joining the centers of the two spheres. This force will be one of repulsion if the product $(Q_1 Q_2)$ is positive. This, of course, will be the case whenever Q_1 and Q_2 are alike—either both are positive, or both are negative. If, however, $(Q_1 Q_2)$ is negative, then $\mathbf{F}$ will be a force of attraction.

Equation (1) represents a fundamental law in electrostatics, first discovered by Coulomb (1785–1789).

The choice of the constant A is arbitrary. In the *rationalized MKS* (meter-kilogram-second) system of units, A is given by

$$A = 4\pi\kappa, \tag{2}$$

where κ is defined as the dielectric constant of the medium in which the

29

spheres are placed. For vacuum, $\kappa = \kappa_0$, and

$$\kappa_0 = 10^{-9}/36\pi = 8.854 \times 10^{-12} \text{ farad/meter.} \qquad (3)$$

The dielectric constant κ can be expressed in terms of κ_0 for vacuum by

$$\kappa = \kappa_r \kappa_0. \qquad (4)$$

The quantity κ_r is called the relative dielectric constant.

In view of Eqs. (1) and (2), Coulomb's law may be expressed in the MKS system as

$$F = (Q_1 Q_2)/4\pi\kappa r^2. \qquad (5)$$

In this system of units, F is measured in newtons, r in meters, and Q_1 and Q_2 in coulombs.

Coulomb's law actually serves to determine the unit of electric charge—in this case, the Coulomb.

2.2 Electric Field Intensity

In the neighborhood of an electric charge Q, any test charge will experience a force. At any point P, the magnitude of this force per unit positive charge, together with the direction of the force, completely defines at P what is called the *electric field intensity* **E**, or simply the *electric field* at point P.

Accordingly, from Eq. (5), it follows that, at a distance r from the center of a sphere, with a charge Q, the electric field will be given by

$$\mathbf{E} = (Q/4\pi\kappa r^2)\, \mathbf{a}_r. \qquad (6)$$

Here $\mathbf{a}_r$ is a unit vector whose direction is radial.

It should be noticed here that if the test charge δQ is actually used to measure the electric field at a point P, then δQ must be sufficiently small so that it will not disturb appreciably the electric field it is supposed to measure. Ideally, δQ should be infinitesimally small.

2.3 Electric Flux and Electric Flux Density

The concept of electric flux lines was arrived at by Faraday (1832a, 1832b, 1833) as a consequence of a fundamental experiment. Faraday put a conducting sphere, having an electric charge Q, in another larger, hollow conducting sphere, which was initially uncharged. The two spheres were not electrically connected. The outer sphere was momentarily grounded. Then the inner charged sphere was removed. When the charge on the outer sphere was measured, it was found to be $-Q$, that is, equal in magnitude and opposite in sign to the charge of the inner sphere.

If the inner sphere is positively charged, then the outer sphere will be negatively charged. To explain this experiment, Faraday has postulated that there exist *electric flux lines* which emanate from the inner (positively-charged) sphere and terminate on the outer (negatively-charged) one. Always the number of electric flux lines emanating from a charged sphere is proportional to the charge. The constant of proportionality depends only on the system of units used. Figure 1 represents electric flux lines with the outer sphere designated by the dashed circle.

In the MKS system, the total number of electric flux lines Ψ emanating from a sphere, whose charge is Q, is simply given by

$$\Psi = Q. \tag{7}$$

In the MKS system, the unit of Ψ, like that of Q, is the coulomb.

Equation (7) can now be used to determine how at any point the electric field $\mathbf{E}$ is related to the electric flux density $\mathbf{D}$. The quantity $\mathbf{D}$ may be defined to be the number of electric flux lines crossing a small area (δs), per unit area. The area δs is transverse to the direction of $\mathbf{E}$ at the point of interest.

To relate $\mathbf{E}$ to $\mathbf{D}$ at any point, consider an isolated charge Q on a sphere of radius R, such as that shown in Fig. 1. For the argument to follow, let the dashed circle in that figure represent a fictitious sphere of radius r. At any point on this sphere, the electric flux density $\mathbf{D}$ is radial and has a constant magnitude. Thus, $\mathbf{D}$ will simply be equal to Ψ divided by the total surface area ($4\pi r^2$) of the sphere, and

$$\mathbf{D} = \mathbf{a}_r \Psi / 4\pi r^2, \tag{8}$$

where $\mathbf{a}_r$ is a radial unit vector.

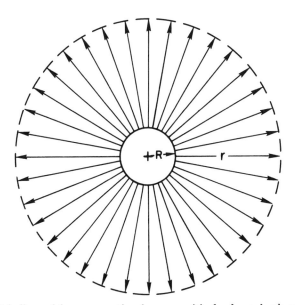

Fig. 1. Electric lines of force emanating from a positively-charged sphere of radius R.

But at any point on the fictitious sphere, the electric field

$$\mathbf{E} = \mathbf{a}_r Q / 4\pi \kappa r^2. \tag{9}$$

Hence, from Eqs. (7), (8), and (9), it follows that

$$\mathbf{D} = \kappa \mathbf{E}. \tag{10}$$

Equation (10) is valid for any isotropic medium.

Continuity of the electric flux lines and the inverse square law. The significance of the concept of electric flux lines actually stems from the inverse square law, which is applicable to the electric field around an isolated charged sphere. For this case, in the spherical coordinate system, the components $E_\theta = 0$, and $E_\phi = 0$. Then, from Eq. (78) [Chapter 2], it follows that

$$\nabla \cdot \mathbf{E} = (1/r^2)\ \partial(r^2 E_r)/\partial r, \tag{11}$$

where E_r is the radial component of $\mathbf{E}$. Substituting Eq. (6) into Eq. (11), we then get

$$\nabla \cdot \mathbf{E} = 0. \tag{12}$$

Therefore, introducing the concept of electric flux density $\mathbf{D}$, such that as expressed by Eq. (10), makes at once $\nabla \cdot \mathbf{D} = 0$. This, in turn, means that the electric flux lines will be continuous outside a charged sphere. Then, one can consider any space charge to consist of an infinite number of charged spheres properly distributed in space. In this way one can reason directly that the continuity of flux lines holds outside a charged region of any geometry, a result suggested by Faraday's experiment.

If, however, the electric field were not to obey an inverse square law, then it follows from Eq. (11) that $(\nabla \cdot \mathbf{E})$ would not have vanished. In such a case, the concept of electric flux lines, for the most part, would have been utterly useless. Quite fortunately, this is not the case.

2.4. *Gauss's Law*

Gauss's law may be stated in the MKS system of units as follows: *the total number of flux lines penetrating* (outwardly, or inwardly) *through any closed surface equals the total* (positive, or negative) *charge enclosed.* The geometry of the surface is totally unimportant. The surface may further be metallic, insulating, or even fictitious.

Gauss's law is a generalization of Faraday's conclusions arrived at on the basis of the experiment of two concentric spheres. For, if the two spheres were to be replaced by other nonspherical closed surfaces of any geometry, Faraday's results must still hold true. Namely, the outer, initially uncharged body, when grounded, will retain a charge equal in magnitude and opposite in sign to the charge on the inner body.

Mathematically, Gauss's law may be expressed as

$$\oint_{S} \mathbf{D} \cdot d\mathbf{s} = \int_{\mathcal{U}} \rho \, dv. \tag{13}$$

The left-hand side of Eq. (13) represents the integral over any closed surface S of the component of $\mathbf{D}$ normal to the infinitesimal area ds. The quantity ρ is the *volume-charge density*, or the charge per unit volume evaluated at various points. The product (ρdv) is the amount of charge contained within an infinitesimal volume dv. The right-hand side of Eq. (13), therefore, represents the integral of ρ over the entire volume $\mathcal{U}$ bounded by the closed surface S.

2.5. *The Electric Voltage V*

Definition. The voltage V_{ab} between any two points a and b (along a specified path C) is defined to be the work done (by some source of mechanical energy) on a unit positive charge, as the charge is moved from b to a on the path C.

The definition just stated, although convenient, lacks some rigor. A unit charge, especially in the MKS system, is so large in magnitude that it would profoundly disturb the electric fields, the effects of which we are trying to measure. The intent of the above definition, however, is that a positive test charge of sufficiently small magnitude is used. The work on this test charge, as it is moved from b to a, divided by the charge, is actually V_{ab}.

From the definitions of V and $\mathbf{E}$, we may write

$$V_{ab} = - \int_{b}^{a} \mathbf{E} \cdot d\mathbf{l} = \int_{a}^{b} \mathbf{E} \cdot d\mathbf{l}. \tag{14}$$

Here $d\mathbf{l}$ is an infinitesimal increment of length on the path C.

To solve Eq. (14) for $\mathbf{E}$, consider V_{ab} which can be written as

$$V_{ab} = V(a) - V(b) = - \int_{a}^{b} dV. \tag{15}$$

The quantities $V(a)$ and $V(b)$ are the values the function V assumes at points a and b, respectively. It is a mathematical identity, however, that

$$dV = \nabla V \cdot d\mathbf{l}. \tag{16}$$

For a proof of Eq. (16), see Eq. (21) [Chapter 2]. Substituting Eq. (16) into Eq. (15), we get

$$V_{ab} = - \int_{a}^{b} \nabla V \cdot d\mathbf{l}. \tag{17}$$

Comparison of Eq. (14) and (17), leads to

$$\mathbf{E} = -\nabla V. \tag{18}$$

The absolute voltage near a charged sphere. The absolute voltage V at any point P near a charged sphere is defined to be the relative voltage of point P with respect to points at infinity.

Accordingly, if P is at a distance r_0 away from the center of a sphere whose charge is Q, then

$$V = \int_{r_0}^{\infty} \mathbf{E} \cdot d\mathbf{r} = \int_{r_0}^{\infty} E \, dr, \tag{19}$$

where r is the distance measured from the center of the sphere along a radial line. But

$$E = Q/4\pi\kappa r^2. \tag{20}$$

Therefore,

$$V = \frac{Q}{4\pi\kappa} \int_{r_0}^{\infty} \frac{dr}{r^2} = \frac{Q}{4\pi\kappa r_0}. \tag{21}$$

Equipotential surfaces. In Chapter 2, we have seen that the gradient of scalar function is perpendicular at all points to the surfaces of constant values of that function. In view of Eq. (18), the electrostatic field $\mathbf{E}$ is always perpendicular to the surfaces of constant voltage (or potential) V. Such surfaces are called *equipotential*.

Accordingly, the electrostatic field is always perpendicular to the surface of a charged conductor, no matter what the geometry of the conductor may be. For, all points on the surface of a conductor must have the same voltage. Otherwise, there will be an electric current and the problem will not be one of electrostatics.

3. ELECTRIC CURRENT AND THE MAGNETIC FIELD

3.1. *The Electric Current*

The electric current i passing through any given area A is defined to be the amount of charge Q crossing A per second. This definition would be satisfactory if the rate of flow is constant. More generally, however, it may be stated that

$$i = dQ/dt. \tag{22}$$

In the MKS system of units, i is measured in amperes.

It is sometimes desirable to express the *current density* $\mathbf{J}$ (current per unit area) at a point in terms of the (average) drift velocity $\mathbf{v}$ of the charge and the volume charge density ρ. To do so, consider a volume (Fig. 2),

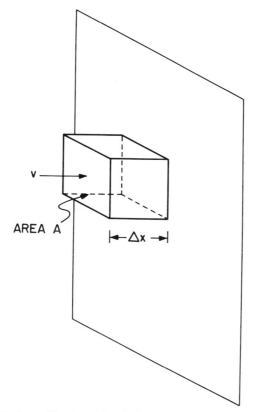

Fig. 2. A particle flux with velocity v crossing a small area A.

sufficiently small so that ρ is uniform within the volume. Suppose, now that during a small time interval Δt, the charge has moved a distance Δx normal to the small area A. Then, the distance

$$\Delta x = v \, \Delta t. \tag{23}$$

During Δt, the area A will be crossed by an amount of charge

$$\Delta Q = \rho A \, (\Delta x) = \rho A v (\Delta t). \tag{24}$$

Therefore, the current density $J = (1/A) \, dQ/dt$ will be given by

$$\mathbf{J} = \rho \mathbf{v}. \tag{25}$$

If the charges constituting ρ are electrons, whose concentration is n, then

$$\mathbf{J} = -qn\mathbf{v}, \tag{26}$$

where q is the magnitude of the electron charge.

From experiment, it is found that, for electrical conductors, the electron drift velocity **v** is proportional to the applied electric field E, provided that E is less than a certain critical value, which is usually large. Accordingly,

$$\mathbf{v} = -\mu\mathbf{E}. \tag{27}$$

The constant of proportionality μ is defined as the *mobility*. According to Eq. (27), the electron mobility is a positive quantity. For the electron, being negatively charged, always moves against **E**.

From Eqs. (26) and (27), it follows that

$$\mathbf{J} = q\mu n\mathbf{E}. \tag{28}$$

Equation (28) may be written as

$$\mathbf{J} = \sigma\mathbf{E}, \tag{29}$$

which is a more familiar form of Ohm's law. The quantity σ is known as the electrical conductivity and equals $(q\mu n)$.

3.2. *Magnetic Flux Density*

If a wire, carrying an electric current I, is placed near a magnet, it will be acted on by a force. The force $d\mathbf{F}$, acting on a length $d\mathbf{l}$ of the wire, is found to be given by

$$d\mathbf{F} = I\, d\mathbf{l} \times \mathbf{B}, \tag{30}$$

The quantity **B** is defined as the *magnetic flux density*, which represents the number of magnetic flux lines (penetrating a transverse area) per unit area. In the MKS system, the unit of B is *weber/meter²*.

3.3. *Nonexistence of Magnetic Sources or Sinks*

Isolated electric charges are of common occurrence. However, magnetic charges have never, so far, been found isolated. A magnet (Fig. 3), for example, must have a north and a south pole. Furthermore, there are as many magnetic flux lines approaching each pole as leaving it. Hence, even a magnetic pole is not, strictly speaking, a source, or a sink of magnetic flux lines. Invariably then each magnetic flux line constitutes a closed loop. Mathematically, for any closed surface S, we must have

$$\oint_S \mathbf{B} \cdot d\mathbf{s} = 0. \tag{31}$$

3.4. *Ampère's Law and the Magnetic Field Intensity*

It has been found by experiment that around any closed loop C, linked by a current I, the line integral

$$\oint_C (\mathbf{B}/\mu) \cdot d\mathbf{l} = I. \tag{32}$$

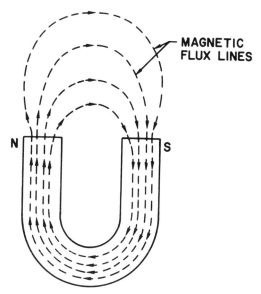

Fig. 3. Magnetic flux lines of a magnet emanating and terminating on themselves.

The quantity μ is called the *(magnetic) permeability*,* which depends on the medium. In the rationalized MKS system, the permeability μ_0 of free space is found to be

$$\mu_0 = 4\pi \times 10^{-7} \text{ henry/meter}. \tag{33}$$

The ratio $(\mathbf{B}/\mu)$ is defined as the *magnetic field (intensity)*, which is usually denoted by $\mathbf{H}$. Accordingly,

$$\mathbf{B} = \mu\mathbf{H}. \tag{34}$$

Thus, Eq. (32) may be rewritten as

$$\oint_C \mathbf{H} \cdot d\mathbf{l} = I. \tag{35}$$

The direction of rotation of $\mathbf{H}$ around I (Fig. 4) follows the rule of the right-hand corkscrew. If the axial motion of the screw is in the same direction as that of I, then the direction of rotation of the screw is the same as that of $\mathbf{H}$.

Equation (35) was a consequence of measurements, first conducted by Ampère (1826, 1883).

---

* To conform with the literature, μ is used to designate both mobility and permeability, which are entirely different quantities. There should be no confusion about this symbology, since the two quantities generally do not occur in one problem.

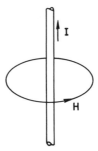

Fig. 4. Magnetic field **H** induced by a current I in a straight wire. Direction of rotation of **H** around I follows the rule of the right-hand cork screw.

3.5. *Faraday's Law*

It has been experimentally observed that if a wire forms a closed loop, which is linked by a time-varying magnetic flux Φ, then an emf e is induced across the loop such that

$$e = -d\Phi/dt. \tag{36}$$

Here t signifies time. Equation (36) was first discovered by Faraday (1832a, b, 1833).

As shown in Fig. 5, if the flux Φ increases in time along the direction of the arrows, then the emf e will be induced with the polarity as indicated in the figure. The relation of $d\Phi/dt$ and e is opposite to the rule of the right-hand corkscrew. Specifically, if $d\Phi/dt$ increases along the axial motion of the corkscrew, then the induced emf will be against the direction of rotation of that screw. With the rule of a right-hand corkscrew establishing a reference, Eq. (36) must retain a negative sign.

φ MAGNETIC FLUX LINES

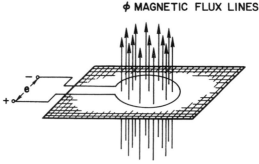

Fig. 5. An emf e induced in a wire forming a closed loop by a time-varying magnetic flux Φ which links the loop.

By definition

$$\Phi = \int_S \mathbf{B} \cdot d\mathbf{s}. \tag{37}$$

The integration of **B** is carried over the surface S bounded by the closed loop C. Therefore, Eq. (36) may be rewritten as

$$e = -(\partial/\partial t) \int_S \mathbf{B} \cdot d\mathbf{s}. \tag{38}$$

4. ENERGY STORED IN ELECTRIC AND MAGNETIC FIELDS

The existence of an electric and/or a magnetic field in a medium represents the storage of energy in the medium. We shall determine next the amount of energy per unit volume associated with an electric and a magnetic field.

4.1. *Energy Stored in an Electric Field*

The parallel-plate capacitor. When two electrically-isolated bodies are in sufficient proximity, they form what is called a capacitor. The two bodies may be two parallel (metallic) plates, as illustrated in Fig. 6.

When an initially uncharged capacitor is connected to a constant emf source, a charging current will be established temporarily. The current i relaxes to zero. The temporary flow of current may be explained on the basis of Gauss's law. Impressing a voltage across the capacitor requires the existence of an electric field between the two plates of the capacitor. But the electric field cannot exist in space without emanating from one plate and terminating on the other. According to Gauss's law, this action cannot take place unless there is a positive surface charge on one plate and a negative charge on the other. As the charges build up, a current must flow.

If the distance d separating the two plates is much smaller than the dimensions of the plates, the electric field **E** between the plates will be sub-

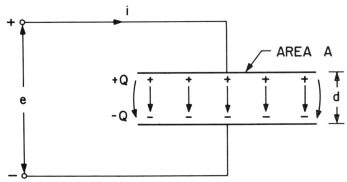

Fig. 6. Electric field lines between two electrically charged plates forming a capacitor. Except for the plate edges, the electric field lines between the plates are uniform.

stantially uniform (Fig. 6). For, the electric field must be perpendicular to the surface of any metal. This property has been explained in Subsection 2.5. Furthermore, most of the charge will be on the surfaces of the plates facing each other. The insignificant remaining part of the charges will cause what is called *edge* or *fringe effects*.

Energy associated with an electric field. If there are no ohmic losses during charging a capacitor, then all the energy furnished by the charging source will be expended to build up the electric field between the two plates of the capacitor. This energy, designated as W_e, will be expressed as

$$W_e = \int_0^T ei \, dt. \tag{39}$$

Here e and i are the charging voltage and current, respectively, as illustrated in Fig. 6; and T is the time period of charging the capacitor.

Neglecting for the moment the edge effects, we may say that the electric field $\mathbf{E}$ is uniform between the plates. Likewise will be the flux density $\mathbf{D}$.

By definition,

$$D = Q/A, \tag{40}$$

where A and Q are, respectively, the area of, and magnitude of the charge on, each plate. But

$$E = D/\kappa, \tag{41}$$

$$E = e/d, \tag{42}$$

and

$$i = dQ/dt. \tag{43}$$

From the preceding five equations, it follows that

$$W_e = \int_0^T (Ed) \frac{dQ}{dt} \, dt = \frac{Ad}{\kappa} \int_0^T D \frac{dD}{dt} \, dt$$

$$= \left(\frac{Ad}{\kappa}\right) \int_0^D D \, dD = \tfrac{1}{2}(Ad) E D. \tag{44}$$

The product (Ad) represents the volume between the two plates which the uniform electric field occupies. Therefore, the amount of energy, w_e, stored by the electric field per unit volume will simply be

$$w_e = \tfrac{1}{2}\kappa E^2. \tag{45}$$

We have stated earlier that the edge effects were to be neglected. Actually, one can devise a means whereby the edge effects, at least in principle, would be completely eliminated. One can imagine that the two parallel plates are infinite, although still separated by the finite distance d. In this case the value of i used in our calculation represents only the finite current which charges the finite partial area A of each plate.

From the preceding argument, it is apparent that Eq. (45) is exact.

4.2. *Energy Stored in a Magnetic Field*

Consider the solenoid, shown in Fig. 7. Let the permeability of the core be μ. If we ignore for the moment the edge effects, at and near both ends, we may say that in the zone covered by the N turns, the magnetic field H will be uniform and confined within the core. We may, therefore, calculate H in that zone by applying Ampère's law to the dashed rectangular closed loop $b_1b_2b_3b_4$. We shall consider that the vertical sides b_3b_2 and b_4b_1 extend sufficiently far, even to infinity, so that H vanishes along the finite portion b_1b_2. Since there are no components of H along b_2b_3 and b_4b_1, the line integral of H around the closed loop $b_1b_2b_3b_4$ will simply be (Hd), contributed by H integrated along b_3b_4.

Since the closed path links the current i, N times, invoking Ampère's law leads to

$$Hd = Ni, \tag{46}$$

or

$$H = Ni/d. \tag{47}$$

In order to establish a finite current, which supports a magnetic field H, an amount of energy has to be supplied from the electric source. If there

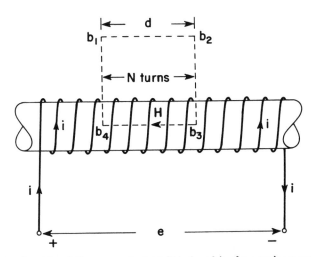

Fig. 7. A solenoid and the magnetic field H induced in the core by a current i.

are no ohmic losses, then this energy,

$$W_m = \int_0^T ei\,dt, \tag{48}$$

where T is the time period during which the final value of i has been established. Notice that when i attains a constant value, e vanishes as required by Faraday's law, and no further energy is transferred from the electric source to the solenoid.

From Faraday's law, however, the emf generated across N turns will be

$$e = N\,d\Phi/dt, \tag{49}$$

where Φ is the total magnetic flux linking each turn. But

$$\Phi = AB, \tag{50}$$

$$B = \mu H. \tag{51}$$

Therefore,

$$W_m = \int_0^T (Ad)\frac{dB}{dt}H\,dt = \mu(Ad)\int_0^T H\,dH$$

$$= \tfrac{1}{2}\mu(Ad)H^2 = \tfrac{1}{2}(Ad)HB. \tag{52}$$

The product (Ad) represents the volume hosting the magnetic field to which the energy W_m has been transferred. Hence, the amount of energy w_m per unit volume stored in the magnetic field will be given by

$$w_m = \tfrac{1}{2}\mu H^2. \tag{53}$$

The edge effects, we chose earlier to ignore, would not change the fact that Eqs. (52) and (53) are exact. For, it is possible, at least in principle, to eliminate the edge effects entirely. For example, imagine that the solenoid is infinitely long and its coil has an infinite number of turns. Our concern still will be over the finite number of N turns covering a finite part of the solenoid. In that case, e will designate that portion of voltage impressed across the N turns.

5. MAXWELL'S EQUATIONS OF ELECTROMAGNETISM

Thus far, we have briefly reviewed the theory of electricity and magnetism as known prior to the work of Maxwell (1864, 1876, 1892)—Coulomb's law, Faraday's concepts of electric and magnetic flux lines, Ampère's law and Faraday's law. All these are products of a profound understanding of electricity and magnetism. But they cannot possibly lead to a complete theory of electromagnetism, explaining, for example, propagation in free space.

From an esthetic point of view, the symmetry of the laws just mentioned is lacking. Specifically, Faraday's law essentially asserts that a time-varying magnetic field generates an electric field. But none of the pre-Maxwell laws suggest, even remotely, that a time-varying electric field generates a magnetic field. Maxwell's work has introduced the missing link, thereby establishing the beautiful symmetry in the laws of electromagnetism.

Maxwell's conclusions were arrived at by observing that a fundamental paradox existed in one of the then well-established laws of circuit theory. Resolving this paradox has led at once to postulating the existence of what is called a *displacement current.* This fundamental physical quantity is to be discussed next.

5.1. *Maxwell's Displacement Current*

Kirchhoff's current law (Kirchhoff 1847) states that the total electric current entering any node equals the total current leaving the node. The law holds equally well, if one considers any closed surface, real, or fictitious, rather than a node.

But Maxwell has observed that this law, as sound as it seems, breaks down completely in at least one fundamental case: namely, that of a capacitor. To explain this point, consider Fig. 8. If the capacitor is being charged, the charging current i will enter the fictitious closed surface, represented by the dashed closed loop. But no current, in the usual sense, ever leaves

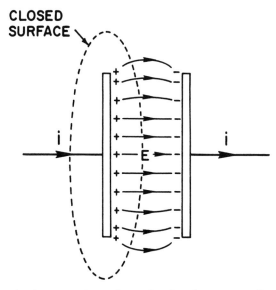

Fig. 8. A net conduction current entering a closed surface surrounding one plate of a capacitor—an exception to Kirchhoff's current law in its pre-Maxwell sense.

the closed surface. For ideally, the space between the two plates of the capacitor is a perfect electrical insulator, such as free space.

To resolve this serious paradox, Maxwell postulated that there existed some nonconduction current i_D, called a *displacement current*, such that

$$i = i_D. \tag{54}$$

Thus, as the conduction current i enters the closed surface, simultaneously, the displacement current i_D leaves it. In this way, the paradox in Kirchhoff's current law has been completely resolved. Furthermore, i_D can be determined immediately, since i can be found from the pre-Maxwell results. Specifically, for the capacitor of Fig. 8,

$$i = dQ/dt = A \ dD/dt, \tag{55}$$

where Q is the charge on the positive plate of the capacitor, and A is the area of each plate. Clearly, $Q = AD$ is a consequence of Gauss's law, when the edge effects are absent.

Equations (54) and (55) suggest at once that the displacement current density $\mathbf{J}_D$ will be expressed at any point in space as

$$\mathbf{J}_D = \partial \mathbf{D}/\partial t. \tag{56}$$

Generally, $\mathbf{D}$ is a function of position and time.

5.2. *Maxwell's Equations*

Maxwell's formulation (Maxwell 1864, 1876, 1892) of the theory of electromagnetism is based on four differential vector equations to be derived next.

The first equation. Faraday's law, expressed by Eq. (38), may be written as

$$\oint_C \mathbf{E} \cdot d\mathbf{l} = - \frac{\partial}{\partial t} \int_\mathbf{S} \mathbf{B} \cdot d\mathbf{s}, \tag{57}$$

where $\mathbf{S}$ is the surface surrounded by the closed loop C. But Stokes's theorem requires that for any vector, such as $\mathbf{E}$,

$$\oint_C \mathbf{E} \cdot d\mathbf{l} = \int_\mathbf{S} \nabla \times \mathbf{E} \cdot d\mathbf{s}. \tag{58}$$

Equations (57) and (58) lead to

$$\nabla \times \mathbf{E} = - \partial \mathbf{B}/\partial t, \tag{59}$$

which is the first of Maxwell's four equations.

The second equation. Ampère's law [Eq. (35)], in its classical form, states that

$$\oint_C \mathbf{H} \cdot d\mathbf{l} = I, \tag{60}$$

where I is the conduction current linking the closed loop C. Maxwell then has postulated that I is made not only of the conduction current, but also of the displacement current. Expressed in terms of the conduction current density $\mathbf{J}_c$ as well as the displacement current density $\mathbf{J}_D$, Eq. (60) may be rewritten as

$$\oint_C \mathbf{H} \cdot d\mathbf{l} = \int_S (\mathbf{J}_C + \mathbf{J}_D) \cdot d\mathbf{s}. \tag{61}$$

Here $\mathbf{J}_D$ is as expressed by Eq. (56). But from Stokes's theorem

$$\oint_C \mathbf{H} \cdot d\mathbf{l} = \int_S \nabla \times \mathbf{H} \cdot d\mathbf{s} = \int_S (\mathbf{J}_C + \mathbf{J}_D) \cdot d\mathbf{s}. \tag{62}$$

or

$$\nabla \times \mathbf{H} = \mathbf{J}_c + \partial \mathbf{D} / \partial t. \tag{63}$$

Equation (63) is the second of Maxwell's equations. In free space, $\mathbf{J}_C = 0$, and the implication then is that a time-varying electric field generates a magnetic field. Thus, the counterpart of Faraday's law and the symmetry of the laws of electricity and magnetism are established.

The third equation. If, in a medium, there is a space charge of volume density ρ, then Gauss's law states [Eq. (13)] that

$$\oint_S \mathbf{D} \cdot d\mathbf{s} = \int_v \rho \, dv. \tag{64}$$

But from Gauss's theorem, it follows that

$$\oint_S \mathbf{D} \cdot d\mathbf{s} = \int_v \nabla \cdot \mathbf{D} \, dv. \tag{65}$$

Therefore, Eqs. (64) and (65) lead to

$$\nabla \cdot \mathbf{D} = \rho, \tag{66}$$

which is the third of Maxwell's equations.

The fourth equation. As explained in Section 3.3, magnetic flux lines do not have sources and sinks, a property expressed by Eq. (31), which is

$$\oint_S \mathbf{B} \cdot d\mathbf{s} = 0,$$

for any closed surface S. Applying Gauss's theorem to the preceding equation, it follows immediately that

$$\nabla \cdot \mathbf{B} = 0. \tag{67}$$

Equation (67) is the last of Maxwell's equations. This equation expresses the property that the magnetic flux density is solenoidal.

5.3. Boundary Conditions for Electric and Magnetic Fields

In principle, any electromagnetic problem can be solved by solving Maxwell's four equations subject to the boundary conditions, which the electric and magnetic fields must satisfy. These conditions will be determined next.

Tangential components of the electric and magnetic fields at the boundary between two media. Consider Fig. 9 which represents a small closed loop crossing the boundary surface between two different media, I and II. Medium I has a permeability μ_1, and a dielectric constant κ_1. Medium II has correspondingly μ_2 and κ_2. The components of the electric field, tangential to the surface, are E_{1t} and E_{2t}. The first is just within medium I and the second is just within medium II. The normal components on either end of the loop are approximately E_n and E_n'. We now want to determine how E_{1t} is related to E_{2t}.

To do so, let us apply Faraday's law to the closed loop shown in Fig. 9. We may, therefore, write

$$(E_{1t}-E_{2t})\,\Delta l+(E_n-E_n')\,\Delta w=\pm\,(\Delta w\Delta l)\,\partial B/\partial t. \qquad (68)$$

Letting Δw and Δl both tend to zero, in the limit, E_{1t} and E_{2t} will be the tangential components at the boundary in the two respective media. If we now let Δw tend to zero before Δl, then Eq. (68) reduces to

$$E_{1t}-E_{2t}=0, \qquad (69)$$

that is,

$$E_{1t}=E_{2t}. \qquad (70)$$

By a similar procedure, using Maxwell's second equation [Eq. (61)] in its integral form, it can be shown that

$$H_{1t}=H_{2t}. \qquad (71)$$

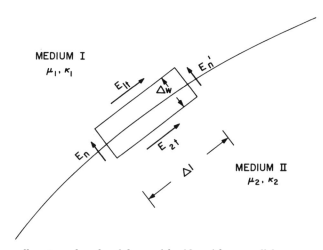

Fig. 9. A small rectangular closed loop with sides either parallel, or normal, to and crossing the boundary between two different media.

The quantities H_{1t} and H_{2t} are the components of the magnetic field tangential to the boundary surface between the two media, I and II. The components H_{1t} and H_{2t} are just within media I and II, respectively.

In conclusion, it may be stated that the components of the electric and of the magnetic field, tangential to the boundary between any two different media, are continuous at the boundary.

Normal components of the electric and magnetic flux densities at the boundary between two different media. Fig. 10 shows a small volume which includes part of the boundary surface between two different media. The top and bottom parts of the volume are parallel to the boundary. The components of the electric flux density normal to the boundary is D_{1n} in medium I and D_{2n} in medium II. We wish now to relate D_{1n} to D_{2n}.

To do so, let us apply Gauss's law to the small volume of Fig. 10. We, therefore, write

$$(D_{1n} - D_{2n})\Delta A + \smallint_{\Delta S} \mathbf{D} \cdot d\mathbf{s} = \rho(\Delta A \ \Delta w), \tag{72}$$

where the integration is carried over the cylindrical surface ΔS of the volume.

As ΔA and ΔS both tend to zero, in the limit, D_{1n} and D_{2n} will be the normal components of the flux densities at the boundary in both respective media. If we now let ΔS tend to zero before ΔA, Eq. (72) reduces to

$$D_{1n} - D_{2n} = 0, \tag{73}$$

that is,

$$D_{1n} = D_{2n}. \tag{74}$$

It has been assumed, of course, that there are no surface charges between the two media.

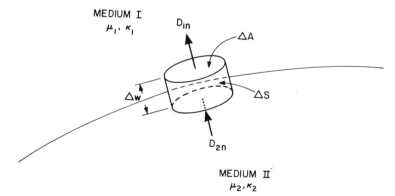

Fig. 10. A small cylinder with top and bottom parallel to the boundary between two media. The side surface of the cylinder is normal and crosses the boundary.

By a similar argument, using Eq. (31), applied to the volume of Fig. 10, it can be shown that

$$B_{1n} = B_{2n}, \tag{75}$$

where B_{1n} and B_{2n} are the normal components of the magnetic flux density in the two respective media at the boundary.

In summary, we may state that the components of the electric and of the magnetic flux density, normal to the boundary between any two media, are continuous at the boundary.

6. NEWTON'S LAW OF GRAVITY AND THE GRAVITATIONAL FLUX LINES

Newton's law of gravity (Newton 1687) states that the force of attraction F between any two spherical masses M_1 and M_2 is proportional to M_1, M_2 and the inverse square of the distance r between their centers. The distance r is supposed to be much larger than the radii of the respective bodies, a condition usually satisfied in nature. Accordingly,

$$F = G \, M_1 M_2 / r^2, \tag{76}$$

where G is the constant of proportionality.

In the MKS system of units, from experiment

$$G = 6.67 \times 10^{-11} \text{ meter}^3/\text{kilogram-second}^2. \tag{77}$$

There are contrasts between some of the laws of electrostatics and others of gravitation. Like charges, for example, repel each other, and attraction occurs only between dissimilar charges. However, like (positive) masses attract each other, rather than suffer a repulsion.

Nevertheless, there are some striking similarities between the laws of electrostatics and those of (static) gravitation. Newton's law of gravity is an inverse square law. So is Coulomb's law. Parallel to the definition of an electric field, therefore, we may define the *gravitational field* $\mathbf{E}_g$ at any point P to be the force acting on a unit mass. Thus, at any point outside an isolated spherical mass M, from the definition of $\mathbf{E}_g$, and Eq. (76), it follows that

$$\mathbf{E}_g = -\mathbf{a}_r GM / r^2, \tag{78}$$

where r is the distance between point P and the center of the mass, and $\mathbf{a}_r$ is a radial unit vector.

As explained earlier [Eq. (12)], any force obeying an inverse square law must be solenoidal, at all points where the law applies. The gravitational field $\mathbf{E}_g$ is, therefore, solenoidal outside a spherical mass. It will be shown shortly that $\mathbf{E}_g$ is solenoidal outside any mass, or masses of any geometry. If we now define the gravitational flux density to be proportional to E_g, then at once the gravity flux lines will be continuous in free space. Furthermore, like in electrostatics, the gravitational flux lines must terminate on (positive) masses and conceivably emanate from negative masses, if they do exist.

Let us define the gravitational flux density by

$$\mathbf{D}_g = \mathbf{E}_g / 4\pi G. \tag{79}$$

We can now calculate the total number of gravitational flux lines Ψ_g terminating on any (positive) mass M, regardless of its geometry. If the mass density is ρ_m, then the mass within an infinitesimal volume dv will be $(\rho_m \, dv)$.

Now imagine a finite fictitious sphere of radius R and center coinciding with that of dv. The gravitational field $d\mathbf{E}_g$ induced by the mass $\rho_m \, dv$ at various points of the sphere will be given by

$$d\mathbf{E}_g = -\mathbf{a}_r G \rho_m \, dv / R^2, \tag{80}$$

where $\mathbf{a}_r$ is a unit radial vector. But the flux density $d\mathbf{D}_g$, associated with $d\mathbf{E}_g$, will be

$$d\mathbf{D}_g = -\mathbf{a}_r \rho_m \, dv / 4\pi R^2. \tag{81}$$

Thus, the total gravitational flux lines terminating on the infinitesimal mass $(\rho_m \, dv)$ will simply be

$$d\Psi_g = \rho_m \, dv. \tag{82}$$

Furthermore, the total gravitational flux lines Ψ_g terminating on the macroscopic mass M, of any geometry, will be

$$\Psi_g = \int_v \rho_m \, dv. \tag{83}$$

The integration in Eq. (83) is carried over the entire volume of the mass M. Equation (83) leads to

$$\Psi_g = M. \tag{84}$$

Equation (83) has a second interesting consequence. From the meaning of divergence, expressed as Theorem A [Subsection 3.2, Chapter 2], Eq. (83) may be written as

$$\Psi_g = \int_v \nabla \cdot \mathbf{D}_g \, dv = \int_v \rho_m \, dv. \tag{85}$$

whence,

$$\nabla \cdot \mathbf{D}_g = \rho_m. \tag{86}$$

In view of Eq. (79) and (86), we have

$$\nabla \cdot \mathbf{E}_g = 4\pi G \rho_m. \tag{87}$$

Equation (87) has a particularly interesting implication. At any point within a mass, $\nabla \cdot \mathbf{E}_g \neq 0$, that is, the gravitational field is nonsolenoidal. However, in free space surrounding any number of masses of any geometry, the gravitational field will be necessarily solenoidal. For ρ_m vanishes in free space. This will mean that in the neighborhood of a spherical mass, the gravitational field must obey an inverse square law.

PROBLEMS

1. The capacitance C between any two bodies having equal and opposite charges is defined generally by

$$C = Q/V,$$

where Q is the positive charge and V is the voltage difference between the two bodies. In the MKS system, C is measured in farads.

Neglecting the edge effects, show that for the parallel-plate capacitor (see Fig. 6),

$$C = \kappa A/d.$$

Hint. Assume Q to be known and from Gauss's law, calculate D, from which E follows. Integrate E to get V.

2. Show that the capacitance C per unit length between any two coaxial cylinders is given by

$$C = 2\pi\kappa/\ln(R_2/R_1),$$

where R_1 and R_2 are the radii of the internal and external cylinders, respectively.

Hint. Assume a known surface charge ρ per unit length on the internal cylinder. Use Gauss's law to calculate D at any point between the two cylinders. Then find E and integrate to get V.

3. Show that the absolute voltage induced at any point P by a cloud of charge contained in a volume $\mathcal{V}$ of any geometry is related to the volume charge density ρ at various points within $\mathcal{V}$ by

$$V = (\pi\kappa)^{-1} \int_{\mathcal{V}} (\rho/r)\ dv.$$

Here r is the distance of point P from the origin of reference.

4. Show that the capacitance C between two concentric spheres is given by

$$C = 4\pi\kappa\ r_1 r_2/(r_2 - r_1),$$

where r_1 and r_2 are the radii of the internal and external spheres, respectively.

5. Calculate the capacitance between two parallel plates of area $A = 100$ cm², and separated by a distance $d = 0.1$ cm. Assume that the medium between the plates is free space (see Appendix D for the value of κ_0).

6. A parallel-plate capacitor of area $A = 1$ m², is charged to a voltage $V = 10,000$ volts. The plates are separated by a distance $d = 10$ cm. A slab

of thickness $a = 5$ cm, and of the same area A, is inserted between the two capacitor plates such that it touches the lower plate. Calculate the flux density D between the plates.

[Ans. $D = 1.418 \times 10^{-6}$ coulomb/meter^2.]

7. An imaginary sphere with a radius $R = 1$ m, encloses a space charge of volume-charge density ρ, given by: $\rho = kr$. Here r is the distance measured from the center of the sphere, and $k = 10^{-6}$ coulomb/m^4. Calculate the total charge Q contained in the sphere and the electric field E_R at the surface of the sphere. Consider that $\kappa = \kappa_0$.

[Ans. $Q = \pi k R^4 = \pi \times 10^{-6}$ coulomb, $E = Q/4\pi\kappa R^2 = 9000\pi$ volt/meter.]

8. For Problem 7, derive an expression for the absolute voltage V_r at any point inside the sphere, at a distance r away from the center.

Hints. Integrate E to get V, and evaluate the constant of integration from the boundary conditions at the surface. Two different methods can be used to determine E. Method 1: use Maxwell's third equation, expressed in the spherical coordinates and solve for E. Method 2: apply Coulomb's law for any fictitious sphere of radius r, by calculating the charge Q_r within the sphere.

[Ans. $E = kr^2/4\kappa$, $V = -kr^3/12\kappa + V_0$, $V_0 = kR^3/3\kappa$, which is a constant of integration.]

9. Neglecting edge effects, show that the total flux between any two coaxial cylinders, linking the inner cylinder, is given by

$$\Phi = (d\mu I/2\pi) \ln(r_2/r_1),$$

where d is the axial length of each cylinder, and r_1 and r_2 are the radii of the inner and outer cylinders, respectively. The currents carried by the two cylinders are equal in magnitude, which is I, and opposite in direction.

10. A straight wire of circular cross section is carrying a uniformly-distributed current. Show that, outside the wire,

$$H = I/2\pi r$$

and, inside the wire,

$$H = (I/2\pi R^2) r.$$

Here I is the total current carried by the wire, R is the radius of the wire cross section, and r is the shortest distance between any point and the axis of the wire.

11. The electric field E at a point in free space is expressed by

$$E = E_0 \sin\omega t,$$

with $E_0 = 10$ volts/m,

(a) Determine the maximum value of the energy in joules stored in the electric field per unit volume.

(b) Calculate the maximum value of the displacement current density J_D at $\omega = 10^3$, 10^6, and 10^9 radians/sec.

[Ans. (a) $w_e = 4.425 \times 10^{-10}$ joules/m³;
        (b) $J_D = 8.85 \times 10^{-8}$, 8.85×10^{-5}, and 8.85×10^{-2} amperes/m².]

12. The magnetic field H in free space is 10 amperes/meter. Calculate the amount of energy stored in the magnetic field per unit volume.

[Ans. $w_m = 4\pi \times 10^{-5}$ joules/m³.]

13. Using Maxwell's equations, show that in free space

$$\nabla^2 \mathbf{E} = \mu\epsilon(\partial^2 \mathbf{E}/\partial t^2), \qquad \nabla^2 \mathbf{H} = \mu\epsilon(\partial^2 \mathbf{H}/\partial t^2),$$

where ∇^2 signifies $(\nabla \cdot \nabla)$. Each one of the preceding two equations represent what is known as the *wave equation*.

Hint. To derive the first wave equation, operate by $(\nabla \times)$ on both sides of the first of Maxwell's equations. Then, expand $\nabla \times (\nabla \times \mathbf{E})$ using identity (46) [Chapter 2].

14. An electromagnetic wave is propagated along the positive y direction of the Cartesian coordinates. The electric field $\mathbf{E}$ is given by

$$\mathbf{E} = \mathbf{k}E_z = \mathbf{k}E_0 \sin(\omega t - \beta x),$$

where ω and β are constants, known as the angular frequency (radians per second), and phase constant (radians per unit length), respectively. An electromagnetic wave described by the preceding equation constitutes what is defined as a *plane wave*.

Sketch E at various instants ($t_0 = 0$, $t_1 = \pi/2\omega$, $t_2 = \pi/\omega$, $t_3 = 3\pi/2\omega$, and $t_4 = 2\pi/\omega$). On the basis of the sketch, verify the following:

(a) The wavelength λ (defined to be the length between two successive maxima, or minima, of E at any one instant) is given by

$$\lambda = 2\pi/\beta.$$

(b) The period of oscillation T (defined as the time elapsing between two successive maxima, or minima of E at any one point in space) is given by

$$T = 1/f,$$

where the frequency,

$$f = \omega/2\pi \text{ cycles/second, or hertz.}$$

(c) The velocity c of propagation of the wave will be expressed as

$$c = \omega/\beta.$$

15. It is convenient to describe the electric field in Problem 14, in the exponential form, as

$$E_z = E_0 \exp[i(\omega t - \beta x)],$$

where $i = (-1)^{1/2}$.

(a) Show that the preceding expression for E_z represents a solution (in one dimension) of the first wave equation cited in Problem 13.

(b) Verify that the velocity of propagation c of the wave is given by

$$c = (\mu\epsilon)^{-1/2}.$$

(c) Evaluate $c = c_0$ of free space. Compare the result with the velocity of light in free space (see Appendix D).

16. Using any one of the first two of Maxwell's equations, derive an expression for the magnetic field **H** associated with the electric field E_z, expressed in Problem 15.

17. The ratio of the maximum value of E to that of H, for a plane wave, equals the magnitude of what is defined as the intrinsic impedance Z_{in} of the medium in which the wave is propagated. Calculate Z_{in} for free space. [Ans. $Z_{in} = 120\pi$ ohms.]

18. A hypothetical infinite cylindrical body has a circular cross section and a mass per unit axial length, σ_m, which is uniform throughout the body. Using the concept of gravitational flux lines, derive an expression for the gravitational field intensity $\mathbf{E}_g$ at points exterior to the cylindrical body whose cross-sectional radius is ρ_0.

19. Derive an expression for the gravitational field $\mathbf{E}_g$, for the body described in Problem 18, at points interior to the body.

REFERENCES

Ampère, A. M. 1826, Chez Crochard, Paris. (Microfilm of the original is in the University of Chicago Library.)

—— 1883, Théorie mathématique des phénomènes électrodynamiques, uniquement déduite de l'expérience (second edition); A. Hermann, Paris.

de Coulomb, C. A. 1785–1789, Memoires sur l'Electricité et le Magnétisme, Bachelier Paris.

Faraday, M. 1832a, Phil. Trans. 122, pp. 125–162.

—— 1832b, Recherches Expérimentale sur l'Electricité, Ann. Chem. Phys. **50**, 5–69, 113–163.

—— 1833, Phil. Mag., (Series 3) **3**, pp. 161–171, 253–263, 353–363.

Kirchhoff, G. 1847, Pogg. Ann. Phys. **72**, 497.

Maxwell, J. C. 1864, Roy. Soc. Proc., "A Dynamical Theory of Electromagnetic Field," **13**, pp. 531–536.

—— 1876, "Theory of Electrical Induction," Nature **14**, pp. 27–28.

—— 1892, A Treatise on Electricity and Magnetism (third edition), Clarendon Press, Oxford.

Newton, I. 1687, Philosophiae Naturalis Principia Mathematica (London: Jessu Societatis Regiae ac Typis Josephi Streater), English Translation by Andrew Motte 1729. Revised by Florian Cajori, 1934 (Berkeley; University of California).

Chapter 4

FOUNDATION OF THE THEORY OF GENERALIZED FIELDS IN RELATION TO CLASSICAL THERMODYNAMICS

1. INTRODUCTION

Thermodynamics, in its classical formulation, is founded on a number of laws. The first (Carnot 1824; Mayer 1842–1845, 1867; Joule 1845, 1850; Helmholtz 1847) expresses the conservation of energy in all of its forms. The second (Clausius 1850) pertains to the important aspects of entropy. The third (Nernst 1912) concerns the unattainability principle of the absolute zero. Another significant principle relates to what is known as the mechanism of detailed balancing, characterizing thermal equilibrium in its broadest sense.

In Chapter 1, we have broadly discussed the aspects of natural philosophy which justify the existence of any theoretical framework. In that respect, we have arrived at a number of fundamental conclusions. Of these, we shall consider in this chapter at least three crucial questions relevant to the classical thermodynamic framework. The first concerns whether classical equilibrium thermodynamics has been formulated as a natural limiting case of a nonequilibrium situation. We shall see that this was not the case. The second question is not unrelated to the first. Has the second law been used, in the classical thermodynamic formulation, in a strict sense? We shall find that if it has, it can still be done in a stricter and seemingly more rigorous way. The question of validity of the classical interpretation of the second law, for systems in nonequilibrium, has, in fact, been raised by some eminent thermodynamicists (Mayer 1955, Meixner 1970, Kestin and Rice 1970). The third and perhaps the most serious question to be raised: are there any paradoxes or inconsistencies clearly arising in classical thermodynamics within its own framework?

As we attempt to answer the questions raised, we shall see that the first and second laws of thermodynamics lend themselves to new interpretations which differ significantly from those of classical thermodynamics. We shall further observe that the fundamental propositions of the Thermodynamic Theory of Generalized Fields (TTGF) naturally follow. A number of fundamental aspects of the TTGF will be deduced in this chapter before they are stated and more extensively discussed in Chapter 6.

As the theory of generalized fields is developed, it will become apparent that consequences of the third law of thermodynamics are of more crucial relevance to this theory than it has been to the classical thermodynamic formulation. Considerations of the third law, however, cannot be treated effectively in this chapter. They will be left to Chapters 8, 9, and 10, after sufficient insight into the understanding of the new thermodynamic theory has been developed.

2. INTERPRETATIONS OF THE FIRST AND SECOND LAWS IN CLASSICAL THERMODYNAMICS

Nearly a century ago, the first and second laws of thermodynamics were interpreted by Gibbs (1875-8). This interpretation evolved into a general formulation providing a basis for subsequent developments in equilibrium thermodynamics as well as in its younger offshoot which is concerned with nonequilibrium. These two branches of thermodynamics, as known today, underlie directly or indirectly much of the understanding in the various diversified areas of the physical, life and engineering sciences.

In this section, we shall attempt to briefly discuss the Gibbs equation and some of its fundamental consequences.

2.1. *The Gibbs and Gibbs-Duhem Equations*

Consider a one-constituent thermodynamic system whose particles are not subject to electric, magnetic, or gravitational fields. Let part of that system consist of N particles occupying an appropriately small* volume V in which the pressure is p. Let η and U be the entropy and internal energy of the N particles, respectively, and T be their absolute temperature. In an infinitesimal *quasistatic* change involving a reversible process for which N is constant, it has been reasoned that the first and second laws of thermodynamics would lead to

$$dU = T\,d\eta - p\,dV. \tag{1}$$

Here $(T d\eta)$ represents the increment of heat energy given to the N particles and (pdV) is the amount of mechanical work done by the particles on their surroundings.

If the number of particles within V changes by an amount dN, then according to Gibbs, Eq. (1) would be modified to

$$dU = T\,d\eta - p\,dV + \tilde{\mu}\,dN. \tag{2}$$

The quantity $\tilde{\mu}$ is generally known as the *chemical potential* and has been

---

* The statement "appropriately small volume V," wherever used, is meant to signify that V is sufficiently small so that the pressure, temperature, and other thermodynamic parameters, if nonuniform in the system, may be considered uniform within V. However, V must not be too small, otherwise the fluctuations may not be insignificant.

defined by Gibbs to be given by

$$\tilde{\mu} = (\partial U / \partial N)_{\eta, V}. \tag{3}$$

From Gibbs's equation, a fundamental relation follows. The coefficients of the differentials are all *intensive* quantities* or *variables* in the sense that none of these coefficients depend on the mass (or number of particles) within the volume V considered. On the other hand, the quantities U, η, V and N are all *extensive* variables* since each one depends on the mass (or number) of particles within V.

We have stated earlier that V is an appropriately small volume. Now because U, η, V and N are extensive variables, if we change η, V and N to $a\eta$, aV, and aN, where a is a constant, we must change U to aU. We may, therefore, put

$$dU = a_0 U, \quad d\eta = a_0 \eta, \quad dV = a_0 V, \quad dN = a_0 N. \tag{4}$$

In this case a_0 is an infinitesimal constant.

From Eqs. (2) and (4), it follows that

$$U = T\eta - pV + \tilde{\mu}N. \tag{5}$$

We shall call Eq. (5) the *Euler equation* corresponding to Eq. (2).

Differentiating Eq. (5), we get

$$dU = T\,d\eta + \eta\,dT - p\,dV - V\,dp + \tilde{\mu}\,dN + N\,d\tilde{\mu}. \tag{6}$$

Subtracting Eq. (6) from Eq. (2) makes it possible to solve for $d\tilde{\mu}$. Carrying out the steps, we obtain

$$d\tilde{\mu} = -(\eta/N)\,dT + (V/N)\,dp. \tag{7}$$

Equation (7) is generally known as the Gibbs–Duhem equation.

The case just discussed would become more general, if particles within V were subject to other effects, such as electric and gravitational. Such fields have been accounted for classically by replacing the chemical potential $\tilde{\mu}$ by what has been termed the generalized potential $\tilde{\mu}_t$. In this case Eq. (2) would be more generally expressed as (Guggenheim 1967)

$$dU = T\,d\eta - p\,dV + \tilde{\mu}_t\,dN. \tag{8}$$

Again, since $\tilde{\mu}_t$ is supposedly an intensive variable, then the Euler equation corresponding to Eq. (8) will be identical with Eq. (5), with $\tilde{\mu}$ replaced by $\tilde{\mu}_t$. The resulting equation together with Eq. (8) makes it possible to solve for $d\tilde{\mu}_t$, which can be expressed as

$$d\tilde{\mu}_t = -(\eta/N)\,dT + (V/N)\,dp. \tag{9}$$

---

* For a rigorous definition of the terms intensive and extensive, see Subsection A.1, Appendix A, p. 239.

A detailed discussion concerning the derivation of Eq. (9), and its mathematical uniqueness, may be found in Appendix A, pp. 239–245.

2.2. *Thermal Equilibrium in Classical Thermodynamics*

In the classical formulation, the state of thermal equilibrium in any system is invariably characterized by the condition that, everywhere in the system, the generalized potential

$$\tilde{\mu}_t = C, \tag{10}$$

where C is a constant. This result is applicable to each constituent in a multicomponent system.

One component of $\tilde{\mu}_t$ is, of course, the chemical potential $\tilde{\mu}$. If the other components of $\tilde{\mu}_t$ are $\tilde{\mu}_1, \tilde{\mu}_2, \cdots, \tilde{\mu}_i$, then the criterion of thermal equilibrium in classical thermodynamics may be expressed, for constituent j, by

$$\tilde{\mu}_j + \tilde{\mu}_{1j} + \tilde{\mu}_{2j} + \cdots + \tilde{\mu}_{ij} = C. \tag{11}$$

Thus,

$$\nabla \tilde{\mu}_{tj} = \nabla \tilde{\mu}_j + \nabla \tilde{\mu}_{1j} + \nabla \tilde{\mu}_{2j} + \cdots + \nabla \tilde{\mu}_{ij} = 0. \tag{12}$$

Since each of the terms in Eq. (12) is a force, or at least has the dimension of a force, then this equation may be rewritten as

$$\mathbf{f}_j + \mathbf{f}_{1j} + \mathbf{f}_{2j} + \cdots + \mathbf{f}_{ij} = 0, \tag{13}$$

where the forces, or virtual forces, are given by

$$\mathbf{f}_j = \nabla \tilde{\mu}_j, \quad \mathbf{f}_{1j} = \nabla \tilde{\mu}_{1j}, \quad \mathbf{f}_{2j} = \nabla \tilde{\mu}_{2j}, \cdots, \quad \mathbf{f}_{ij} = \nabla \tilde{\mu}_{ij}. \tag{14}$$

A consequent interpretation of Eq. (13) is that, at thermal equilibrium, the balancing for each constituent at each point in a multicomponent system must be established by *all* the force fields *combined*. The balancing of a constituent, of course, means that there will be as many particles crossing in one direction a given area per unit time as there are particles crossing in the opposite direction. Accordingly, Eq. (13) expresses what is generally defined as the *mechanism of detailed balancing*, which characterizes generally the state of thermal equilibrium in the framework of classical thermodynamics.

As is well known, the mechanism of detailed balancing underlies the basic formulation of classical nonequilibrium thermodynamics.

3. ARE THERE LIMITATIONS IN THE CLASSICAL THERMODYNAMIC FORMULATION?

We shall discuss in this section some questions which concern the internal-energy equation, the mechanism of detailed balancing, and the definition of entropy for systems in nonequilibrium.

3.1. *On the Question of Consistency of the Classical Criteria of Thermal Equilibrium*

In the framework of classical thermodynamics, it has been considered that at every point in a system, the generalized potential $\tilde{\mu}_t$ is a constant at thermal equilibrium. Let us see now what this result means first for a liquid-vapor system at thermal equilibrium. In such a system there are no electric or magnetic effects. Ignoring gravity, then $\tilde{\mu}_t$ reduces to the chemical potential $\tilde{\mu}$.

Consider now two points A and B on either side of the liquid-vapor interface. Imagine that l is a path linking A to B, and that dl is a differential increment of length along l. Let $d\tilde{\mu}$, dT, and dp be the changes in $\tilde{\mu}$, T, and p along dl.

At thermal equilibrium, of course, $dT=0$. Furthermore, the classical result that $d\tilde{\mu}=0$ will then require in Eq. (7) that $dp=0$. If we now interpret that the pressure p is the externally measurable pressure for the liquid—not, for example, the kinetic pressure—we can explain at once that p of the liquid equals the pressure on the vapor side. We have at once complete consistency between Eqs. (9) and (12) when applied to the liquid-vapor system. This conclusion, of course, is well known.

Let us, however, consider Eqs. (9) and (12) for other systems which include effects such as electric and gravitational.

The atmospheric gas at thermal equilibrium. It is well known that if the state of thermal equilibrium in an atmospheric gas around a planet is established, the gas will be isothermal and the gas pressure p will decrease monotonically with altitude. The generalized potential $\tilde{\mu}_t$ in this case must consist of two components: the chemical potential $\tilde{\mu}$ and a gravity potential $\tilde{\mu}_g$. Now according to classical thermodynamics, at thermal equilibrium,

$$d\tilde{\mu}_t = d\tilde{\mu}_g + d\tilde{\mu} = 0. \tag{15}$$

Yet we know that, although $dT=0$ throughout the system, $dp \neq 0$ along the vertical axis; and, from Eq. (9), it follows that

$$d\tilde{\mu}_t = (V/N)\, dp \neq 0. \tag{16}$$

Are Eqs. (15) and (16) consistent? Hardly! For, unlike the liquid-vapor problem, it is not possible to define p in such a way as to make $dp=0$ along the vertical axis. It should be noted here, however, that avoiding the inconsistency between Eqs. (15) and (16) is usually accomplished in the literature by a certain mathematical procedure. Appendix A (pp. 239–245) presents a discussion of this procedure which is investigated from the point of view of the conditions required for mathematical existence.

Conduction electrons in solid interfaces. Consider next conduction electrons in the interface between any two different solids. Such solids could be metals and semiconductors. In the latter, the electron concentration can vary over an extremely wide range. This matter is discussed in considerable detail in Chapter 5. For the moment, let us assume that the electron concentration in the semiconductor is, say, $10^{16}/cm^3$. If we now choose the metal to be copper, the concentration of electrons is known to be about $8.4 \times 10^{22}/cm^3$ (see Appendix C, p. 247). The variation in concentration through the interface is large. We shall come back to consequences of this point shortly.

For charged particles, such as electrons, subject to no other than an electric field, the generalized potential $\tilde{\mu}_t$ consists of two components: the chemical potential and the electric potential. In this case $\tilde{\mu}_t$ is generally called the *electrochemical potential*. If the interface conduction electrons are in thermal equilibrium, then in the classical thermodynamic framework,

$$d\tilde{\mu}_t = 0. \tag{17}$$

Consider now Eq. (9). Since $dT = 0$, the equation reduces to

$$d\tilde{\mu}_t = (1/n)\, dp. \tag{18}$$

Here, $n = N/V$, which represents the electron concentration at various points.

If we wish to make Eqs. (17) and (18) look consistent, we must find a way to define the pressure so that $dp = 0$ throughout the interface. After all, it seemed like we succeeded in the liquid-vapor system, although we really have not in the case of an atmosphere.

If we were not too desperately in need to reconcile Eq. (17) with Eq. (18), we may then give the matter independent considerations. Conduction electrons in a solid constitute a gas for which the pressure can most reasonably be defined as two-thirds the average kinetic energy per unit volume. We need not be concerned about second and higher-order virial terms, for electrons have none.

The preceding definition of pressure associated with an electron gas, whether in a solid, or free, is not at all new. In fact, it has been used by many authors including Chandrasekhar (1939, p. 357) and Kittel (1971, p. 264).

We now return to our copper-semiconductor interface. By the well-established methods of quantum and statistical mechanics (see Chapter 5), the electron pressure in the copper can be found to be 37.6×10^9 newtons/m². On the other hand, in our semiconductor, with an electron concentration of only $10^{16}/cm^3$, the ideal gas laws apply at $T = 300°K$ (see Chapter 5). At that temperature the electron pressure will be 41.4 newtons/m². The interface, however, may be only about 500 angstroms wide. Through that microscopically-small width, the electron pressure decreases continuously from its highest value of 37.6×10^9 newtons/m² in copper to its lowest value of 41.4 newtons/m² in the semiconductor. Is the gradient of the electron pressure in the interface insignificantly small? Hardly!

Are Eqs. (17) and (18) then consistent? Not unless we are willing to drastically change our conception of what electron pressure is. If we should succeed to do so, we still cannot ignore the inconsistencies encountered in the case of the atmospheric gas.

3.2. *The Question of Completeness of the Classical Internal Energy Equation*

Let us consider once more the generalized classical internal energy equation, restated next for convenience:

$$dU = T\,d\eta - p\,dV + \tilde{\mu}_t\,dN. \tag{8}$$

We recall that the first term on the right-hand side of the equation represents the heat added to an appropriately small volume V containing a number of particles N. The second term represents the mechanical work done on the surroundings of the N particles. The third accounts for the change in the number of particles N within V in the presence of effects such as electric, magnetic, and gravitational.

Suppose now that we have a number of particles r that entered the volume V and then left it. Suppose further that during this process no change in volume takes place and no particles enter V without leaving it. In this case, clearly $dN = 0$, and $dV = 0$. Equation (8) then reduces to

$$dU = T\,d\eta. \tag{19}$$

There does not seem to be a term in Eq. (8) involving explicitly the quantity r representing those particles that have crossed the volume. One, of course, may say at first glance that the crossing of r particles implies nonequilibrium, which would represent a situation not considered in Eq. (8). Or it may be said that for nonequilibrium $(T\,d\eta)$ would account for the crossing of r particles. The preceding two statements are somewhat questionable. The crossing of a finite number of particles is not at all incompatible with thermal equilibrium, since the crossing time t_0 has not been specified. If we let t_0 approach infinity, then the system may be considered in the limit to be at thermal equilibrium. The question whether $(T\,d\eta)$ can be allowed to account for the change in U caused by the crossing of V by r particles, when the system is in nonequilibrium, will be taken up shortly in the next section.

4. MODIFIED INTERPRETATIONS OF THE FIRST AND SECOND LAWS OF THERMODYNAMICS FOR SYSTEMS IN NONEQUILIBRIUM

The central objective in this section is to arrive at a fundamental equation expressing the differential change in the internal energy, subject to a *strict* interpretation of the second law, for a system which may generally be in a state of nonequilibrium. The system may further involve electric, magnetic, and gravitational fields.

4.1. *A Search for a New Fundamental Equation*

Before proceeding with constructing our equation, we must review the primary points of difficulties in the classical internal energy equation. For, we must make every effort to avoid transplanting these difficulties in a new equation. First, we recall that Eqs. (8) and (9) lead to inconsistent answers when applied to systems involving gravitational and electric fields, and, by analogy, magnetic fields. But contributions of these fields are accounted for in the term involving the so-called generalized potential $\tilde{\mu}_t$. We, therefore, conclude that we cannot account for the electric, magnetic and gravity fields by any of the terms in the existing internal-energy equation. New terms must then be sought.

The second point of difficulty in the quasiequilibrium, as classically viewed, is that particles crossing our appropriately small volume V are not at all accounted for by the term involving the generalized potential $\tilde{\mu}_t$. If the contribution of these particles to dU is not accounted for by the term involving the entropy η, we must then account for such particles in a new, different way.

We must now consider whether the entropy η can possibly account for particles crossing V, particularly in cases involving finite particle fluxes. Such cases may seem to be beyond what Eq. (8) describes. However, Eq. (8) cannot be viewed to describe other than a limiting case of a situation in which particle fluxes tend to zero. For, one cannot conceive of a system falling into an equilibrium state discontinuously. If it did, we would be deprived of all the advantages of differential calculus for describing changes in the system.

That the entropy η cannot account for the change in the internal energy of an appropriately small volume V due to a finite particle flux has been the concern of a number of prominent thermodynamicists. For example, it has been stated by Meixner (1970):

"Thermostatics (equilibrium thermodynamics) is a well-established subject with many successful applications during the hundred years of its existence. It has also found an excellent corroboration by statistical mechanics. The concepts of the thermodynamic temperature and entropy are well defined without any ambiguity and it is well known how numerical values of all sorts of variables, in particular of the entropy as a function of state, can be obtained by appropriate measurements.

The situation is very different in the thermodynamics of processes (nonequilibrium thermodynamics). Although there is a long history of irreversible thermodynamics, its foundation has not received sufficient attention. Since the time of Clausius' work, it has been taken for granted that, in nonequilibrium states a unique entropy exists and there was not much discussion either about what temperature in nonequilibrium states means.

A careful study of the thermodynamics of electrical networks (Meixner 1968) has given considerable insight into these problems and also produced a very interesting result: *the nonexistence of a unique entropy value in a state which is attained during an irreversible process.*

A closely related result has been obtained by Schlögl (1968) on the basis of statistical and information theoretical arguments. It states that *the entropy of a system is not an objective quantity* but also depends upon the observer through the information he has about the system."

The preceding statements of Meixner are by no means isolated ones in the literature. Similar conclusions have been expressed by Mayer (1955), Kestin and Rice (1970), and others.

4.2. *A Generalized Interpretation of the First and Second Laws for Systems in Nonequilibrium*

Consider an appropriately small volume V in which there are N particles of one constituent. Let the absolute temperature of the particles be T, their entropy S, internal energy U, and pressure P. Imagine that our small system has gone through an infinitesimal quasistatic change involving a *reversible* process. During the occurrence of the process, an amount of heat dQ has been added reversibly to the system, and the volume has changed by dV. If no particles entered or left the volume, then the first law of thermodynamics requires that

$$dU = dQ - P \, dV. \tag{20}$$

Here $(P \, dV)$ represents the mechanical work done by the N particles on their surroundings. We shall avoid further discussion of dQ until the most general situation is treated.

Consider a point A just on the boundary of the volume V (Fig. 1). Let A also lie on a prescribed path C. Imagine now that dN particles, originating from point A, entered V on the path C. These particles must then contribute to the change dU in the internal energy U within V.

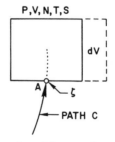

Fig. 1. Path C of a small number of particles entering an appropriately small volume V which changes by an amount dV.

Let us now define the quantity ζ, *at point A*, to be the *total amount of energy introduced statistically into V by each particle originating from point A and entering V*. It is assumed here, of course, that the system is not subject to any electric, magnetic, or gravitational fields. The definition of ζ at A may similarly be extended to all points on the path C. We shall call ζ *the intrinsic transport energy coefficient*.

The choice of a prescribed path, in the definition of ζ, has not been without reason. In case ζ depends on the path, as we shall see later on, ζ cannot exist mathematically at all points of a continuum without specifying the path.

Now from the definition of the intrinsic energy coefficient, we observe that $(\zeta\,dN)$ represents the total amount of energy added to the particles within V when dN particles originate just outside the boundary of V and enter V on the prescribed path C. Thus, for the system under consideration, the first law of thermodynamics requires that Eq. (20) should be modified to

$$dU = dQ - P\,dV + \zeta\,dN. \qquad (21)$$

Imagine now that we have r particles at point A that entered the volume V, but then proceeded on, along path C, and left the volume at point B (Fig. 2). We observe then that the contribution of these particles to dU is not accounted for by the term $(\zeta\,dN)$. For, in this case $dN = 0$. We shall next calculate the contribution to the change in U by the r particles crossing V.

From the definition of ζ, the total amount of energy given to the N particles as the r particles enter the volume at point A is $(r\zeta)$. If the r particles are to cause U to increase, then, by definition of ζ, at point B, where the

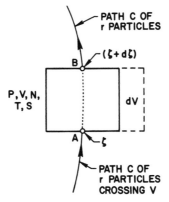

Fig. 2. Path C of a small number of particles crossing an appropriately small volume V which changes by an amount dV.

particles depart volume V, the intrinsic energy coefficient must decrease infinitesimally to $(\zeta - d\zeta)$. Accordingly, the total energy extracted from the N particles as the r particles depart from V at point B will be $[r(\zeta - d\zeta)]$. Consequently, the total amount of energy given to the N particles as r particles cross the volume will be

$$r\zeta - [r(\zeta - d\zeta)] = r\,d\zeta.$$

Thus, for the system under consideration, the law of conservation of energy requires that Eq. (21) be modified to

$$dU = dQ - P\,dV + \zeta\,dN + r\,d\zeta. \tag{22}$$

Now suppose that the system within V is subject to fields such as electric, magnetic, etc., which all originate within V. Such force fields are defined to be *intrinsic*. Accordingly, if r particles cross V, each particle will be acted on by a force $\mathbf{f}_R$ (Fig. 3). This intrinsic force field (per particle) is associated with all the fields (electric, magnetic, etc.) to which the particles are subjected.

If in crossing V, the r particles are displaced a distance $d\mathbf{l}$, then the mechanical work $d\xi_R$ done statistically on each one of these particles by $\mathbf{f}_R$ as they cross V will be

$$d\xi_R = \mathbf{f}_R \cdot d\mathbf{l}. \tag{23}$$

Since all the fields originate inside V, the law of conservation of energy requires that the internal energy of our N particles decrease by $d\xi_R$. Conse-

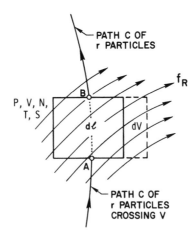

Fig. 3. Path C of a small number r of particles crossing an appropriately small volume V which changes by an amount dV. While crossing V, the particles are subject to a resultant force field $\mathbf{f}_R$ associated with electric, magnetic, and gravitational fields.

quently, in the general case, Eq. (22) must further be modified to

$$dU = dQ - P\,dV + \zeta\,dN + r\,(d\zeta - d\xi_R).\tag{24}$$

Equation (24) essentially expresses the first law of thermodynamics accounting for intrinsic fields of any nature. This Generalized Equation of Conservation of Energy (GECE) has some interesting fundamental consequences to be discussed in the next subsection.

It should be pointed out here that the quantities of energy* $(\kappa E^2 V/2)$ and $(\mu H^2 V/2)$ within V, associated with the electric and magnetic fields, respectively, have extremely negligible effects on dU, at least for all the problems to be treated in this volume. For simplicity, therefore, we neglect these two quantities in Eq. (24), although we shall consider them in Appendix A.

4.3. *Some Consequences of the Generalized Equation of Conservation of Energy*

Thus far, we have defined the heat quantity dQ appearing in the GECE only in a rather vague way. In this subsection, we shall first define dQ in a manner which meets the strictest requirements of the second law. Subsequently, we shall derive from the GECE two relations of fundamental significance to the theory of generalized fields.

The entropy. Consider once more the N particles in our appropriately small volume V. We shall define the quantity dQ to be strictly *the amount of reversible heat added to the system of N particles by other than flow.*

Now it is possible to define rigorously the change dS in the entropy of the N particles in our small volume V. Specifically, from the second law of thermodynamics (Clausius equality), we have

$$T dS = dQ.\tag{25}$$

From the preceding discussion, it is apparent that our entropy S is different from the entropy η, which is used in classical irreversible thermodynamics. Briefly, $(T dS)$ includes *no other than purely reversible heat.* Any heat produced irreversibly is shifted to other terms in the generalized equation of conservation of energy.

Infinitesimal change of the intrinsic energy coefficient. We are to derive next a general expression for the differential $d\zeta$.

Substituting Eq. (25) into Eq. (24), we get

$$dU = T\,dS - P\,dV + \zeta\,dN + r\,(d\zeta - d\xi_R).\tag{26}$$

We now observe that r represents the number of particles that cross the volume V. Hence, r is not a function of position as ζ and ξ_R are. Thus, we

---

* These quantities have been derived in Section 4, Chapter 3.

may write $r \, d\zeta = d(r\zeta)$, and $r \, d\xi_R = d(r\xi_R)$. It can be shown that each of the differentials $d(r\zeta)$ and $d(r\xi_R)$ is proportional to V (which in the limit is a differential). Thus $d(r\zeta)$ and $d(r\xi_R)$ are extensive differentials. For a general proof, see Subsection A.4, Appendix A. We may then rewrite Eq. (26) in the following more useful form:

$$dU = T \, dS - P \, dV + \zeta \, dN + d(r\zeta) - d(r\xi_R). \qquad (27)$$

Since all the differential quantities in Eq. (27) are extensive variables, and all their coefficients are intensive variables, or constants, as explained for Eq. (2), it follows that the corresponding Euler equation will be

$$U = TS - PV + \zeta N + r\zeta - r\xi_R. \qquad (28)$$

Therefore,

$$dU = T \, dS + S \, dT - (P \, dV + V \, dP) + \zeta \, dN + N \, d\zeta + [d(r\zeta) - d(r\xi_R)]. \qquad (29)$$

Subtracting Eq. (27) from (29), and solving for $d\zeta$, we get

$$d\zeta = -s \, dT + (1/n) \, dP, \qquad (30)$$

where

$$s = S/N, \quad n = N/V. \qquad (31)$$

It is particularly interesting to note in Eq. (30) that, while $d\zeta$ pertains strictly to the transported particles, the entropy s per particle, the temperature T, concentration n, and pressure P all belong entirely to the *nontransported* particles within our volume V. Thus, there is no trouble whatsoever in determining the entropy, temperature and pressure according to the most rigorous rules of equilibrium thermodynamics.

The generalized transport energy function and its differential change. So far, we have been mainly concerned with the factors contributing to the change in the internal energy U of N particles occupying an appropriately small volume V. Among these factors, we have considered the amount of energy given to the N (*nontransported*) particles by the r particles which crossed the volume V.

As we shall see in this and subsequent chapters, it is particularly useful to think in terms of the statistical amount of total transport energy given to, rather than given by, a particle crossing our volume. Suppose now that in crossing this volume, the particles are subject to fields such as electric, magnetic, etc. As the particles cross V, then the *total energy statistically given to each particle transported through* V will be designated by $d\nu_t$. Here ν_t is defined as the *generalized transport energy function*. The total energy given to r particles transported through V will, of course, be $(r \, d\nu_t)$.

Let us determine next the precise contribution of changes in the generalized transport energy function ν_t to the changes in the internal energy U of a system as r particles cross that system.

Consider again the N particles within an appropriately small fictitious volume V. To calculate the change dU in U caused by *no other than* the crossing of r particles: firstly, we must add no heat to the volume V. Thus $dQ = 0$, and $dS = 0$. Secondly, the volume is not made to change, while the particles are crossing. That $dV = 0$ can always be satisfied, since V is a fictitious, imagined volume. Thirdly, since all particles that enter V depart from it, then $dN = 0$. Accordingly, Eq. (26) reduces to

$$dU = r(d\zeta - d\xi_R),\qquad(32)$$

and from Eq. (23),

$$dU = r(d\zeta - \mathbf{f}_R \cdot d\mathbf{l}).\qquad(33)$$

We observe now that: the total amount of energy dU, given by the r transported particles to the N nontransported particles, is equal and opposite in sign to the amount of total energy given by the N particles to the r particles. This result, of course, is a consequence of the law of conservation of energy—first law—and the way we have defined the entropy S. The definition of S is in accordance with the most precise interpretation of the second law.

From the definition of the generalized transport energy function, we may write

$$dU = -r\,d\nu_t.\qquad(34)$$

Comparison of Eq. (33) and (34) gives at once that

$$d\nu_t = -d\zeta + \mathbf{f}_R \cdot d\mathbf{l}.\qquad(35)$$

We now recall that $d\nu_t$ pertains entirely to particles transported in any system. Eq. (35) signifies that at any point in a system, $d\nu_t$ is determined from $\mathbf{f}_R$, which is uniquely defined in classical mechanics, and $d\zeta$, which is uniquely determined for nontransported particles in an appropriately small volume. As explained earlier in this subsection, $d\zeta$ can be uniquely determined with the strictest rules of equilibrium thermodynamics.

5. FORMULATION OF THE DIFFUSION AND THERMOMOTIVE FIELDS

Classical mechanics and Maxwell's theory of electromagnetism are most conveniently expressed in a force formalism. In the particular case of the theory of electromagnetism, the use of a force formalism even extends somewhat beyond mere convenience. As we have seen in Chapter 3, time-varying electric and magnetic (force) fields are necessarily nonconservative. The electric voltage V, being the negative of the line integral of the electric field $\mathbf{E}$, necessarily depends on the path. Thus, the voltage—representing transport energy—does not exist mathematically at all points in a continuum without a path, unless the electric field **E** is conservative. On the other hand, **E** exists mathematically at every point in a continuum, regardless of whether **E** is conservative. Thus, the choice by Maxwell of a force formalism to express the electromagnetic relations is actually a natural one from a mathematical point of view. The alternative would have been to use inexact differentials of voltage V, and constantly specify paths.

As our thermodynamic theory develops, we shall observe that under nonequilibrium conditions, the differential $d\nu$ of the intrinsic transport energy function may be an inexact differential. Other Newtonian-type force fields constituting $\mathbf{f}_R$ also may become nonconservative. To conform with mechanics and the theory of electromagnetism, we shall use the force formalism, rather than inexact differentials with specified paths.

In this section, we shall develop the force formalism corresponding to the intrinsic transport energy function. In addition, we shall investigate the nature of the pressure P which occurs in the generalized equation of conservation of energy [Eq. (26)], as well as the intrinsic transport energy function. We shall pursue the second objective first.

5.1. *The Intrinsic Transport Energy Function*

Earlier in this chapter, we have seen that the interpretations of the first and second laws in the framework of classical thermodynamics and that of the theory of generalized fields are significantly different. The differences have arisen because of the differences in the interpretations of entropy, and in the schemes of accounting for electric, magnetic, gravitational and other Newtonian-type force fields.

In this subsection, we shall show that, at least in some systems, the interpretation of the pressure can also be significantly different in our thermodynamic theory and in classical thermodynamics.

To do so, consider Eq. (35). In the absence of electric, magnetic, and gravitational fields, this equation reduces to

$$d\nu = -d\zeta. \tag{36}$$

Substituting Eq. (30) into Eq. (36), we have

$$d\nu = s\,dT - (1/n)\,dP. \tag{37}$$

We shall define ν to be the *intrinsic transport energy function* (Melehy 1966b).

Let us now investigate a quasistatic transport in any system in which $\mathbf{f}_R = 0$. For such a system $d\nu_t$ reduces to $d\nu$. To be specific, let that system consist of a liquid and its vapor which are both in a container (Fig. 4). Imagine a fictitious volume V which is bounded by the vertical sides of the container and two planes parallel to, and on either side of, the liquid-

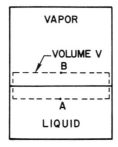

Fig. 4. A volume containing a liquid vapor interface.

vapor interface. Let A and B be any two points on the lower and upper surfaces of V, respectively.

Suppose now that we let r particles cross uniformly through the volume V from the liquid to the vapor. According to Eq. (34), the net amount of change ΔU in the internal energy of (the subsystem within) V will be

$$\Delta U = -r \int_{\nu_a}^{\nu_b} d\nu. \tag{38}$$

Here ν_a and ν_b are the values of the intrinsic transport energy functions at points A and B, respectively.

If the entire liquid-vapor system is isothermal, then by virtue of Eq. (37), we may write

$$\Delta U = r \int_{P_a}^{P_b} (1/n) \, dP. \tag{39}$$

Here P_a and P_b are the pressures at points A and B, respectively.

Letting r particles cross V quasistatically amounts to evaporating r particles without any viscous losses. From well-known observations, this process inevitably leads to cooling within V. For, the system within V must supply the latent heat of vaporization. Therefore, we must expect ΔU in Eq. (39) to be a finite negative quantity. This conclusion must help define the nature of P, whose occurrence can, of course, be traced back to the generalized equation of conservation of energy [Eq. (26)].

Let us now ask whether P can be the externally measurable pressure for both the liquid and its vapor. If the vapor is an ideal classical gas, there is every reason to believe that the pressure in the vapor is the measurable pressure. If P for the liquid, however, is taken also to be the externally measurable pressure, $dP = 0$, at all points within and without the liquid-vapor interface. For, in our system the evaporation has proceeded quasistatically. Accordingly, from Eq. (39), it follows that $\Delta U = 0$. This result is, of course, in fundamental conflict with what has been explained earlier; namely, that ΔU must be a finite negative quantity.

Therefore, we arrive at the important conclusion that *in the expression for dv [Eq. (37)], the pressure P for a liquid is not at all the externally measurable pressure.* Using similar arguments, the same conclusion can be reached for solids. Thus, at least for liquids and solids, the quantity P is completely different from the externally measureable pressure p, which is invariably used in the Gibbs's equation and in classical thermodynamics. We shall define P as the *internal* or *thermodynamic pressure.*

The internal pressure P. For a number of systems, the internal pressure P is quite simple to define exactly. For others, one can only speculate, at this stage, about what it might be.

For ideal classical gases, we must expect that the internal and external pressures are equal. Thus, for such gases, we simply define the internal pressure at a point A by

$$P = knT. \tag{40}$$

Here n and T are the gas concentration and absolute temperature at A, respectively, and k is Boltzmann's constant.

A free eléctron gas, and those electrons responsible for electrical conduction in any form of matter, are examples of systems which have well-defined internal pressure. At any point A in a system, the electron internal pressure P_n is given by

$$P_n = (2/3) \text{ average kinetic energy per unit volume at } A. \tag{41}$$

Calculations of P_n for electrons when quantum-mechanical effects are important will be done in considerable detail in the next chapter.

For liquids, however, it is believed that the internal pressure P_l could be expressed as

$$P_l = \sigma_l k n_l T. \tag{42}$$

Here n_l is the concentration of the liquid and σ_l is a factor which weakly depends on temperature. The order of magnitude of σ_l is about unity. Estimation of σ_l may be done on the basis of the compressibility experiments. In case of water, for example, from the measured parameters of the Tait's equation, one can estimate P_l. At 25°C, $P_l \simeq 3 \times 10^9$ dynes/cm². Since for water $n_l = 3.35 \times 10^{22}$/cm³, then $k n_l T = 1.379 \times 10^9$ dynes/cm². Thus, at 25°C, for water, $\sigma_l = 2.18$.

5.2. The Diffusion and Thermomotive Fields

Consider once more the differential dv of the intrinsic transport energy function v. This differential is expressed by Eq. (37), which, for constituent

j, may be written as

$$dv_j = s_j \, dT - (1/n_j) \, dP_j. \tag{43}$$

Here s, T, n, and P represent the entropy per particle, absolute temperature, particle concentration and internal pressure, respectively. It is significant to note that the four preceding quantities pertain to the nontransported particles of constituent j which occupy an appropriately small volume V.

By definition, dv_j represents the total amount of transport energy given statistically to a particle of constituent j crossing V, on a prescribed path, by all the nontransported particles within V. The quantity dv_j excludes the work done on the transported particle by electric, magnetic, gravitational fields.

Suppose that in crossing V, the transported particle is displaced an infinitesimal distance $d\mathbf{l}$, which has a magnitude dl, and a specified direction. We shall define the thermodynamic field $\mathbf{f}_t$ (Melehy 1966b) within V to be such that

$$dv_j = \mathbf{f}_{tj} \cdot d\mathbf{l}. \tag{44}$$

From Eq. (43) and (44), we have

$$\mathbf{f}_{tj} \cdot d\mathbf{l} = s_j \, dT - (1/n_j) \, dP_j. \tag{45}$$

The temperature T and internal pressure P may vary from point to point in a system. As explained in Chapter 2, it is a mathematical identity that

$$dT = (\nabla T) \cdot d\mathbf{l}, \qquad dP_j = (\nabla P_j) \cdot d\mathbf{l}. \tag{46}$$

Substituting Eq. (46) into Eq. (45), it follows that

$$\mathbf{f}_{tj} \cdot d\mathbf{l} = [s_j \, \nabla T - (1/n_j) \, \nabla P_j] \cdot d\mathbf{l}. \tag{47}$$

Therefore,

$$\mathbf{f}_{tj} = \mathbf{f}_{Tj} + \mathbf{f}_{dj}, \tag{48}$$

where

$$\mathbf{f}_{Tj} = s_j \, \nabla T, \tag{49}$$

$$\mathbf{f}_{dj} = -(1/n_j) \, \nabla P_j. \tag{50}$$

The quantities $\mathbf{f}_{Tj}$ and $\mathbf{f}_{dj}$ have been defined (Melehy 1966b) as the *thermomotive field* and *diffusion field*, respectively. Since the (internal) pressure P_j is an actual force per unit area, then $\mathbf{f}_{dj}$ is a force per particle in the Newtonian sense. The idea of a diffusion field consisting of a mechanical force was recognized in 1963 (Melehy a, b). The thermomotive field $\mathbf{f}_{Tj}$, however, is only a virtual force per particle. The line integral of the two force fields $\mathbf{f}_{Tj}$ and $\mathbf{f}_{dj}$ between any two points A and B, along a prescribed path C in a system, represents the total statistical transport energy given to a particle, as the particle is transported between points A and B along the path C. The transport energy given to the particle does not include electric, magnetic or gravitational effects.

In view of the preceding discussion, and Eqs. (35), (36), (37), (44), and (47), we may rewrite Eq. (34), for constituent j, as

$$dU_j = -r[\mathbf{f}_{Tj} \pm \mathbf{f}_{dj} \pm \mathbf{f}_{Rj}] \cdot d\mathbf{l}. \qquad (51)$$

Here $\mathbf{f}_{Rj}$ represents the resultant of the force per particle associated with electric, magnetic and gravity fields. The differential dU_j represents the change in U_j strictly caused by the transport of r particles through a distance $d\mathbf{l}$ while subject to the force fields $\mathbf{f}_{Tj}$, $\mathbf{f}_{dj}$, and $\mathbf{f}_{Rj}$. The choice of the proper algebraic sign is an important matter which will be discussed in Section 7.

6. THERMAL EQUILIBRIUM IN THE FRAMEWORK OF THE THERMODYNAMIC THEORY OF GENERALIZED FIELDS

The primary objective in this section is to show briefly the novel manner in which the state of thermal equilibrium is attained in a system, if the system is viewed in the framework of the thermodynamic theory of generalized fields.

6.1. *Generalized Conditions of Thermal Equilibrium*

Without loss of generality, consider conduction electrons—that is, electrons responsible for electrical conduction—in some solid body. To be general, let the concentration n of electrons vary spatially. This condition will be established, even at thermal equilibrium, if the body, for example, consists of a large number of different solids, each of which has a different electron concentration. All the constituent parts are, of course, in physical contact, and separated by interfaces. Within these interfaces the gradient of n will be nonvanishing.

Imagine now that the body is mechanically at rest. Imagine further that the electron system in this body is approaching thermal equilibrium. Let us then identify all the possible force (per particle) fields the electrons are subject to. These force fields are (1) a thermomotive field $\mathbf{f}_T$; (2) a diffusion field $\mathbf{f}_d$; (3) an electrostatic force (per particle) field $\mathbf{f}_e$, which is due to space charge in the interfaces; and (4) a gravity force (per particle) $\mathbf{f}_g = m\mathbf{g}$. Here, m is the mass per electron and $\mathbf{g}$ is the gravitational acceleration.

At thermal equilibrium, we cannot have any dissipative processes anywhere in the system. Under such conditions, we observe, from Eq. (49), that

$$\mathbf{f}_T = 0. \qquad (52)$$

Since a static gravitational field is conservative, we may then express the line integral for $\mathbf{f}_g$, around any closed loop within the body as

$$\oint \mathbf{f}_g \cdot d\mathbf{l} = m \oint \mathbf{g} \cdot d\mathbf{l} = 0. \tag{53}$$

The electrostatic force field $\mathbf{f}_e = -q\mathbf{E}$, where q is the magnitude of the electron charge and $\mathbf{E}$ is the electric field intensity at various points. We now notice that

$$\oint \mathbf{f}_e \cdot d\mathbf{l} = -q \oint \mathbf{E} \cdot d\mathbf{l} = 0. \tag{54}$$

For the electrostatic field $\mathbf{E}$ is conservative, as required by Maxwell's equations of electromagnetism (Chapter 3).

Let us next investigate the closed-loop line integral of the diffusion field $\mathbf{f}_d$. For simplicity, we shall confine our discussion in this section to the case for which conduction electrons in the system behave like ideal classical gases. Such an assumption, although special, is sufficiently general and not unrealistic. For, there are classes of materials, known as semiconductors, in which electrons can have concentrations $n = 10^{19}/\text{cm}^3$, and practically any smaller values of n we wish to specify. At room temperature, and above, such conditions guarantee that electrons will behave as ideal, classical gases. Reasons underlying these results will be discussed in the next chapter.

For ideal, classical electrons, the electron internal pressure $P = knT$. Since at thermal equilibrium, T is constant throughout the system, then Eq. (50), expressing the diffusion field $\mathbf{f}_d$, reduces to

$$\mathbf{f}_d = -(kT/n)\,\nabla n. \tag{55}$$

Recalling from Chapter 2 that $(\nabla n \cdot d\mathbf{l}) = dn$, we may then write

$$\oint \mathbf{f}_d \cdot d\mathbf{l} = -kT \oint n^{-1}(\nabla n) \cdot d\mathbf{l}$$
$$= -kT \oint n^{-1}\,dn$$
$$= -kT \oint d(\ln n),$$

or

$$\oint \mathbf{f}_d \cdot d\mathbf{l} = 0, \tag{56}$$

since $d(\ln n)$ is an exact differential.

We now observe that at thermal equilibrium, in the framework of the thermodynamic theory of generalized fields, each identifiable force (per particle) field becomes conservative, or vanishes. This interesting result will be shown, in Chapter 6, to hold for each constituent in a multicomponent system, no matter how many identifiable fields the system may have. It will be further shown in Chapter 6 that Eq. (56) holds, even when quantum-mechanical and relativistic effects are important in any system.

These *generalized conditions of thermal equilibrium* were first discovered in the latter part of 1963, after recognizing (Melehy 1963a, b) the mechanical nature of $\mathbf{f}_d$. The results were published shortly afterwards (Melehy 1964, 1965). The observed simplicity, generality, and mathematical beauty of these conditions intensely stimulated this author to look for the relevant general thermodynamic formulation, which is treated in this volume.

6.2. *The Mechanism of Detailed Self-Balancing*

We shall further interpret the generalized conditions of thermal equilibrium just discussed. The implication of these conditions is that under the action of each identifiable force field, the total transport energy given statistically to each particle—of a given constituent—around every possible closed loop is zero. Since there is no dissipation at thermal equilibrium, the situation has then a striking analogy with that of circuit theory. For, if in any network the sum of the emf (of voltage sources) around every closed loop is zero, there can be no electric currents, or dissipation, anywhere in the system. Electrons in the entire system may then be said to be in thermal equilibrium.

We observe that in the framework of the TTGF, at thermal equilibrium, where there is no dissipation whatsoever, every field f_i and its corresponding transport energy function v_i is purely *motive*, or *active*, that is, *emf-like*. Furthermore, all the existing laws of nature (pertaining to gravity, electromagnetism, etc.) require that every motive field be conservative at thermal equilibrium. Thus, every identifiable motive field leads to a vanishing total motive transport energy for each constituent around every closed loop in the system.

In conclusion, we may state that in the framework of the thermodynamic theory of generalized fields, the state of thermal equilibrium may be defined (Melehy 1964, 1965, 1966a, b, c, d, e) to be one for which each identifiable force field for each constituent is in *self-balance* in the sense that:

> *under the action of each identifiable force field, there are as many particles of any one constituent crossing an area per unit time as there are particles crossing in the opposite direction.*

The *mechanism of detailed self-balancing*, just defined, characterizes thermal equilibrium in our thermodynamic formulation. This mechanism is in *sharp contrast* with that generally called the mechanism of detailed balancing characterizing thermal equilibrium in classical thermodynamics. As explained in Section 2, in the Gibbsian framework, it is necessary to consider that the balancing at thermal equilibrium would be established for each constituent by *all* the processes collectively, rather than by each one individually.

7. THE TRANSPORT CORRESPONDENCE PRINCIPLE AND ACTIVE AND PASSIVE FIELDS

In this section, we shall determine, on the basis of the generalized equation of conservation of energy, the time rate of change of internal energy per unit volume at various points in a system, under the conditions of non-equilibrium. Having determined the rate of change of internal energy, corresponding to each identifiable force field, we shall point out identical properties existing in electric networks and thermodynamic systems generally. Recognizing these properties leads to the conclusion that regardless of the nature of the force fields in a thermodynamic system, there exist two distinctly different types of fields. One is emf-like, and will be called *active*, or *motive*. The other type of fields is always associated with heat dissipation, generated only under nonequilibrium conditions. Such fields will be called *passive*, or *dissipative*.

It is a primary objective in this section to clearly identify active and passive fields and determine their interactions under certain restricted conditions of nonequilibrium.

7.1. *Time Rate of Change of Internal Energy per Unit Volume*

Consider an appropriately small cubic volume V in a one-constituent thermodynamic system. Let the edges of the cube be parallel to the three Cartesian coordinates x, y, and z, as shown in Fig. 5. Suppose that throughout the system and within V the particles are subject to a number of force fields which can generally be: a thermomotive field $\mathbf{f}_T$; a diffusion field $\mathbf{f}_d$; an electric force (per particle) field $\mathbf{f}_e$; etc. Let $\mathbf{f}_i$ represent any one of these force fields. If we have r particles transported along x through the volume, while subject to the x-component f_{ix} of $\mathbf{f}_i$, then the corresponding change ΔU_{ix} in the internal energy within V can be expressed, by virtue of Eq. (51), as

$$\Delta U_{ix} = \mp r f_{ix}\, \Delta x. \tag{57}$$

The minus or plus signs correspond to whether f_{ix} is along, or against the direction of flow of the r particles. Further discussion of this matter will follow shortly.

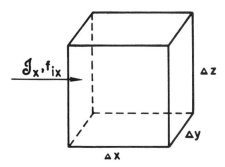

Fig. 5. The x-component of a particle flux density $\mathcal{J}_x$ crossing along x a small volume $(\Delta x\, \Delta y\, \Delta z)$.

In a realistic situation, r particles can be transported a distance Δx during a time interval Δt, if there exists a particle flux density $\mathcal{J}$ with a component $\mathcal{J}_x$ along x, such that

$$r = \mathcal{J}_x \, \Delta y \, \Delta z \, \Delta t. \tag{58}$$

By definition, $\mathcal{J}_x$ represents the number of particles crossing, along x, a sufficiently small area, per unit area, per unit time. The area is perpendicular to the x axis—the quantities Δy and Δz being the dimensions of V along the y and z axes, respectively.

From Eqs. (57) and (58), it follows that

$$\Delta U_{ix} = \mp \, (\mathcal{J}_x \, f_{ix}) \, (\Delta x \, \Delta y \, \Delta z) \, \Delta t. \tag{59}$$

In the limit as Δt tends to zero, Eq. (59) becomes

$$(1/V) \, \partial U_{ix}/\partial t = \mp \mathcal{J}_x \, f_{ix}, \tag{60}$$

where

$$V = \Delta x \, \Delta y \, \Delta z. \tag{61}$$

By similar arguments, it can be shown that the time rates of change $(\partial U_{iy}/\partial t)$ and $(\partial U_{iz}/\partial t)$, corresponding to the y-components f_{iy}, $\mathcal{J}_y$ and z-components f_{iz}, $\mathcal{J}_z$ of $\mathbf{f}_i$ and $\mathcal{J}$, will be given by

$$(1/V) \, \partial U_{iy}/\partial t = \mp \mathcal{J}_y \, f_{iy},$$

$$(1/V) \, \partial U_{iz}/\partial t = \mp \mathcal{J}_z \, f_{iz}. \tag{62}$$

We can, therefore, see that at any point A in the system, the total time rate $[(\partial U_i/\partial t)/V]$ of change of U_i per unit volume corresponding to all the components of $\mathbf{f}_i$ and $\mathcal{J}$ will be

$$(1/V) \, \partial U_i/\partial t = \mp [\mathcal{J}_x \, f_{ix} + \mathcal{J}_y \, f_{iy} + \mathcal{J}_z \, f_{iz}],$$

or

$$(1/V) \, \partial U_i/\partial t = \mp \mathcal{J} \cdot \mathbf{f}_i. \tag{63}$$

We may express Eq. (63) in a more convenient way as

$$\partial \mathfrak{u}_i/\partial t = \mp \mathcal{J} \cdot \mathbf{f}_i. \tag{64}$$

Here $(\partial \mathfrak{u}_i/\partial t)$ may be defined as the time rate of change of the internal energy at any point A per unit volume. The point A is a limiting case of appropriately small volume V.

7.2. *The Generalized Equation of Conservation of Energy and Circuit Theory*

In this subsection, we shall interpret, for the fundamental case of circuit theory, Eq. (64) and the generalized equation of conservation of energy.

Sources of electromotive force. Consider a dc source of electrical energy. Without loss of generality, let this emf source be a lossless battery. This basic element of electric networks is represented in Fig. 6.

Imagine that the battery is feeding a current to some network. Details of the network are of no concern to our discussion. Let I_B be the battery current, which has the direction indicated in Fig. 6. The direction of electron flow is against that of I_B.

Let us now consider a rather fundamental question. How does a battery, or any other source of electrical energy, produce an emf? In answering this question, we do not intend to get involved with the chemical reactions, or other specific processes, that produce the emf in an electrical energy source. Rather, regardless of the nature of these processes, we can say generally that the electrons in the source must experience a pumping action, much like that produced by a pump in a hydraulic system consisting of a closed loop. If a battery is connected to a resistor, electrons in the closed circuit (loop), acting as a fluid, will continuously be pumped by the battery into the resistor, from which they return to the battery. The circulation of the electrons goes on and on as long as the loop is kept closed. The battery pumping action is precisely what makes the electrons able to overcome the forces of friction (or virtual friction) within the resistor. Electrons transported through the battery gain (transport) energy which is exactly lost in the resistor in counteracting the forces of friction within that element.

While the electron stream in the battery is gaining transport energy as it advances, the internal energy of the battery itself is continuously decreasing as long as no energy is being added to the battery. On the other hand, as the electron stream moves ahead into the resistor, the electron transport energy decreases. Correspondingly, heat is dissipated in the resistor, whose internal energy steadily rises, if the heat is not lost to the surroundings.

Let us now represent the pumping action that the electrons experience in the battery by a statistical force $\mathbf{f}_a$ per particle. This force we shall call *active*, or *motive*. We may now imagine that the active force field $\mathbf{f}_a$ is de-

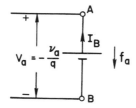

Fig. 6. Active electron force field $\mathbf{f}_a$ leading to an active voltage V_a in an emf source—a battery.

fined at all points within the battery. Generally, f_a is a vector quantity. In the case of our battery, the direction of $\mathbf{f}_a$ is as indicated in Fig. 6.

According to Eq. (64), the time rate $(\partial \mathfrak{U}_B/\partial t)$ of change of internal energy per unit volume at any point within the battery is given by

$$\partial \mathfrak{U}_B/\partial t = -\mathfrak{g} \cdot \mathbf{f}_a. \tag{65}$$

The minus sign in Eq. (65) signifies that, if the direction of flow of electrons inside the battery is along $\mathbf{f}_a$, a decrease in the internal energy of the battery inevitably results.

Since the electron current density $\mathbf{J}$ is simply related to the electron flux density $\mathfrak{g}$ by

$$\mathbf{J} = -q\mathfrak{g}, \tag{66}$$

we may then rewrite Eq. (65) as

$$\partial \mathfrak{U}_B/\partial t = \mathbf{J} \cdot \mathbf{f}_a/q. \tag{67}$$

The total time rate of increase of electrical energy P_B (watts) in the battery can now be determined by integrating Eq. (67) over the entire interior volume of the battery. Thus,

$$P_B = q^{-1} \iiint_{\text{vol.}} (\mathbf{J} \cdot \mathbf{f}_a) \, dx \, dy \, dz. \tag{68}$$

For the battery illustrated in Fig. 6, it can be easily shown that Eq. (68) reduces to

$$P_B = -(I_B/q)(\nu_a)_{A\to B}, \tag{69}$$

where

$$(\nu_a)_{A\to B} = \int_A^B f_a \, dx. \tag{70}$$

By definition, the transport energy function ν_a of the battery represents the total amount of transport energy given statistically to an electron crossing the battery from point A to B (Fig. 6). It is common to use the concept of battery emf, or voltage V_a. By definition, $(V_a)_{A\to B}$ is the work done per unit positive charge as the charge is imagined to move from point A to B. Accordingly,

$$(V_a)_{A\to B} = -(1/q)(\nu_a)_{A\to B}. \tag{71}$$

The emf $(V_a)_{A\to B}$ may also be defined as the voltage rise from A to B.

From Eqs. (69) and (71), it follows that

$$P_B = I_B(V_a)_{A\to B} = -I_B(V_a)_{B\to A}. \tag{72}$$

Equation (72) indicates that the time rate of increase of the internal energy is *negative*. For, $(V_a)_{B\to A}$ represents the voltage rise in the direction of I_B. Equation (72) is a well-known consequence of (electric) circuit theory.

Resistive elements. Let us next investigate how heat is generated in a resistor carrying an electric current. To do so, consider the resistor R represented in Fig. 7. Let the current in that resistor be I_R and its direction be as indicated in the figure. This resistor may actually symbolize a resistive medium.

When an electron stream is pumped by a battery into a resistor R, the electrons experience forces of (virtual) friction, which will be established against the direction of their flow. This action is much like the viscous forces in a fluid pumped into a porous medium. In the medium constituting R, these forces are caused by a scattering mechanism, the details of which are of no concern to our present discussion. Regardless of how the forces of friction are established, we may represent the effect by a statistical force $\mathbf{f}_f$ per electron. The force field $\mathbf{f}_f$ essentially represents the statistical force exerted by the lattice on each electron in an electron stream. We shall call $\mathbf{f}_f$ the (electron) *impeding force field.* We may imagine that this field is defined at every point in the medium constituting the resistor. The direction of the impeding force field is always against the electron flow.

We may now directly use Eq. (64) to express the time rate $(\partial \mathfrak{U}_R/\partial t)$ of increase of internal energy per unit volume at various points of the resistor. In terms of $\mathbf{f}_f$ and the electron flux density $\mathfrak{g}$, we may write

$$\partial \mathfrak{U}_R/\partial t = -\mathbf{f}_f \cdot \mathfrak{g}. \tag{73}$$

The minus sign here is consistent with that in Eq. (65). If the direction of electron flow is against $\mathbf{f}_f$, as is indeed the case, an increase of internal energy—heating—of the resistive medium inevitably results.

In connection with the flow of electric current in a resistor, it is customary to think in terms of an applied voltage, and an applied electric field. We shall denote these two quantities by V_s and $\mathbf{E}_s$, respectively. Both V_s, and the force $\mathbf{f}_{es}$ per electron associated with $\mathbf{E}_s$, are represented in Fig. 7. The electric field $\mathbf{E}_s$ is usually considered to exist at various points of the resistive medium.

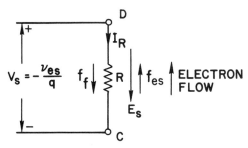

Fig. 7. A passive electrostatic force field $\mathbf{f}_{es}$ (per electron) and the impeding electron force field $\mathbf{f}_f$ in a resistive element, or medium.

We may now define an electrostatic force field (per electron) $\mathbf{f}_{es}$, at any point within the resistive medium, to be given by

$$\mathbf{f}_{es} = -q\mathbf{E}_s. \tag{74}$$

This electrostatic force field is actually equal and opposite to the electron impeding force field. Accordingly,

$$\mathbf{f}_f = -\mathbf{f}_{es}. \tag{75}$$

Since $\mathbf{f}_{es}$ is strictly generated by a current and is always associated with heat dissipation, we shall call it *passive* or *dissipative*. To distinguish between active and passive force fields, we shall invariably use the second subscript s to signify that the field is passive.

We may now calculate the time rate of increase of the internal energy P_R in the resistor R, when R is carrying an electric current. This can be done by integrating Eq. (73) over the entire volume of the resistor. Carrying out this step, and in view of Eqs. (66), (74), and (75), we get

$$P_R = \iiint_{\text{vol}} \mathbf{E}_s \cdot \mathbf{J} \, dx \, dy \, dz. \tag{76}$$

Here the quantity P_R represents the time rate of dissipating heat in the resistor R.

For evaluating Eq. (76), it is convenient to choose one of the three Cartesian axes, such as x, to be along the axis of R. Recalling that $\mathbf{E}_s$ and $\mathbf{J}$ have the same directions, Eq. (76) then reduces to

$$P_R = I_R \int_D^C E_s \, dx. \tag{77}$$

Here D and C are points on opposite sides of the resistor R, as shown in Fig. 7.

The time rate of heat dissipation P_R as described by Eq. (77) can further be expressed as

$$P_R = I_R V_s. \tag{78}$$

Here V_s is the voltage drop in the direction of I_R. Equation (78) is, of course, a well-known result of circuit theory.

Electric transport energy function for a resistor. We shall define the infinitesimal change in the electric transport energy function $d\nu_{es}$ as an electron is transported a distance $d\mathbf{l}$ in a resistive medium to be given by

$$d\nu_{es} = \mathbf{f}_{es} \cdot d\mathbf{l}. \tag{79}$$

The second subscript, s, designates that $d\nu_{es}$ is a passive quantity, for it is associated with the passive force field, $\mathbf{f}_{es}$. Significance of distinguishing active from passive quantities will become apparent shortly.

The passive electric transport energy function through the resistor R from point C to D (Fig. 7) will be

$$(\nu_{es})_C^D = \int_C^D \mathbf{f}_{es} \cdot d\mathbf{l} = -q \int_C^D \mathbf{E}_s \cdot d\mathbf{l}$$

$$= -qV_s. \tag{80}$$

Here V_s signifies the voltage drop from point C to D.

The generalized equation of conservation of energy. In Section 7.1, we have considered the change in the internal energy within a fictitious, appropriately small, constant volume V, which is within a one-constituent system. In particular, we have seen that any particle flux density $\mathcal{g}$ established in a force field $\mathbf{f}_i$, of any nature i, will cause in V during a time interval dt, a change in the interval energy dU such that

$$dU = \mp (\mathcal{g} \cdot \mathbf{f}_i) V \, dt. \tag{81}$$

Equation (81) follows directly from Eq. (63).

Equations (63) and (81) have taken this simple form because of the way entropy is defined in our thermodynamic theory.

As discussed earlier in this section, if V is within a lossless emf source, then Eq. (81) takes the form

$$dU = -\mathcal{g} \cdot \mathbf{f}_a V \, dt. \tag{82}$$

Here $\mathbf{f}_a$ is the electron active force field and $\mathbf{J}$ is the electron flux density. On the other hand, if V is within a resistive (lossy) medium, then Eq. (81) becomes

$$dU = \mathcal{g} \cdot \mathbf{f}_{es} V \, dt. \tag{83}$$

Here $\mathbf{f}_{es}$ is the electron electrostatic passive force field, which is related to the electron impeding force field $\mathbf{f}_f$ by

$$\mathbf{f}_{es} = -\mathbf{f}_f. \tag{84}$$

The force field $\mathbf{f}_f$ does not exist in a lossless source of emf. It is obvious, however, that $\mathbf{f}_f$, because of its friction-like nature, must exist as a consequence of any dissipative process.

7.3. *The Transport Correspondence Principle*

It is significant to note that for any given force field $\mathbf{f}_i$ in a system, the generalized equation of conservation of energy takes essentially one form, which does not depend on the nature of $\mathbf{f}_i$. Specifically, this force field could be the thermomotive or diffusion field. It could also be an electric, magnetic, or gravity force field; or it could be one of the two types of force fields in the two fundamental elements of circuit theory—an active force field in a battery, or a passive electrostatic force field in a resistor.

The existence of an equation, whose validity does not depend on the nature of the possible force fields, suggests that there are even more common properties to explore for various fields. For example, we can identify in circuit theory between an active and a passive force field, and depending on just this property only one of the algebraic signs in Eq. (81) must be used. We must be able to uniquely specify this algebraic sign for any force field, no matter what its nature may be.

Further common properties between various force fields have been shown in connection with the mechanism of detailed *self*-balancing (Sections 6.1 and 6.2). This mechanism characterizes thermal equilibrium in our thermodynamic theory. At thermal equilibrium, each identifiable force field, regardless of its nature, becomes conservative. So will the active force field associated with emf sources in any electric network in which the current vanishes at all points of the system. Under such conditions the emf around every closed loop is zero.

We, therefore, observe a pattern of correspondence developing between circuit theory and processes generally in a thermodynamic system. We may then ask whether the generalized equation of conservation of energy has the information that determines all the interactions between various force fields in any system. The answer to this fundamental question is actually a negative one. Reasons for such an answer are at least two. The first is that the fundamental properties inherent in the mechanism of detailed self balancing in the framework of our thermodynamic theory do follow from the established laws of nature—electromagnetism, gravitation, circuit theory, etc.—and indeed not from the generalized equation of conservation of energy. The second reason is that, for the well-known case of circuit theory, f_{es}, in Eq. (83), can only be calculated from Ohm's law, as we shall see. Moreover, the interaction between f_a and f_{es} can only be determined from Kirchhoff's voltage law, which only exists because of a fundamental distinction made between active voltage (across a battery for example) and passive voltage (across a resistor).

We must, therefore, try to find the fundamental generalized laws relevant to the determination of the various force fields and their interactions in any system. We shall attempt to do so, under some restricted conditions of nonequilibrium, on the basis of a self-evident proposition which is to follow.

The transport correspondence principle. This proposition may be stated (Melehy 1966b) as follows:

To every time-independent law in (electric) network theory, there corresponds another, to hold, in general, in a thermodynamic system, provided that the network law and its conditions are entirely describable in terms of nonrestrictive physical quantities.

The term nonrestrictive used here is meant to describe physical quantities, which are not characteristic of only one process of a specific nature. Rather, they must signify a universal physical quantity. Thus, we may describe the electron force field, transport energy, and particle concentration as nonrestrictive physical quantities. On the other hand, the electric or magnetic field intensities, according to our definition here, are restrictive physical quantities. Each one is characteristic, and indicative of the existence of a specific physical situation of a specific nature.

We shall next discuss at least two fundamental consequences of this interesting general proposition.

7.4. *Passive and Active Force Fields and Their Interactions*

In this subsection, we shall formulate two fundamental, generalized relationships. The first concerns how a passive force field $\mathbf{f}_{isj}$, of nature i, pertaining to particles of constituent j, is expressed in terms of the particle flux density $\mathfrak{J}_{ij}$ at every point in a system. Characteristically, each one of such fields is, at each point in the system, equal in magnitude and opposite in direction to an impeding force field. The second relationship is concerned with how passive fields interact with active (motive) fields. The latter force fields are those for which there exists no impeding force fields, even under nonequilibrium conditions.

Without loss of generality, our discussion will mainly concern electrons. Generalization of the conclusions to other constituents, however, will become an obvious matter.

The particle flux density-passive force field generalized relationship. Consider Fig. 8, which represents a lossless battery with an emf V_a connected to a resistor R. The current I_R through R may be described in terms of the voltage V_s across R by Ohm's law (Ohm 1825, 1826a, b) as follows:

$$I_R = V_s/R. \tag{85}$$

Notice here that all the three quantities in Eq. (85) belong to one element—namely, the resistor R.

Let us next write an expression for the battery current I_B. This will be

$$I_B = V_a/R. \tag{86}$$

Notice here that, while I_B and V_a both belong to the battery, R does not belong to that circuit element. Rather, it belongs to an element outside the battery. Thus, we may state the following: The current through any resistor is determined by Ohm's law in terms of all the variables of that resistor. However, the current through a (pure) emf source cannot be determined by all the variables of the source. Rather complete information for the whole closed loop is needed to determine the current in the emf source.

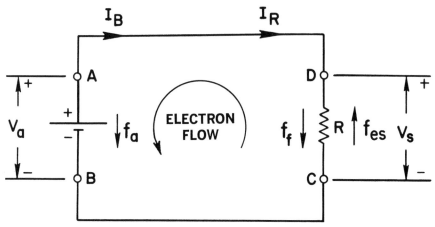

Fig. 8. Passive electrostatic and impeding force fields (f_{es} and f_f, respectively) per electron in a resistor, connected to an emf source hosting an active force field f_a.

Let us next transform Eq. (85) and the statement just made into a non-restrictive form so that the transport correspondence principle may be applied.

At any point G within a resistor if the concentration of electrons is n and their drift velocity is $\mathbf{v}_n$, then the electron flux density $\mathcal{J}_n$ can be shown to be given by

$$\mathcal{J}_n = n\mathbf{v}_n. \qquad (87)$$

Therefore, the electron current density $\mathbf{J}$ will be

$$\mathbf{J}_n = -qn\mathbf{v}_n. \qquad (88)$$

Equation (88) is the same as Eq. (26), derived in Chapter 3.

From well-known experimental observations, in a resistive medium, if a (passive) electric field $\mathbf{E}_s$ is applied, then, at any point G, the electron drift velocity v_n is proportional to E_s so that

$$\mathbf{v}_n = -\mu_n\mathbf{E}_s. \qquad (89)$$

The constant of proportionality μ_n is defined as the *electron mobility*. This quantity is a phenomenological coefficient, which is constant, so long as the magnitude of $\mathbf{E}$ is below a certain value. Otherwise, μ_n will have some dependence on $\mathbf{E}$.

From Eqs. (88) and (89), it follows that at point G

$$\mathbf{J}_n = -\mu_n n(-q\mathbf{E}_s). \qquad (90)$$

Equation (90) is another form of Ohm's law, expressed earlier by Eq. (85).

It is apparent that $(-q\mathbf{E}_s)$ in Eq. (90) represents the electrostatic force field $\mathbf{f}_{esn}$ acting on each electron at point G. As designated by the second subscript, this force field is passive. For, $\mathbf{f}_{esn}$ is at every point equal in magnitude and opposite in direction to an impeding electron force field. The first subscript in $\mathbf{f}_{esn}$ designates the nature of $\mathbf{f}_{esn}$, and here e stands for electrostatic. The last subscript signifies pertinence to a specific constituent, which consists in our case of electrons. The letter n is usually chosen as a reminder of the *negative* charge each electron has.

Let us now imagine that $\mathbf{f}_{esn}$ at point G has been replaced somehow by another equal force of any nature i. Evidently, the electron current density $\mathbf{J}_{in}$ would remain unchaged, provided that $(\mu_n n)$ remained constant. Therefore, we may write

$$\mathbf{J}_n = -\mu_n n \mathbf{f}_{isn}, \tag{91}$$

and say that $\mathbf{f}_{isn}$ is a generalized passive force per electron at G. The nature of this force here, of course, is totally unimportant.

By a similar argument, it can be reasoned that for any constituent j, the particle flux density $\mathcal{g}_{ij}$, of nature i, is related to the passive generalized force field, $\mathbf{f}_{isj}$, by

$$\mathcal{g}_{ij} = A_j n_j \mathbf{f}_{isj}. \tag{92}$$

Here, n_j is the concentration of particles of constituent j, and A_j is a phenomenological constant coefficient pertinent to the same constituent.

It should be remembered here that Eq. (92) holds for all magnitudes of $\mathcal{g}_{ij}$ below a certain value. Otherwise, A_j will have some dependence on $\mathbf{f}_{isj}$.

Conservation of transport energy around closed loops in the real space. It is a common problem in circuit theory to be given full information concerning all emf sources in, say, a known resistive network, and it is then the objective to determine the currents through every resistor in the network. It is well known that using Ohm's law is not sufficient to solve this problem. Rather, Kirchhoff's current and voltage laws (Kirchhoff 1847) must additionally be invoked.

Kirchhoff's current law in the differential form will be

$$\nabla \cdot \mathbf{J}_n = 0, \tag{93}$$

for electrons, and generally for any constituent j

$$\nabla \cdot \mathcal{g}_j = 0. \tag{94}$$

Here $\mathbf{J}_n$ is the total electron current density, and $\mathcal{g}_j$ is the total particle flux density pertaining to constituent j.

If Eq. (93) is not satisfied, the problem is no more one pertinent to circuit theory. Since we are here transforming by correspondence the circuit theory laws into generalized laws, we must for the time being restrict ourselves to cases for which Eqs. (93) and (94) are satisfied. Both equations are in nonrestrictive forms. Hence, the two equations are meant to be satisfied, regardless of the nature of the components of J_n and g_j.

That J_n and g_j are solenoidal (of vanishing divergence) at every point in a system, means further that there are no force fields in the system that are varying in time. Furthermore, there are no chemical reactions and there are no net generation or recombination of charge carriers of opposite polarity.

Consider now Kirchhoff's voltage law, which is generally stated as follows: around every closed loop in an electric network, the sum of the emf's minus the (passive) voltage drops across resistors must vanish. Symbolically, we have

$$\sum_{i=1}^{i=N_a} E_{ia} - \sum_{i=1}^{i=N_s} V_{is} = 0, \tag{95}$$

where E_{ia} is any emf (active voltage), and V_{is} any voltage drop (passive voltage), and N_a and N_s are the numbers of emf sources and resistive elements, respectively, in any closed loop in the network under consideration.

It is evident that

$$q\left[\sum_{i=1}^{i=N_a} E_{ia} - \sum_{i=1}^{i=N_s} V_{is} \right] = 0, \tag{96}$$

where q is the magnitude of the electron charge. In the integral form, Eq. (96) may be rewritten as

$$\oint (f_a - f_s) \cdot dl = 0, \tag{97}$$

where f_a and f_s are the active and passive force fields, respectively, evaluated at various points of the system. The integration is carried, of course, around every closed loop in the network.

Let us now imagine that the electron active force field f_a within the batteries are replaced by any number of active force fields (of any nature) whose resultant is f_{ta}. Imagine further that the electron passive force field f_s within the resistors are replaced by any number of passive force fields (of any nature) whose resultant is f_{ts}. It is then evident that corresponding to Eq. (97), we may write

$$\oint (f_{ta} - f_{ts}) \cdot dl = 0. \tag{98}$$

There is no restriction whatever on the number of closed loops in the system. This number can be imagined then to increase as large as we please. In the limit, the system under consideration would be essentially a continuum.

Clearly, Eq. (98) is expressed in a nonrestrictive form. Thus, from the transport correspondence principle, it follows that Eq. (98) is applicable to any constituent in a multicomponent system, provided, of course that, each identifiable particle flux density is solenoidal.

Equation (98) essentially expresses the conservation of transport energy in the *real* (three-dimensional, position) space. This result was first arrived at in 1966 (Melehy a, b, c). The reader may prove for himself that Eq. (98) leads directly to the mechanism of detailed *self*-balancing at thermal equilibrium. This mechanism has been briefly discussed in Subsections 6.1 and 6.2. A detailed discussion of this mechanism, and how it follows from Eq. (98) is presented in Chapter 6.

7.5 *The Generalized Equation of Conservation of Energy*

In Section 4, and earlier in this section, we have developed in steps the generalized equation of conservation of energy. In each step we have accounted for more force fields as they were developed. Now that the concepts of active and passive force fields have been formulated, it is then possible to write the generalized equation of conservation of energy in its most complete form.

Consider an appropriately small volume V in a one-constituent system. Let there be any number N_a of active force fields and N_s of passive force fields. These fields may be of any nature. Suppose that an amount of heat is added reversibly, and r is the number of particles that have crossed the volume in a given period of time t_0. If the volume happens to change quasistatically by an amount dV, then correspondingly the change dU in the internal energy within V will be

$$dU = T\,dS - P\,dV + \zeta\,dN - r\,(\mathbf{f}_{ta} - \mathbf{f}_{ts})\cdot d\mathbf{l}, \tag{99}$$

where

$$\mathbf{f}_{ta} = \sum_{i=1}^{N_a} \mathbf{f}_{ia}, \qquad \mathbf{f}_{ts} = \sum_{i=1}^{N_s} \mathbf{f}_{is}. \tag{100}$$

The integration of $\mathbf{f}_{ta}$ and $\mathbf{f}_{ts}$ is carried along the increment of length $d\mathbf{l}$ through the volume V.

It is important to remember that dN represents the number of particles that entered V quasistatically and never came out. Also, dN, if negative, will represent the number of particles that left V quasistatically and never came back. The term $(\zeta\,dN)$, therefore, represents a purely reversible process. So does each one of the two terms $(T\,dS)$ and $(P\,dV)$.

The number of particles r which cross V may be described as

$$r = \int_0^{t_0}\!\!\int_{A_0} (\mathbf{g}\cdot d\mathbf{A})\,dt, \tag{101}$$

Here $d\mathbf{A}$ is a vector whose magnitude represents a differential of area. The direction of the vector is that perpendicular to the differential area. The quantity A_0 represents the area of the surface of V crossed by the particles.

The finiteness of the number r does not in any way specify whether the system is in a state of thermal equilibrium, or of nonequilibrium. For $\mathcal{J}$ may be approaching zero as closely as we please, if t_0 tends to infinity. In the limit, it can be said that the system is in a state of thermal equilibrium. If, however, t_0 is finite, then $\mathcal{J}$ will be nonvanishing. Correspondingly, the system will be in a state of nonequilibrium.

8. SUMMARY

In this chapter, one objective has been to discuss a number of paradoxes and inconsistencies inherent in the classical interpretation of the first and second laws of thermodynamics when used to express the infinitesimal changes in the internal energy of a system. Specifically, the central points of criticism discussed include the following: (1) the classical definition of entropy for a state attained during an irreversible process; (2) the absence, in the classical internal energy equation, of a fundamental term which allows a system to approach thermal equilibrium continuously; and (3) the lumping of electric, magnetic, and gravitational effects in what is called the generalized potential.

In attempting to remove the paradoxes and inconsistencies, each term in the classical internal energy equation has been radically reinterpreted. Additional terms have been introduced to account for particles transported. The new terms involve five distinguishable force fields (forces per particle) for each constituent in a multicomponent system. These force fields consist of the thermomotive, diffusion, electric, magnetic and gravitational force fields.

We have shown that the state of thermal equilibrium in the framework of classical thermodynamics is one characterized by the balancing for each constituent by *all force fields* combined. Thus, this balancing is detailed only by constituents, but *not* by fields. By contrast, we have seen that in the framework of the thermodynamic theory of generalized fields, the balancing at thermal equilibrium is detailed *both on the basis of fields as well as constituents*.

Fundamental in the theory of generalized fields is a strong distinction made between passive and active force fields. Regardless of their nature, passive fields are equal and opposite to impeding (frictional) forces established at various points of a system. Consequently, regardless of direction, passive fields are associated with real particle fluxes and heat dissipation. At thermal equilibrium, passive fields, therefore, necessarily vanish individually, thereby establishing in the system a state of *self*-balancing. Active fields, by contrast, are not associated with impeding force fields.

Such force fields produce emf or emf-like effects, and can, hence, exist at thermal equilibrium. Under such a condition, however, each active field becomes conservative. Thus, at thermal equilibrium each identifiable active field leads to a vanishing transport work around every closed loop in the system. In this way active fields attain a state of detailed *self*-balancing at thermal equilibrium.

We have seen that passive fields and the corresponding particle flux densities are related by a fundamental equation, which is totally inapplicable to active force fields. Whenever particle fluxes are solenoidal for each constituent, active and passive force fields are related through the conservation of transport energy for each constituent around every closed loop in the real (three-dimensional position) space.

It will be demonstrated in Chapter 8 that such loops represent a special case of a more general type of loop, consisting of closed loops in a four-dimensional hyperspace. This hyperspace consists of the three position coordinates of the real space and a fourth independent axis of temperature. Around every closed loop in this hyperspace, the conservation of transport energy will also be conserved for each constituent.

REFERENCES

Carnot, S. 1824, Réflexions sur la Puissance Motrice du Feu, et sur les Machines Propres a Développer cette Puissance, a memoir published at Bachelier, Libraire, Paris. English translation by R. H. Thurston 1890, John Wiley, New York, and also Macmillan, London. Thurston's translation edited by E. Mendoza 1960, Reflections on the Motive Power of Fire and on Machines Fitted to Develop that Power, pp. 1–60, Dover Publications.

Chandrasekhar, S. 1939, An Introduction to the Study of Stellar Structure, Chap. 10, p. 357, The University of Chicago Press, Chicago.

Clausius, R. 1850, Pogg. Ann. Phys. **79**, 368, 500; English translation 1960, edited by E. Mendoza, On the Motive Power of Heat, and on the Laws which can be Deduced from it for the Theory of Heat, pp. 109–152, Dover Publications, New York.

Gibbs, J. W. 1875–8, Trans. Conn. Acad. Arts. Scie **30**, 108, 343; reprinted (1961) in Collected Works "Thermodynamics," vol. 1, Dover Publications, New York.

Guggenheim, E. A. 1967, Thermodynamics (5th ed.), pp. 22–25, 298–300, 327–328, North Holland Publ. Co., Amsterdam.

von Helmholtz, H. 1847, "On the Conservation of Force," a paper read to the Physical Society of Berlin. Later published in 1853, in Natural Philosophy (Taylor Scientific Mem.), pp. 114–162.

Joule, J. P. 1845, Phil. Mag. (Series 3) **27**, pp. 205–207.

—— 1850, Phil. Trans. **140**, pp. 61–82.

Kestin, J. and Rice, J. R. 1970, Proc. of the Pittsburgh, Pennsylvania 1969 International Symposium on "A Critical Review of Thermodynamics," p. 275, Mono Book Corp., Baltimore.

Kirchhoff, G. 1847, Pogg. Ann. Phys. **72**, 497.

Kittel, C. 1971, Introduction to Solid-State Physics, p. 264 (fourth edition), John Wiley and Sons, New York.

Mayer, J. E. 1955, "Two Unresolved Problems of Statistical Mechanics," Comm. Pure Appl. Math. **8**, 73.

von Mayer, J. R., 1842–1845, Uber die Erhaltung der Energie (On the Preservation of Energy). Letters by Mayer to W. Griesinger and their replies in the three-year period. Edited by W. von Preyer, 1889, Berlin.

—— 1867, Die Mechanik der Wärme in gesammelten schriften, Stuttgart, J. G. Cotta.

Meixner, J. 1968, Beziehungen Zwischen Netzwerktheorie und Thermodynamik, Sitzungsberichte der Arbeitsgemeinschaft für Forschung des Landes Nordrheinwestfalen, Köln and Opladen, Westdeutscher Verlag.

—— 1970, Proc. of the 1969 Pittsburgh, Pennsylvania International Symposium on "A Critical Review of Thermodynamics," pp. 37–47, Mono Book Corp., Baltimore.

Melehy, M. A. 1963a, Nature **198**, 980; 1963b, Proc. IEEE **51**, 1028.

—— 1964, Nature **202**, 864–868.

—— 1965, Nature **205**, 456–464.

—— 1966a, Bull. Am. Phys. Soc. **11**, 114; 1966b, Nature **209**, 670–677; 1966c, Proc. MIT Annual Phys. Electron. Conf. **26**, 402–415; 1966d, Bull. Am. Phys. Soc. **11**, 641; 1966e, Proc. National Electron. Conf. **22**, 165–170.

Nernst, W. 1912, S. B. Preuss. Akad. Wiss., p. 134.

Ohm, G. S. 1825, Pogg. Ann. **4**, 79.

—— 1826, *Ibid.* **6**, 459.

—— 1826, *Ibid.* **7**, 45.

Schlögl, F. (Same as Meixner, J. 1968).

Chapter 5

CLASSICAL AND DEGENERATE GASES

Electrons and Holes in Semiconductors and Electrons in Metals

1. INTRODUCTION

Ideal classical gases may be defined phenomenologically to be those for which the pressure is proportional to the concentration and temperature. Such gases are also called *nondegenerate*. In some cases, gas particles may be so light and so dense that quantum-mechanical effects are particularly important. Under such conditions these gases are said to be *degenerate*.

In Chapter 8, it will be seen that one of the fundamental results of the Thermodynamic Theory of Generalized Fields (TTGF) relates the interactions in any system with important conditions satisfied generally at the absolute zero. At that particular temperature, however, any gas, with nonvanishing concentration, must be degenerate. An appreciation, therefore, of certain general properties of the TTGF calls for considering some results of the quantum theory and quantum statistical mechanics.

In this chapter, we shall briefly review those consequences of quantum and statistical mechanics of particular relevance to the TTGF, and to the problems treated in this volume. In a number of these problems, the gases of primary interest are electrons and what are known as holes in semiconductors. Because their (effective) masses are sufficiently small, electrons and holes will even be degenerate above a concentration of about 10^{19} cm^{-3}, at room temperature. Thus, for example, electrons in metals, with concentrations $\approx 10^{22}$ cm^{-3}, will be highly degenerate between the absolute zero and temperatures much higher than room temperature.

2. FUNDAMENTAL ASPECTS OF THE QUANTUM THEORY

2.1. *Basic Postulates and Schrödinger's Equation*

Particles of atomic and subatomic sizes, in many respects, do not obey Newtonian mechanics. For example, an electron in an atom cannot attain just any kinetic energy as can a macroscopic particle. Rather, an electron in an atom can only possess certain *discrete energy levels*.

When an electron makes a complete transition from an energy level ϵ_2 to a lower level ϵ_1, energy is released in the form of a radiant electromagnetic wave. The frequency ν of the electromagnetic energy is related to ϵ_1 and

ϵ_2 by

$$\epsilon_2 - \epsilon_1 = h\nu. \tag{1}$$

Here h is a universal constant known as Planck's constant. When an electron makes the transition as just described, it is said that a *photon* is emitted with the *quantized energy* $h\nu$.

Any *classical* particle (macroscopic particle) is localized in space in the sense that it has a well defined location and geometry. By contrast, an electron in an atom is not localized. Rather, it is in continuous motion which, when averaged in time, makes the electron appear like a cloud of charge. The volume charge density ρ_e of this cloud has been postulated to be equal to the electron charge $(-q)$, times the square of the magnitude of a wavefunction Ψ, which is a solution of

$$(h^2/8\pi^2 m)\nabla^2\Psi - V\Psi = (h/2\pi i)\,\partial\Psi/\partial t. \tag{2}$$

Here m and V are the electron mass and potential energy, respectively, t is time, and $i = (-1)^{1/2}$. The definition of Ψ just stated is equivalent to saying that $|\Psi|^2\,dV$ is the probability of finding the electron within the infinitesimal volume dV. Thus $|\Psi|^2$ represents a volume-probability density.

Equation (2) was first derived by Schrödinger (1926). The derivation[*] of *Schrödinger's equation* is based on two fundamental postulates. In order to explain the spectral distribution of radiant energy from a black body, Planck (1901) postulated the following. The radiant electromagnetic energy from a black body proceeds as though there were oscillators whose energies ϵ_n are quantized such that

$$\epsilon_n = nh\nu, \qquad n = 1, 2, 3, 4, \cdots. \tag{3}$$

de Broglie (1924, 1925) further postulated that, associated with the momentum p of any particle, there exists a wavelength λ such that

$$\lambda = h/p. \tag{4}$$

de Broglie's wavelength is profoundly small compared with the actual size of any macroscopic particle. Therefore, Eq. (4) has no significance whatsoever for such particles, which, in any event, obey Newtonian mechanics.

de Broglie's postulate expresses *dual properties* peculiar to classical experience. Any particle has wave properties and any wave has particle properties. Thus, for example, an electromagnetic wave with a given wavelength has a well defined momentum; and an electron having a given momentum is associated with a specific wavelength.

---

[*] A simple derivation may be found in many textbooks, including Dicke and Wittke (1960), p. 36.

2.2. *Quantum States and Their Volume-Energy Density*

Planck's and de Broglie's postulates, together with Schrödinger's equation, endow a microscopic particle with a wavefunction Ψ which has some properties analogous to mechanical and electromagnetic waves.

For example, a *conduction electron* (one-contributing to electrical conduction) in a cubic crystal has a finite probability distribution inside the crystal, but not outside it. This will mean that the probability density $|\Psi|^2$ associated with the electronic space charge is finite only inside the crystal. Accordingly, Ψ vanishes outside, and will assume finite values within the crystal. Solutions must satisfy the *boundary condition* that $\Psi = 0$, say, just at the surface. Thus, it would be expected that possible solutions of Ψ consist of spatial variations involving only integral numbers of half wavelengths along each one of the three perpendicular crystal axes.

An analogous situation would be an elastic cube whose surfaces are fixed to six rigid plates. Again, the possible modes of vibration must be restricted to waves with only integral numbers of half wavelengths along the three axes.

If the numbers of half wavelengths for Ψ along the three perpendicular axes are l, m, and n, then any combination of these numbers correspond to a possible solution of Schrödinger's equation. The integers l, m, and n are called *quantum numbers*.

Electron spin and quantum states. In addition to its motion in space, an electron rotates around its axis. It is found that this rotation leads to a fourth quantum number, which may be $+\frac{1}{2}$ or $-\frac{1}{2}$, depending on whether the spin is positive or negative.

It is now possible to state the following important definitions:

An *electron quantum state* consists of a single wavefunction, and either a positive or negative electron spin. Thus, an electron quantum state is specified by four quantum numbers, three of which pertain to space and the fourth one is either a positive or a negative spin.

Pauli exclusion principle. This principle (Pauli 1927) states that there can be no more than one electron occupying the same state in any atom, or system of atoms.

The Pauli exclusion principle constitutes a foundation stone in the theory of matter. If it were not for the existence of a law of nature as such, as philosophically described by Shockley (1950), electrons in various atoms would have dropped to the lowest energy level. Consequently, the structure of the periodic table, the diversity of chemistry, and even life as we know, would not exist.

Distribution of quantum states. Suppose that we have a unit volume in which the particle concentration is uniform. It is particularly important to be able to express how the states in that volume are distributed as a function of energy ϵ. To do so, let $(g\, d\epsilon)$ be the number of states per unit volume lying between ϵ and $(\epsilon+d\epsilon)$. Accordingly, the function g may be defined as the *volume-energy density* of *quantum states*, or simply, the *density of quantum states*.

The function g can generally be obtained for any system of particles from Schrödinger's equation. A case of special interest is that of what is to be called free particles, such as those of a vapor, and conduction electrons in solids. If the concentration of these particles is uniform, then the *free particle theory* assumes that the potential energy for a particle is approximately zero throughout the volume enclosing the gas. The basis of this assumption for the vapor particles is that most of the time the particles are sufficiently far apart so that the binding forces are negligibly small. In the case of conduction electrons, each one is far removed from any one nucleus. Thus, due to all the nuclei and other electrons in the crystal, the resultant *coulomb force* (electrostatic force) acting on any one electron is zero.

The free electron theory in metals is due to Sommerfeld (1928). It has been extended to semiconductors, as we shall see below in this chapter.

From Schrödinger's equation, under the assumptions of the free particle theory, it can, be shown* that

$$g(\epsilon) = C\epsilon^{1/2}, \tag{5}$$

$$C = (4\pi\sigma_d/h^3)\,(2m_{\text{eff}}^3)^{1/2}, \tag{6}$$

where ϵ is the electron energy which, if zero, represents the bottom of the allowable energy band; h is Planck's constant; m_{eff} is the particle effective mass; and σ_d may be defined as a degeneracy factor. For vapor particles, m_{eff} is equal to the actual mass per particle and $\sigma_d = 1$. For conduction electrons, however, m_{eff} is equal to the electron's effective mass m_e, which is not necessarily equal to the free electron mass. Because an electron can have two possible spins, $\sigma_d = 2$ for electrons.

As we shall see in this and subsequent chapters, a *parabolic density of states* [Eq. (5)] is fairly simple to manipulate mathematically. Furthermore, it is considered satisfactory, at least for some metals. It is also found to be quite satisfactory for all the semiconductor problems treated in this volume. For these reasons, we shall use invariably a parabolic distribution for the density of quantum states.

---

* For our treatment, it is not necessary to know how Eqs. (5) and (6) are derived. Readers interested in the derivations, however, will find them in a number of references. For electrons, see Kittel (1971), pp. 241–243. Identical results can be obtained for a vapor except that, because of the absence of a spin, the states are just half those of the electrons.

3. QUANTUM STATISTICS

We have seen in the previous section that the concept of a quantum state is a fundamental consequence of the quantum theory. We must, however, realize that the existence of a state does not guarantee that the state is occupied by one or more particles. Given a large number of states with the same energy level, how can we then determine the fraction of these states occupied by particles? This question is actually central in statistical mechanics. The results will be discussed here without proofs for two types of gases which either have symmetric, or antisymmetric wavefunctions.

3.1. *The Fermi–Dirac Distribution Function*

The probability that a quantum state at an energy level ϵ is occupied depends primarily on the type of gas, and its temperature. For gases, with antisymmetric wavefunctions, this probability is described by what is known as the *Fermi–Dirac distribution function* (Fermi 1926; Dirac 1926) given by*

$$F = \{\exp[(\epsilon - \epsilon_f)/kT] + 1\}^{-1}. \tag{7}$$

Here the quantity ϵ_f is called the *Fermi (energy) level*. When ϵ_f is measured from the zero reference of ϵ, then we shall call ϵ_f the *Fermi energy*. Particles for which the Fermi-Dirac distribution function is applicable are referred to as *fermions*.

Equation (7) provides another definition for ϵ_f. Notice that when $\epsilon = \epsilon_f$, $F = 0.5$, at any temperature. We may, therefore, say that the Fermi energy is that for which the probability of occupation of its states is one-half.

For a given value of ϵ_f, the dependence of F on ϵ at two temperatures is represented in Fig. 1. At $T = 0$, F becomes either 1, for $\epsilon < \epsilon_f$; or 0, for $\epsilon > \epsilon_f$. As T increases above the absolute zero, F gradually decreases from unity to zero.

In view of Eq. (7) and Fig. 1, we may say that states with energies less than the Fermi energy ϵ_f by several kT's are nearly filled. On the other hand, states with energies higher than ϵ_f by several kT's are nearly empty. In the latter case, Eq. (7) reduces to the *Boltzmann* distribution function given by

$$F = \exp[-(\epsilon - \epsilon_f)/kT]. \tag{8}$$

Equation (8) is a consequence of the Maxwell-Boltzmann statistics (Maxwell 1860, 1952; Boltzmann 1896).

---

* The Fermi–Dirac function is derived in any textbook on quantum statistical mechanics. For a brief and elegant treatment, see Schrödinger (1946).

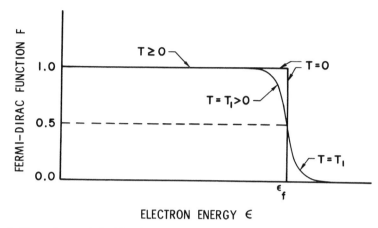

Fig. 1. Dependence of the Fermi–Dirac distribution function F on the electron energy ϵ at the absolute zero and at a higher temperature.

3.2. *The Bose–Einstein Distribution Function*

Gases with symmetric wavefunctions obey the *Bose–Einstein distribution function* (Bose 1924; Einstein 1924). Such gases are called *bosons*. The distribution function is expressed as

$$B = \{\exp[(\epsilon - \epsilon_b)/kT] - 1\}^{-1}, \tag{9}$$

where ϵ_b may be defined as the *Bose level*. When ϵ_b is measured from the zero reference of ϵ, then ϵ_b may be called the *Bose energy*.

The Bose–Einstein distribution function represents the probability that a state with an energy ϵ is occupied by a particle. It is interesting to notice that B can be larger than unity. The implication is that any number of bosons can occupy a state.

It follows from Eq. (9) that as ϵ exceeds ϵ_b by a few kT's, the Bose–Einstein distribution function approaches the classical limit of the Boltzmann distribution function, expressed by Eq. (8). In this equation, ϵ_b replaces ϵ_f.

Many gases in nature are bosons. The lightest of these are hydrogen and helium.* Yet, these two gases have atomic masses still so large that departures of the Bose–Einstein distribution function from the Maxwell–Boltzmann distribution function is negligibly small, except in the close neighborhood of the absolute zero. At such temperatures, these two gases, and heavier ones, will be in the liquid or solid state. Thus, the treatment of bosons for real gases will be too complicated and somewhat unnecessary.

---

* Helium-4 is a boson, although helium-3 is a fermion.

Our treatment will, therefore, be confined to fermions, usually represented by electrons.

4. ENERGY BANDS IN METALS AND SEMICONDUCTORS

4.1. *Band Theory of Solids*

An isolated atom has discrete electron energy levels. Each one of these levels consists of two or more quantum states. When two or more identical atoms are brought in close proximity, the wavefunctions of the two atoms overlap and each one of the original energy levels splits into two nearly equal levels. In the two-atom system, the number of electron states must be conserved. Hence, in this case, the number of states merely doubles. Similar conclusions may be arrived at if N atoms are brought in sufficiently close neighborhood. Specifically, in this case the splitting of energy levels and states will be by a factor of N.

Let us consider next how the splitting of energy levels and states leads to the three different types of solids known as insulators, semiconductors and conductors. To do so, consider a large number N of atoms which occupy, say, a cubic volume V. Let these atoms be uniformly distributed in that volume so that the distance d between each two neighboring atoms is the same throughout V. We shall call d the *atomic distance*. For solid crystals, d is generally called the *lattice constant*.

Imagine now that the N atoms initially occupy a sufficiently large volume so that the coupling between the atoms is nearly zero. In this case, the wavefunctions of the atoms will not overlap and the electron energy levels and states are essentially those of isolated atoms, as shown in Fig. 2, in the extreme right. The range of d, for which atoms behave as though they were isolated, corresponds to the gaseous state.

Suppose now that by some means the atomic distance d is being reduced steadily. As d reaches a certain small value, the closest atoms begin to interact and their wavefunctions will then overlap. Thus, the splitting of energy levels and states begins to take place as represented in Fig. 2. Further reduction in d only means that the domain of interaction involves more and more atoms. The splitting of energy levels and states continues to be more significant. As d assumes its typical values in solids, fully developed allowable energy bands will be established.

Thus one can see the relevance of discrete energy levels in isolated atoms (gases) and the existence of allowable and forbidden energy bands in solids and liquids. It is interesting to observe that as d diminishes, the allowable (energy) bands expand while the forbidden band (*energy gap*) diminishes. It is possible that the allowable bands overlap, which means that the energy gap completely disappears.

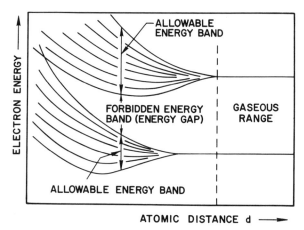

Fig. 2. Dependence of electron energy levels and band formation upon the atomic distance (lattice constant).

4.2. *Conduction and Valence Bands: Metals and Intrinsic Semiconductors*

From the discussion in the preceding subsection, one can understand why atoms in a solid crystal would give rise to many electronic (allowable) energy bands. Of all the energy bands, however, only one, or two at the most are of any significance to electrical conduction.

Metals. In metals the only energy band relevant to electrical conduction is the uppermost one containing electrons (Fig. 3). This band must further be *partially filled* by electrons at the absolute zero. Therefore, when an electric field is applied, electrons in this band will, under the proper conditions, be allowed to climb up to empty states at higher energy levels. Under such conditions, electrons are allowed to absorb energy from the applied electric field.

We have seen in Subsection 3.1 that the Fermi–Dirac distribution function requires that states tend to be completely filled if their energies are smaller than ϵ_f. On the other hand, the states tend to become empty as their energies increase above ϵ_f. Estimation of the energy departure in either direction from ϵ_f must, of course, be done in units of kT. Thus, at the absolute zero, all (allowable) energy bands above the conduction band are totally empty; and all energy bands below the conduction band are totally filled. For all practical purposes, this conclusion holds approximately true at room temperature and even above.

Accordingly, in metals the conduction band is the only band of concern for electrical conduction.

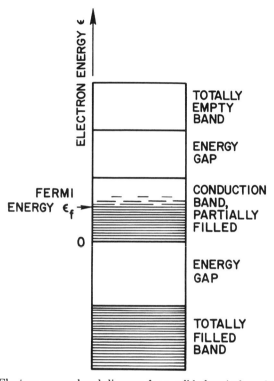

Fig. 3. Electron energy-band diagram for a solid electrical conductor.

Intrinsic semiconductors, and insulators. In some pure crystals, to be called *intrinsic* or *pure* semiconductors, two bands are relevant to electrical conduction (Fig. 4). In such crystals, at the absolute zero, the uppermost band containing electrons is completely filled. This filled band is defined as the *valence band*. The next higher energy band, called the *conduction band*, is completely empty. At the absolute zero, electrical conduction is not possible in the crystal. For, there are no allowable energy levels sufficiently near the (totally filled) valence band for the electrons to climb up to, if they absorbed energy from an applied electric field. Thus, characteristically, at the absolute zero an intrinsic semiconductor should act as a perfect electrical insulator.

Now as the temperature T is imagined to depart from its limiting case of zero, the conduction properties of the semiconductor are altered drastically. As T is increased, more and more electrons acquire sufficiently high thermal energy and evaporate from the valence to the conduction band, where they no longer belong to a specific atom. Rather, they wander freely

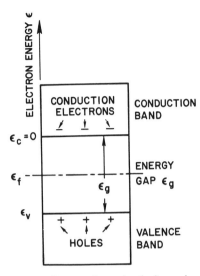

Fig. 4. Electron energy diagram for an instinsic semiconductor crystal.

and randomly in the entire crystal. They can further contribute to electrical conduction, because of the abundance of empty states of proper energy levels. Such electrons are, therefore, called *conduction electrons*.

As an electron rises to the conduction band, it leaves behind an empty state in the valence band. Such an empty state constitutes what is known as a *hole* which has a positive charge equal in magnitude to that of the electron. A hole also has a positive effective mass. Physically, the generation of an *electron-hole pair* involves detaching a valence electron from some atom. So the atom becomes positively charged. At a later instant, the atom borrows a valence electron from a neighboring atom. The first atom becomes neutral, while the second, having lost an electron, becomes positively charged. In this way, the hole shifts in position. This process continues on in a random way involving all atoms in the crystal. Like conduction electrons, holes are mobile in the crystal and, therefore, can contribute to electrical conduction.

From the preceding discussion, it is apparent that in an intrinsic crystal, conduction electrons and holes are created, or annihilated, in equal numbers. Consequently, at any temperature in any intrinsic semiconductor crystal, there are equal numbers of conduction electrons and holes; even though this number is strongly dependent on temperature, as we shall see in Section 6.

If now the energy gap of a crystal, say, exceeds 5 eV, no appreciable electron-hole pairs can be generated to even 500°K. The crystal resistivity in all this temperature range will be exceedingly high. The crystal in this case is said to be an insulator. Thus, a pure semiconductor with a sufficiently wide energy gap is an insulator.

4.3. *Impurity or Doped Semiconductors*

A number of properties of pure semiconductors are altered severely by introducing even minute traces of certain impurity atoms. For example, at room temperature, the resistivity of an intrinsic silicon crystal will be reduced by nearly a million times subsequent to introducing one impurity atom, such as boron, for every 10^6 atoms of silicon. This change in resistivity is a consequence of a profound change in the numbers of conduction electrons and holes. In the intrinsic crystal, both *charge carriers* are equal in numbers; even though, as we shall see in Section 6, these numbers depend strongly on the crystal temperature. Upon *doping* the crystal, that is, introducing impurities in it, one of the two types of charge carriers will drastically outnumber the other; and this can happen in two different ways to be discussed next.

n-Type semiconductors. A certain type of impurity atoms, when added in a semiconductor crystal (such as arsenic in silicon or germanium crystals), introduces an allowable energy level below, and close to, the bottom of the

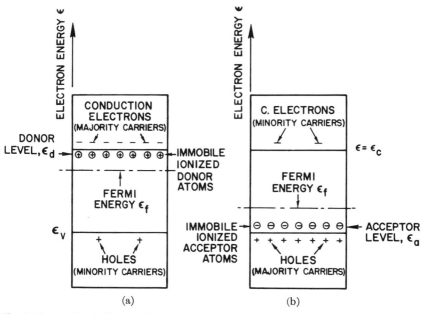

Fig. 5. Energy band diagrams for doped semiconductor crystals: (a) *n*-type; (b) *p*-type.

conduction band (Fig. 5a). At this energy level, the impurity atom commonly has one electron. At room temperature, the probability is extremely high that this electron will be *donated* to the conduction band. In this way, the electron will be completely detached from the impurity *donor* atom and will wander at random in the entire crystal. The donor atom will, therefore, be positively charged and is said, therefore, to be *ionized*. Since the impurity atom is frozen in the crystal, it cannot contribute to electrical conduction.

From the preceding discussion, it is apparent that one can introduce at least one conduction electron per donor atom. Consequently, by adding donor atoms, one can profoundly increase the concentration of conduction electrons above their minutely-small value in the pure semiconductor. As explained in Section 6, the concentration of holes will, in turn, be drastically reduced below their value in the pure crystal because of the profoundly increased chance of electron-hole recombination. Thus, electrical conduction in a crystal having donor atoms will be most predominantly carried by electrons. The semiconductor, in this case, is called an *n-type* (*n* for negative).

The closer the *donor energy level* (introduced by the impurity atom, Fig. 5a) is to the conduction band, the lower will be the minimum temperature required for ionizing most of the donor atoms.

p-Type semiconductors. When a second type of impurity atoms, such as boron, is added to a pure semiconductor, such as Si, the number of holes in the crystal will be profoundly increased. Because of the electron-hole recombination, simultaneously the number of conduction electrons is drastically reduced. Electrical conduction in such crystals is, therefore, carried almost entirely by holes. The semiconductor, in this case, is said to be *p*-type (*p* for positive).

This change of *conductivity type* occurs because the added impurity atoms introduce an allowable energy level in the energy gap above, and close to, the top of the valence band (Fig. 5b). This energy level has usually one state empty. At room temperature, the probability strongly favors that the empty state becomes occupied by an electron from the valence band. In this way, each impurity atom *accepts* an electron from the valence band. The *acceptor atom* at once becomes ionized.

Each empty state in the valence band constitutes a hole. As explained earlier for intrinsic semiconductors, the hole keeps wandering at random in the entire crystal, and can, therefore, contribute to electrical conduction. The ionized acceptor atom, being fixed in position, cannot do so.

Again, the closer the *acceptor level* (Fig. 5b) is to the valence band, the lower will be the minimum temperature required to ionize most of the acceptor atoms.

5. IDEAL CLASSICAL GASES

Earlier in this chapter, we have summarized some basic results of quantum and statistical mechanics. These results include the concept of a state, the density of states per unit energy per unit volume and the probability of occupation of a state by a particle. In the remaining part of this chapter, we shall use these results to derive a number of fundamental relations for some classical and degenerate gases. We shall further interpret the derived relations for conduction electrons and holes in semiconductors and conduction electrons in metals.

In this section, we shall derive an expression for the concentration of an ideal classical gas in terms of the Fermi or Bose level. We shall also show that the average kinetic energy per particle in an ideal classical gas is $(\frac{3}{2}kT)$, which does not depend on the mass.

From the point of view of quantum and statistical mechanics, we may define *ideal classical gases* to be those which: (1) obey the Maxwell–Boltzmann statistics; (2) have a parabolic distribution of the density of quantum states; and (3) have no other than the first virial term. We shall see in Subsection 5.3 that this definition is identical with the phenomenological definition cited earlier.

5.1. *Gas Concentration Under Ideal Classical Conditions*

Consider a fermion or a boson gas, which has approached its classical limit by some means to be determined later. Let ϵ_x represent the Fermi, or Bose energy for this gas, depending on whether its particles are fermions, or bosons, respectively. In the energy interval $d\epsilon$ there are $[g(\epsilon)\,d\epsilon]$ number of states per unit volume. Of these states, the number dn of states per unit volume occupied by particles will be $[g(\epsilon)F\,d\epsilon]$, where F is the probability of occupation. The function F is, in our case, the Boltzmann distribution function. Now that we know the portion dn, of the gas concentration n, is lying in the interval $d\epsilon$, we may proceed to calculate n, which, in view of Eqs. (5) and (8), may be written as

$$n = \int_0^\infty g(\epsilon) F\,d\epsilon = C \int_0^\infty \epsilon^{1/2} \exp[-(\epsilon - \epsilon_x)/kT]\,d\epsilon. \tag{10}$$

The upper energy limit of infinity is a good approximation, even though the energy band does not have to really extend to infinity. The validity of this approximation is based on the fact that the exponential term in the integrand decays much more strongly than $\epsilon^{1/2}$ increases.

Since the integration in Eq. (10) is strictly with respect to ϵ, the Fermi or Bose energy ϵ_x may be considered constant. Equation (10), therefore, may be rewritten as

$$n = C \exp(\epsilon_\chi/kT) \int_0^\infty \epsilon^{1/2} \exp(-\epsilon/kT) \, d\epsilon. \tag{11}$$

This integral can be evaluated by substituting

$$\epsilon = kTx^2. \tag{12}$$

Accordingly, Eq. (11) becomes

$$n = 2C(kT)^{3/2} \exp(\epsilon_\chi/kT) \int_0^\infty x^2 \exp(-x^2) \, dx. \tag{13}$$

The integral in Eq. (13) is of a standard form, and the expression for n is

$$n = (\pi^{1/2}/2)(kT)^{3/2}C \exp(\epsilon_\chi/kT). \tag{14}$$

Substituting into Eq. (14) the appropriate value of C as given by Eq. (6), we get for conduction electrons ($\sigma_d = 2$):

$$n = 2(2\pi m_e kT/h^2)^{3/2} \exp(\epsilon_f/kT); \tag{15}$$

and for other ideal classical gases such as vapors ($\sigma_d = 1$)

$$n = (2\pi mkT/h^2)^{3/2} \exp(\epsilon_\chi/kT). \tag{16}$$

The quantity m_e is the electron effective mass, and m is the mass per particle of the vapor.

Equations (15) and (16) make it possible at once to calculate the Fermi or Bose energy, once the concentration of the gas and the statistics it obeys are known.

It should be recalled, however, that Eqs. (15) and (16) only hold for ideal classical gases for which the Maxwell–Boltzmann statistics is applicable. Under such conditions the Fermi or Bose energies should be negative. We shall next discuss the factors which cause a gas to move either towards stronger degeneracy or the classical limit.

5.2. Borderline of Degeneracy and Nondegeneracy

Consider first the case of a classical (nondegenerate) electron gas for which Eq. (15) applies. We may rewrite this equation as

$$n = N_e \exp(\epsilon_f/kT), \tag{17}$$

$$N_e = 2(2\pi m_e kT/h^2)^{3/2}. \tag{18}$$

According to Eq. (17), ϵ_f will always be negative whenever $n < N_e$. It is convenient to define the borderline between degeneracy and nondegeneracy as that corresponding to $\epsilon_f = 0$. Let the *critical concentration* associated with this value of Fermi energy be n_{ce}. For this concentration, strictly speaking, the gas will not obey exactly the Maxwell-Boltzmann statistics. However, the departure from the classical conditions is not too appreciable.

We may, therefore, conclude that for electrons

$$n > n_{ce} \quad \text{(gas is degenerate)}, \tag{19}$$

$$n < n_{ce} \quad \text{(gas is classical)}, \tag{20}$$

where

$$n_{ce} = 2(2\pi m_e kT/h^2)^{3/2} = N_e. \tag{21}$$

By a similar argument, one can determine the critical concentration n_{cv} for a free vapor to be

$$n_{cv} = (2\pi mkT/h^2)^{3/2}. \tag{22}$$

Figure 6 shows a plot of the dependence on temperature of the critical concentrations of conduction electrons and of a hypothetical vapor with a particle mass equal to that of the hydrogen atom.

In view of Fig. 6, conditions (19) and (20) and Eqs. (21) and (22), we may arrive at the interesting conclusion that: given any gas with fixed concentration, at sufficiently high temperatures the gas becomes classical, and at sufficiently low temperatures the gas becomes degenerate. Furthermore, heavier gases are nondegenerate even at lower temperatures.

5.3. *Average Kinetic Energy per Particle and the Equation of State*

We next calculate the average kinetic energy $\langle \epsilon \rangle$ per particle. To do so, we first calculate from Eqs. (5) and (8) the total amount of thermal energy $[n \langle \epsilon \rangle]$ per unit volume of the gas.

In the energy interval $d\epsilon$, there are $(g \, d\epsilon)$ states per unit volume, of which $[gF \, d\epsilon]$ states are occupied by particles whose energy is ϵ. Accordingly, in the range $d\epsilon$, the thermal energy of the gas is $[gF\epsilon \, d\epsilon]$ per unit volume. Integrating this quantity over all the possible energy range, we simply get the total amount of thermal energy contained in a unit volume of the gas. In terms of the average kinetic energy $\langle \epsilon \rangle$ per particle, the energy per unit volume will be

$$n \langle \epsilon \rangle = \int_0^\infty \epsilon g F \, d\epsilon, \tag{23}$$

or

$$\langle \epsilon \rangle = n^{-1} \int_0^\infty \epsilon g F \, d\epsilon. \tag{24}$$

Equation (24) represents a general expression for the average kinetic energy per particle for any gas. The gas may be degenerate or nondegenerate.

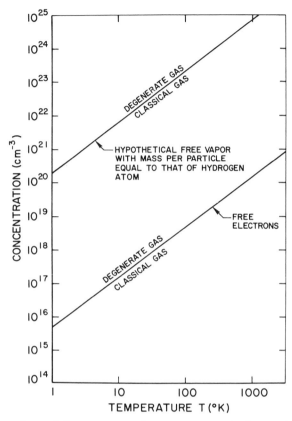

Fig. 6. Dependence of degeneracy–nondegeneracy concentration on the crystal temperature, and particle mass.

If the gas is ideal and classical, then Eqs. (5) and (8) will hold. Equation (24), therefore, reduces to

$$\langle \epsilon \rangle = \frac{C}{n} \int_0^\infty \epsilon^{3/2} \exp[-(\epsilon - \epsilon_x)/kT] \, d\epsilon. \tag{25}$$

It is not necessary to completely evaluate this integral to determine $\langle \epsilon \rangle$. Rather, the integral

$$C \int_0^\infty \epsilon^{3/2} \exp[-(\epsilon - \epsilon_x)/kT] \, d\epsilon = -C(kT) \int_0^\infty \epsilon^{3/2} \, d\{\exp[-(\epsilon - \epsilon_x)/kT]\}$$

$$= \tfrac{3}{2} kT \int_0^\infty C\epsilon^{1/2} \exp[-(\epsilon - \epsilon_x)/kT] \, d\epsilon. \tag{26}$$

The last step in Eq. (26) follows from the integration by parts. It will be recognized here that the integral in the last term represents simply n, as indicated by Eq. (10). Therefore, from Eqs. (25) and (26), we have

$$\langle \epsilon \rangle = \tfrac{3}{2} kT. \tag{27}$$

Thus the average kinetic energy of an ideal classical gas does not depend on the mass per particle.

According to Newtonian mechanics, however,

$$\langle \epsilon \rangle = \tfrac{1}{2} m \langle v^2 \rangle, \tag{28}$$

where m is the mass per particle, and $\langle v^2 \rangle$ the mean square of the particle velocity. From Eqs. (27) and (28), the mean square of the thermal velocity may be expressed as

$$\langle v^2 \rangle = 3kT/m. \tag{29}$$

One can further calculate the gas (internal) pressure P for an ideal classical gas directly from Eq. (27). According to the virial theorem, this pressure is equal to two-thirds the average kinetic energy per unit volume. Thus,

$$P = \tfrac{2}{3} n \langle \epsilon \rangle, \tag{30}$$

and in view of Eq. (27),

$$P = knT. \tag{31}$$

It is interesting to observe that the expressions obtained for $\langle \epsilon \rangle$ and P are valid regardless of the degeneracy coefficient σ_d in Eq. (6). Thus, Eqs. (29) and (31) hold for ideal, classical gases, regardless of whether the particles are electrons, other fermions, or even bosons.

It will be recalled that the results obtained for $\langle \epsilon \rangle$ and P have been based on the Maxwell–Boltzmann statistics, a parabolic density of quantum states and a first-order virial theorem. It is interesting to note that the combination of these three factors leads to the equation of state as defined earlier phenomenologically.

6. ELECTRONS AND HOLES IN NONDEGENERATE SEMICONDUCTORS

In Section 4, we discussed qualitatively intrinsic and doped semiconductors of the n and p types. In this section, we present a quantitative account of how the concentrations of conduction electrons, holes and impurity atoms are interrelated in *nondegenerate* n-type and p-type semiconductors. These semiconductors are those in which both electrons and holes behave like ideal, classical gases.

6.1. *The Mass-Action Law*

Consider a crystal which is uniformly doped either with donor or acceptor atoms. In a nondegenerate crystal, the concentration n of conduction electrons will be expressed as given by Eqs. (17) and (18). This concentration will be

$$n = 2(2\pi m_e kT/h^2)^{3/2} \exp(\epsilon_f/kT). \tag{32}$$

One can then calculate the concentration p of holes by calculating first the number of empty states per unit volume lying in the energy range $d\epsilon$ at ϵ. This can be done by assuming that the density of electron states in the valence band is parabolic. The probability that a state at an energy level ϵ is empty is simply $(1-F)$; where F is the Fermi-Dirac distribution function. Carrying out the necessary steps, it can be shown that

$$p = 2(2\pi m_h kT/h^2)^{3/2} \exp[-(\epsilon_g + \epsilon_f)/kT], \tag{33}$$

where m_h is the hole effective mass, ϵ_g the width of the energy gap, and ϵ_f is measured from the bottom of the conduction band. It should be remembered that ϵ_f is a negative quantity.

From Eqs. (32) and (33), it follows that

$$pn = 4(2\pi kT/h^2)^3 (m_e m_h)^{3/2} \exp(-\epsilon_g/kT). \tag{34}$$

Thus, the product pn does not depend in any way on the *doping levels* (impurity concentrations). Rather, pn depends strongly on the crystal energy gap and temperature, and somewhat weakly on the electron and the hole effective masses.

As explained in Subsection 4.2, in an intrinsic semiconductor crystal, the concentration n_i of electrons is equal to the concentration p_i of holes. Hence, for the crystal under consideration, it follows from Eq. (34) that

$$pn = p_i n_i = p_i^2 = n_i^2. \tag{35}$$

Equation (35) expresses what is generally known as the *mass-action law*, which is applicable only to nondegenerate semiconductors. The *mass-action* law has useful applications as we shall see in the two subsections to follow.

6.2. *Extrinsic and Nearly Intrinsic Semiconductors with Totally Ionized Impurities*

Consider a uniformly-doped semiconductor crystal which may contain generally donor and acceptor atoms of concentrations N_d and N_a, respectively. Let the two impurities be totally ionized, so that the donors will be positively charged, while the acceptors will be negatively charged. Suppose now that N_d and N_a are known and we wish to determine the concentrations p and n of holes and conduction electrons, respectively.

In any part of a uniformly doped crystal, there must be equal amounts of positive and negative charges. This *condition of charge neutrality*, therefore, requires that

$$p+N_d=n+N_a. \tag{36}$$

Equations (35) and (36) make it possible to solve for p and n, whose expressions are

$$p=\tfrac{1}{2}\{(N_a-N_d)+[(N_a-N_d)^2+4n_i^2]^{1/2}\}, \tag{37}$$

$$n=\tfrac{1}{2}\{(N_d-N_a)+[(N_d-N_a)^2+4n_i^2]^{1/2}\}. \tag{38}$$

From Eqs. (34) and (35), we get

$$n_i^2=4(2\pi kT/h^2)^3(m_e m_h)^{3/2}\exp(-\epsilon_g/kT). \tag{39}$$

For simplicity, consider a semiconductor crystal which is only doped with donor impurities. In this case, $N_a=0$, and Eqs. (37) and (38) reduce to

$$p=\tfrac{1}{2}\{[N_d^2+4n_i^2]^{1/2}-N_d\}, \tag{40}$$

$$n=\tfrac{1}{2}\{[N_d^2+4n_i^2]^{1/2}+N_d\}. \tag{41}$$

We now observe that if

$$N_d\gg n_i, \tag{42}$$

then Eqs. (40) and (41) reduce further to

$$p\simeq n_i^2/N_d, \tag{43}$$

$$n\simeq N_d. \tag{44}$$

Equation (43) may be obtained by one of two methods: either directly from Eq. (44) and the mass-action law, or from the binomial expansion of the right-hand side of Eq. (40).

An n-type crystal for which condition (42) holds is defined as an *extrinsic semiconductor*. If, however, N_d is comparable to n_i, the crystal is said to be *nearly intrinsic*. For both extrinsic or nearly intrinsic n-type crystals, once n or p is found, the Fermi energy can be calculated from Eq. (32) or (33), respectively.

Similar conclusions can be made for p-type crystals containing only acceptor atoms. For such crystals, if extrinsic,

$$N_a\gg p_i, \quad p\simeq N_a, \quad n\simeq p_i^2/N_a. \tag{45}$$

In any sufficiently doped semiconductor, one type of carriers outnumbers the other. For example, in an n-type crystal, electrons outnumber holes. Electrons in this case constitute what are called *majority carriers*, whereas holes are the *minority carriers*. In a p-type crystal, however, holes are the majority carriers, while electrons are the minority carriers. As seen in Eqs. (43) and (45), the concentration of minority carriers depends on n_i^2 which, in turn, depends strongly on T and ϵ_g, and somewhat weakly on m_e and m_h.

For illustration, Appendix B lists physical constants for a few common semiconductor materials.

6.3. *The Fermi Energy in Nondegenerate Semiconductors*

We have seen in the preceding subsection how to calculate p and n for any nondegenerate semiconductor in which the impurity atoms are totally ionized. Total ionization usually occurs near room temperature and above. Once p and n are found, the Fermi energy ϵ_f too can be determined. In this section, we shall calculate the Fermi energy in intrinsic and in nondegenerate extrinsic semiconductors accounting for the deionization which usually occurs at low temperatures.

Intrinsic semiconductors. In an intrinsic crystal, at any temperature, the concentration n_i of electrons equals the concentration p_i of holes. Thus, it follows from Eqs. (32) and (33) that

$$n_i/p_i = (m_e/m_h)^{3/2} \exp[(\epsilon_g + 2\epsilon_i)/kT] = 1, \tag{46}$$

where ϵ_i is the Fermi energy in the intrinsic crystal.

Solving Eq. (46) for ϵ_i we get

$$\epsilon_i = -\left[\tfrac{1}{2}\epsilon_g + \tfrac{3}{4}kT \ln(m_e/m_h)\right]. \tag{47}$$

In most cases, the term involving kT is much less than $(\epsilon_g/2)$. Therefore, Eq. (47) may be written approximately as

$$\epsilon_i \simeq -\tfrac{1}{2}\epsilon_g. \tag{48}$$

Equation (48) will be exact, if $m_e = m_h$.

Since ϵ_i is measured from the bottom of the conduction band, Eq. (48) then implies that in an intrinsic semiconductor, the Fermi energy lies nearly in the middle of the energy gap.

On the basis of Eqs. (32), (33), and (48), one can arrive at the following conclusion for nondegenerate semiconductors: the more donor impurities are introduced in a pure crystal, the farther the Fermi level departs from the middle of the gap towards the conduction band. For acceptor impurities, the departure of the energy level is towards the valence band.

Impurity deionization at low temperatures in nondegenerate crystals. As the temperature of a crystal decreases below a certain value, deionization of the impurities significantly proceeds. We shall investigate the temperature dependence of the Fermi energy, accounting for impurity deionization in a special case. The method to be used, however, can be extended to other situations.

The case to be considered is that of a nondegenerate n-type crystal in which there are no other than donor atoms whose concentration is N_d and energy level ϵ_d.* Let the concentration of ionized donor atoms be n_d. Because of the mass-action law, the ratio (p/n) in this crystal will be extremely small. Thus, p can be neglected compared to n. The condition of charge neutrality in the crystal will then require that

$$n \simeq n_d. \tag{49}$$

For maintaining nondegeneracy at and near the absolute zero, ϵ_f must invariably remain below the conduction band. We shall see, however, that at sufficiently low temperatures, ϵ_f will be inevitably above ϵ_d. Hence, we cannot use the Boltzmann distribution function to calculate the probability of ionization for an impurity atom. Rather, we must use the Fermi-Dirac distribution function. Accordingly,

$$n_d = N_d(1 - \{1 + \exp[(\epsilon_d - \epsilon_f)/kT]\}^{-1}). \tag{50}$$

Since ϵ_f is negative, Eq. (32) will hold for n. Therefore, from this equation and Eqs. (49) and (50), we obtain

$$N_d \exp[(\epsilon_d - \epsilon_f)/kT] = BT^{3/2} \exp(\epsilon_f/kT)\{1 + \exp[(\epsilon_d - \epsilon_f)/kT]\}, \tag{51}$$

where

$$B = 2(2\pi m_e k/h^2)^{3/2}. \tag{52}$$

Equation (51) is a quadratic in $\exp(\epsilon_f/kT)$, and has the solution

$$\exp(\epsilon_f/kT) = \tfrac{1}{2}[\exp(2\epsilon_d/kT) + 4(N_d/BT^{3/2}) \exp(\epsilon_d/kT)]^{1/2} - \tfrac{1}{2}\exp(\epsilon_d/kT). \tag{53}$$

Since $\epsilon_d < 0$, then as T tends to zero, the only significant term will be the second one under the square root. Accordingly, it can be shown that

$$\lim_{T \to 0} \epsilon_f = \tfrac{1}{2}\epsilon_d. \tag{54}$$

As the temperature exceeds a relatively high value, the crystal becomes nearly intrinsic and $p \simeq n$. Consequently, Eq. (53) would not hold. It should be noticed, however, that above the temperature for which ϵ_f drops below ϵ_d by several kT's, nearly all the donor atoms will be ionized. At such temperatures ϵ_f can be determined, as outlined earlier, from Eqs. (32) or (33). It can be seen that as T increases sufficiently, crystals will tend to be intrinsic and the Fermi energy approaches about the middle of the energy gap.

From the discussion in this section, it is apparent that under certain conditions, majority carriers in a semiconductor will remain nondegenerate

---

* An extensive list of donors and acceptors and their levels in germanium and silicon is listed in Hanney (1959), pp. 341–342.

at all temperatures, no matter how closely the absolute zero is approached. Minority carriers, of course, are nondegenerate at all temperatures, even in degenerate crystals. It should be noticed, however, that for such a case, at the limiting temperature of 0°K, the concentration of majority and minority carriers must vanish. This result agrees with the general statement made earlier [Section 1] that at the absolute zero, any gas with nonvanishing concentration must be degenerate.

7. STRONGLY AND WEAKLY DEGENERATE IDEAL FERMIONS: METALS AND DEGENERATE SEMICONDUCTORS

We shall deal in this section with what will be called ideal fermions. By definition, such gases are meant to be those which obey the Fermi-Dirac statistics; have a parabolic density of states; and are characterized by an equation of state having no virial terms other than the first one. We shall further be concerned with fermions which are weakly, or strongly degenerate. Weak degeneracy is meant here in the sense that the Fermi energy is, at the most, a few kT's above the bottom of the conduction band, or below the top of the valence band. Therefore, strongly degenerate fermions will have the Fermi energy much more than, say, $10kT$'s above the bottom of the conduction band, or below the top of the valence band. Degenerate holes, of course, can be only in p-type semiconductors, whereas degenerate electrons can be in n-type semiconductors, and are invariably so in metals in a wide temperature range. For metals, this range extends from 0°K to well above room temperature, if not up to and beyond the melting point.

7.1. The Sommerfeld-Bethe Approximation

In treating strongly degenerate fermions, a number of Fermi-Dirac integrals arise. These integrals can be most conveniently evaluated by an approximate method devised by Sommerfeld and Bethe (1934). In this subsection, we shall discuss this useful method of approximation.

Consider the definite integral

$$I = \int_0^\infty (d\phi/d\epsilon) F \, d\epsilon, \tag{55}$$

where

$$\phi = \phi(\epsilon) \tag{56}$$

and F is the Fermi–Dirac distribution function.

Integrating Eq. (55) by parts, and in view of Eq. (56), we obtain

$$I = -\phi(0) - \int_0^\infty \phi(\partial F/\partial \epsilon) \, d\epsilon. \tag{57}$$

The function $(\partial F/\partial \epsilon)$ peaks at $\epsilon = \epsilon_f$, and decays to zero nearly exponentially, after ϵ exceeds ϵ_f by a few kT's (Fig. 7). Therefore, it is only when ϵ is in the close neighborhood of ϵ_f that the integrand in Eq. (57) significantly contributes to the integral. To take advantage of this property, let us expand $\phi(\epsilon)$ by Taylor's series around $\epsilon = \epsilon_f$. Equation (57), therefore, becomes

$$I = -\phi(0) - \int_0^\infty \left[\phi(\epsilon_f) + (\epsilon - \epsilon_f)\phi'(\epsilon_f) + \sum_{\nu=2}^\infty \frac{(\epsilon - \epsilon_f)^\nu}{\nu!} \phi^\nu(\epsilon_f) \right] (\partial F/\partial \epsilon) \; d\epsilon. \quad (58)$$

Of the infinite series of integrals we now have, it is sufficient for all the cases of interest to evaluate only the first three integrals, which we denote by I_1, I_2, and I_3.
The first integral

$$I_1 = \phi(\epsilon_f) \int_0^\infty (\partial F/\partial \epsilon) \; d\epsilon = -\phi(\epsilon_f). \quad (59)$$

The second

$$I_2 = \phi'(\epsilon_f) \int_0^\infty (\epsilon - \epsilon_f)(\partial F/\partial \epsilon) \; d\epsilon$$

$$= \phi'(\epsilon_f) \int_{-\infty}^\infty (\epsilon - \epsilon_f)(\partial F/\partial \epsilon) \; d\epsilon. \quad (60)$$

It has been possible to change the lower limit from 0 to $-\infty$, for the reason

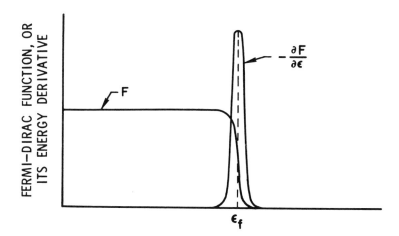

Fig. 7. Dependence on energy ϵ of the Fermi–Dirac distribution function F and its energy derivative at a temperature above 0°K.

that, having $\epsilon_f \gg 10kT$, the integrand will severely decay to zero at $\epsilon = 0$ and more so for $\epsilon < 0$.

If we now make the substitution

$$x = (\epsilon - \epsilon_f)/kT, \tag{61}$$

then

$$\int_{-\infty}^{\infty} (\epsilon - \epsilon_f)(\partial F/\partial \epsilon) \, d\epsilon = -kT \int_{-\infty}^{\infty} \frac{x \, dx}{(e^{x/2} + e^{-x/2})^2} . \tag{62}$$

The integrand on the right-hand side of Eq. (62) is an odd function. Thus, the integral vanishes, and so will I_2.

Finally, the third integral in Eq. (58) will be

$$I_3 = \tfrac{1}{2}\phi''(\epsilon_f) \int_0^{\infty} (\epsilon - \epsilon_f)^2 (\partial F/\partial \epsilon) \, d\epsilon. \tag{63}$$

As explained earlier, the lower limit of the integral can be changed to $-\infty$. Introducing then the variable transformation of Eq. (61), Eq. (63) becomes

$$I_3 = -\tfrac{1}{2}(kT)^2 \phi''(\epsilon_f) \int_{-\infty}^{\infty} \frac{x^2 \, dx}{(e^{x/2} + e^{-x/2})^2} . \tag{64}$$

The integral* equals $(\pi^2/3)$. Hence,

$$I_3 = -(\pi^2/6)(kT)^2 \phi''(\epsilon_f). \tag{65}$$

In view of Eqs. (55), (57), (58), (59), and (65), we may conclude that

$$\int_0^{\infty} (d\phi/d\epsilon) F \, d\epsilon \simeq -\phi(0) + \phi(\epsilon_f) + (\pi^2/6)(kT)^2 \phi''(\epsilon_f), \tag{66}$$

provided that

$$\epsilon_f \gg 10kT. \tag{67}$$

We shall next apply the Sommerfeld–Bethe approximation† to some problems.

7.2. Conduction Electrons in Metals and Strongly Degenerate Semiconductors

In Section 5, we derived expressions for the particle concentration, average thermal kinetic energy per particle, and (internal) pressure, all for ideal classical gases, such as electrons and holes in nondegenerate semiconductors. The three quantities have all been related to the Fermi or Bose

---

* For an excellent reference containing tables of definite integrals, see Bierens de Haan (1858, 1957).

† In the literature, it is commonly assumed that $\phi(0) = 0$. There is no mathematical requirement for it to be so, and, therefore, we consider it here to be of any value.

energy of the gas. In this subsection, we are concerned with determining how these three quantities depart from their classical values for fermions, as the gas becomes increasingly degenerate.

Concentration. If the fermions under consideration are conduction electrons, then, in view of Eqs. (5) and (6), we may express their concentration n by

$$n = (8\pi/h^3)(2m_e^3)^{1/2} \int_0^\infty \epsilon^{1/2} F \, d\epsilon. \tag{68}$$

If the gas is strongly degenerate, then in view of the Sommerfeld–Bethe (SB) approximation, we have

$$n = (16\pi/3h^3)(2m_e^3)^{1/2} \int_0^\infty F(d/d\epsilon)(\epsilon^{3/2}) \, d\epsilon$$

$$= (16\pi/3h^3)(2m_e^3)^{1/2}\epsilon_f^{3/2}[1 + (\pi^2/8)(kT/\epsilon_f)^2]. \tag{69}$$

Equation (69) is applicable to conduction electrons in metals and strongly degenerate semiconductors, provided that the electron energy bands in these solids are of a standard type.

For illustration, Appendix C includes a list of values of the Fermi energy and concentration for eight different monovalent metals.

Average kinetic energy per particle. The (average) thermal kinetic energy per particle may be calculated by dividing the total thermal energy per unit volume by the number n of particles per unit volume. Accordingly,

$$\langle\epsilon\rangle = \left[\int_0^\infty \epsilon^{3/2} F \, d\epsilon\right] \Big/ \left[\int_0^\infty \epsilon^{1/2} F \, d\epsilon\right]. \tag{70}$$

Internal pressure. Since the internal pressure P is two-thirds the average kinetic energy per unit volume, then

$$P = \tfrac{2}{3} n \langle\epsilon\rangle. \tag{71}$$

If the electrons are strongly degenerate, then from the SB approximation, it can be easily shown that

$$\langle\epsilon\rangle \simeq 0.6\epsilon_f[1 + \tfrac{1}{2}\pi^2(kT/\epsilon_f)^2], \tag{72}$$

$$P \simeq 0.4\epsilon_f n[1 + \tfrac{1}{2}\pi^2(kT/\epsilon_f)^2]. \tag{73}$$

In order to see numerically how P and $\langle\epsilon\rangle$ depart from their classical values as the gas becomes degenerate, let us introduce the variable transformation:

$$\eta = \epsilon/kT, \quad \eta_f = \epsilon_f/kT. \tag{74}$$

Consequently, the Fermi–Dirac distribution function will be transformed to

$$F(\eta, \eta_f) = [\exp(\eta - \eta_f) + 1]^{-1}. \tag{75}$$

The quantities $\langle \epsilon \rangle$ and P, can be shown to be given by

$$\langle \epsilon \rangle = \tfrac{3}{2} kT \rho_\epsilon, \tag{76}$$

$$\rho_\epsilon = \frac{2}{3} \left[\int_0^\infty \eta^{3/2} F(\eta, \eta_f) \, d\eta \right] \Big/ \left[\int_0^\infty \eta^{1/2} F(\eta, \eta_f) \, d\eta \right]. \tag{77}$$

It can also be shown that

$$P = nkT \rho_p, \tag{78}$$

$$\rho_p = \rho_\epsilon. \tag{79}$$

The quantity ρ_ϵ may be interpreted as a degeneracy factor. This factor represents the ratio of the average kinetic energy per particle to its classical value of $\tfrac{3}{2} kT$ for a degenerate electron gas. The factor ρ_p also represents the ratio of internal pressure of a degenerate electron gas to its classical value of nkT. Figure 8 represents (Melehy 1965a, b) a plot of ρ_ϵ and ρ_p as a function $\eta_f = (\epsilon_f/kT)$. Numerical values for the Fermi–Dirac functions appearing in Eq. (77) have been taken from the tables of McDougall and Stoner (1938).

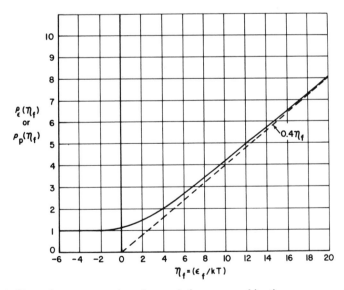

Fig. 8. Dependence on η_f of: ratio ρ_ϵ of the average kinetic energy per (fermion) particle to $(\tfrac{3}{2} kT)$; or ratio ρ_p of particle internal pressure to its classical value (knT). The Fermi energy is measured from the bottom of the (standard) energy band.

It is interesting to notice that ρ_ϵ is very nearly unity as ϵ_f becomes sufficiently negative. This range corresponds to classical gases such as electrons in nondegenerate n-type semiconductors, or in p-type semiconductors with any degree of degeneracy. The coefficient ρ_ϵ increases rather rapidly for $\eta_f > 0$, and approaches asymptotically $0.4\eta_f$. This limit is closely reached for strongly degenerate n-type semiconductors, and metals for which $\langle\epsilon\rangle \simeq 0.6\epsilon_f$, and $P \simeq 0.4n\epsilon_f$. The variation of ρ_p is, of course, the same as that of ρ_ϵ.

PROBLEMS

1. Given a volume $V = 10$ cm³, calculate the number of electronic states in that volume lying between 6 and 7 eV. Assume that the density of states function is given by Eqs. (5) and (6). Assume that the electron effective mass equals the free electron mass.

[Ans. 1.73×10^{23} electronic states.]

2. Calculate the Fermi energy ϵ_f in electron volts at $T = 300°$K, for a classical electron gas whose concentration is 10^{16} cm⁻³.

3. Show that the probability F_p that a state at an energy level ϵ is unoccupied by an electron is given by

$$F_p = \{1 + \exp[-(\epsilon - \epsilon_f)/kT]\}^{-1}.$$

4. Using a parabolic distribution for the density of quantum states in the valence band and the Fermi-Dirac distribution function, show that the concentration p of holes in a nondegenerate semiconductor is given by Eq. (33).

5. Derive Eq. (43) from Eq. (40) using the binomial theorem.

6. Determine the temperature at which the donor atoms are half ionized in a crystal in which $N_d = 10^{16}$ cm⁻³, $\epsilon_d = -0.1$ eV and $\epsilon_g > 1$ eV.

7. Reason that the more donor atoms are added to a nondegenerate semiconductor, the closer the Fermi level gets to the conduction band.

8. Reason that the more acceptor atoms are added to a nondegenerate semiconductor, the closer the Fermi level gets to the valence band.

9. What is the mathematical condition requiring the existence of a critical value of the donor concentration N_{dc} below which majority electrons will remain nondegenerate at all temperatures at and above the absolute zero.

10. Accounting for impurity deionization, derive an expression for $\exp(\epsilon_f/kT)$ for a nondegenerate semiconductor in which there are only acceptor atoms with concentration N_a. Let the acceptor level be ϵ_a.

11. In Problem 10, show that as T tends to $0°K$, ϵ_f tends to be half in between ϵ_a and the top of the valence band.

12. Consider an electron gas for which $\epsilon_f < 0$, but not necessarily that $\epsilon_f \ll -kT$. For that gas, show that if $g(\epsilon) = C_n \epsilon^{1/2}$, then

$$n = \tfrac{1}{2} C_n \pi^{1/2} (kT)^{3/2} \exp(\epsilon_f/kT) \{1 + \sum_{n=1}^{\infty} [(-)^n \exp(n\epsilon_f/kT)] / (n+1)^{3/2}\}.$$

13. Assuming that for copper the Fermi energy $\epsilon_f = 7$ eV, calculate the concentration n of conduction electrons. Consider that the electron effective mass is equal to that in free space.
    [Ans. 8.37×10^{22} cm^{-3}.]

14. Calculate the energy level ϵ in copper for which the probability of occupation by an electron is 10^{-2} at $300°K$.
    [Ans. $\epsilon = 7.1155$ eV.]

15. The mass density ρ_m of a metal can vary somewhat, depending on how the metal is prepared metallurgically. The following are values of ρ_m for some monovalent metals (those having one conduction electron per atom): $\rho_m = 8.89$ g-cm^{-3} for hard-drawn copper, 19.3 for cold-rolled gold, and 10.5 for compressed silver. The atomic weights of the three metals are: 63.54, 197, and 107.9, respectively. Using Avogadro's (MKS) number (number of atoms whose weight in kilograms is equal to the atomic weight), calculate the concentration n of electrons in cm^{-3}, and the Fermi energy ϵ_f in eV for each metal. Assume that the electron effective mass equals the free electron mass. Compare the answers for n and ϵ_f with those values in Appendix C.

16. In Problem 13, what is the average thermal kinetic energy $\langle \epsilon \rangle$ per electron at $0°K$? Calculate $\langle \epsilon \rangle$ in joules and in electron volts.

17. In Problem 13, what is the electron internal pressure P at $0°K$? Calculate the answer in newtons-m^{-2} and in standard atmospheres.

18. Use the Sommerfeld–Bethe approximation to derive approximate expressions for $\langle \epsilon \rangle$ and P, for a highly degenerate electron gas.

19. Calculate the relative error, at $T = 300°K$, for copper arising from neglecting the second term in the expression for P obtained in Problem 18.

20. Show that in Eq. (58), the integral of every term for which ν is odd vanishes.

21. Verify Eq. (62) using Eqs. (7) and (61).

22. Show that for a fermion system

$$\partial\langle\epsilon\rangle/\partial T = -\langle\epsilon\rangle[d(\ln n)/dT] + \tfrac{3}{2}(d\epsilon_f/dT) + (1/T)[\tfrac{5}{2}\langle\epsilon\rangle - \tfrac{3}{2}\epsilon_f].$$

Hint. This equation can be derived, first, by differentiating, with respect to T, the integral set up to express $\langle \epsilon \rangle$. Derivation of this equation will follow in Chapter 9, Subsection 4.2.

REFERENCES

Bierens de Haan, D. 1858, Tables d'Intégrales Définies, Vol. 4 of Memoirs of the Royal Academy of Sciences of Amsterdam; 1867 Edition with English introduction by J. F. Ritt reprinted in 1957 by Haffner Publishing Co., New York.

Boltzmann, I. 1896, Vorlesungen uber Gastheorie, vol. 1, J. A. Barth, Leipzig.

Bose, S. N. 1924, Z. Phys. **26**, 178.

de Broglie, L. 1924, Thesis presented to the University of Paris.

—— 1925, Ann. Physique **10**, 3, 22.

Dicke, R. H. and Wittke, J. P. 1960, Introduction to Quantum Mechanics, Addison Wesley.

Dirac, P. A. M. 1926, Proc. Roy. Soc. **A112**, 661.

Einstein, A. 1924, S. B. Preuss, Akad. Wiss. 261.

Fermi, E. 1926, Z. Phys. **36**, 902.

Hanney, N. B. 1959, Semiconductors, Reinhold.

Kittel, C. 1971, Introduction to Solid State Physics (Fourth Ed.), John Wiley.

McDougall, J. and Stoner, E. C. 1938, Phil. Trans. Roy. Soc. A, **237,** 67.

Maxwell, J. C. 1860, Phil. Mag. (Series 4) **19**, 19.

—— 1952, Scientific Papers, vol. 1 (Edited by W. D. Niven), Dover Publications, p. 377.

Melehy, M. A. 1965a, Nature **205**, 456; 1965b, Proc. IEEE **53**, 536.

Pauli, W. 1927, Physik **41**, 81.

Planck, M. 1901, Ann. Physik **4**, 553.

Schrödinger, E. 1926, Ann. Physik **73**, 361, 489, 748; **80**, 437; **81**, 109.

—— 1946, Statistical Thermodynamics, Cambridge University Press, Cambridge, England.

Shockley, W. 1950, Electrons and Holes in Semiconductors, D. Van Nostrand.

Sommerfeld, A. 1928, Z. Phys. **47**, 1.

Sommerfeld, A. and Bethe, H. 1934, Handbuch der Physik, Vol. 24/2, J. Springer, Berlin.

Chapter 6

REAL-SPACE FORMULATION OF THE THERMODYNAMIC THEORY OF GENERALIZED FIELDS*

1. INTRODUCTION

In Chapter 4, we presented a detailed account of the fundamental reasons which have made it necessary to pursue searching for a thermodynamic framework different from the classical one. Furthermore, in that chapter it has been possible to show that thermal equilibrium and, in some systems, nonequilibrium can be accounted for by a new theory, characterized by the nearly exclusive use of force fields in the Newtonian sense. Important aspects of this theory involve: the possible introduction of seemingly significant quantities of transport energy; and the existence of general physical and mathematical properties common to various fields, regardless of their nature. Central in this *theory of generalized fields* are the new interpretations of entropy, the first law of thermodynamics and the mechanism of detailed *self*-balancing (Melehy 1964, 1965, 1966a, b). This mechanism specifies the state of thermal equilibrium in a manner which is considerably more detailed than it is in classical thermodynamics.

This chapter presents a formalized and an extended account of this new thermodynamic theory. The treatment will be confined to considerations of the real space for systems which are in the steady state and which contain only solenoidal particle fluxes. Although such conditions are somewhat restricting, nevertheless, in the limit they are invariably satisfied in all systems as the state of thermal equilibrium is infinitesimally approached. Thus, it will be possible to derive, on the basis of the material presented, new general conditions for thermal equilibrium. These conditions will be shown to be consistent from the points of view of electromagnetism, gravitation, circuit theory, statistical mechanics, and the first and second laws of thermodynamics.

To illustrate some fundamental aspects of the present thermodynamic theory, two simple examples are considered. These concern the atmospheric gas and the coexistence of the liquid and its vapor under the conditions of thermal equilibrium. For the latter system, an approximate expression is derived for the vapor pressure.

* The content of this chapter was presented, for the most part, at the Pittsburgh, Pennsylvania 1969 International Symposium on "A Critical Review of Thermodynamics." Publication has followed in the Symposium Proceedings (Melehy 1970).

2. PROPOSITION I: THE MECHANISM OF DETAILED SELF-BALANCING

As concluded in Chapter 4, the state of thermal equilibrium, in the framework of the thermodynamic theory of generalized fields, is uniquely characterized by the mechanism of detailed *self*-balancing. This mechanism will be described as follows: *At thermal equilibrium, each identifiable force field pertaining to each constituent in a thermodynamic system is, at each point, in self-balance.*

The preceding statement is equivalent to saying that: as *the state of thermal equilibrium is infinitesimally approached in a system, then each identifiable "actual flux", pertaining to each constituent, tends at each point to vanish individually.*

Clearly, the present definition of the state of thermal equilibrium differs fundamentally from the classical one. For the latter, it is considered that, at each point in a system, the balancing is established for each constituent by all the force fields combined, that is by all the fluxes collectively. This matter has been discussed in detail in Chapter 4.

3. ON THE CONCEPTS OF DIFFUSION AND THERMOMOTIVE FIELDS

The object in this section is to develop from basic physical considerations the concepts of what was defined in Chapter 4 as the diffusion and thermomotive fields.

3.1. *The Diffusion Field for Gaseous Systems*

Consider Fig. 1, which represents a fictitious small cubic volume $\Delta V = (\Delta x\,\Delta y\,\Delta z)$ in a region containing an *electrically neutral*, nonisothermal, nonisobaric, gas of one kind. Let the concentration n of the gas particles be a function of the Cartesian coordinates x, y, and z. The gas pressure $P(x, y_0, z_0)$ will exert at (x, y_0, z_0) on the left side of ΔV, which is parallel to the y-z plane, a force $F_{x1} = P(x, y_0, z_0)\,\Delta y\,\Delta z$. This force will be along the direction of increasing x. Here, y_0 and z_0 are the average values of the y and z coordinates for all points within the volume ΔV. Similarly at $(x + \Delta x, y_0, z_0)$, the pressure $P(x + \Delta x, y_0, z_0)$ will exert a force $F_{x2} = P(x + \Delta x, y_0, z_0)\,\Delta y\,\Delta z$ on the right side of ΔV, which is parallel to the y-z plane. This force will be in the direction of decreasing x. Along the positive x direction, if the pressure is nonuniform, then there will be a net force $F_x = F_{x1} - F_{x2}$ acting on the volume ΔV. This force will be shared by $(n_0\,\Delta V)$ particles. Here, n_0 is the average value of n within ΔV. Thus, on the average the force f_x per particle along x will be

$$f_x = [P(x, y_0, z_0) - P(x + \Delta x, y_0, z_0)](1/n_0\,\Delta x). \tag{1}$$

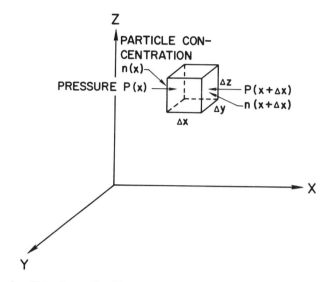

Fig. 1. A sufficiently small cubic volume in a region containing a nonisothermal, nonisobaric gas whose particles are electrically neutral.

In view of Taylor's series, Eq. (1) may be written as

$$f_x = -n_0^{-1}\{(\partial P/\partial x) + \sum_{\nu=2}^{\infty} (\partial^{\nu} P/\partial x^{\nu})[(\Delta x)^{\nu-1}/\nu!]\}. \tag{2}$$

We shall define the *diffusion field* f_{dx} along x to be $\lim_{\Delta x \to 0} f_x$. Therefore, $f_{dx} = -n^{-1}(\partial P/\partial x)$, and in three dimensions this field, for constituent j in a multicomponent system, may be expressed as

$$\mathbf{f}_{dj} = -n_j^{-1} \nabla P_j. \tag{3}$$

It is important to recognize that, according to the derivation of Eq. (3), the diffusion field intensity at any point Q represents a statistical average force per particle of constituent j at Q. Clearly, $\mathbf{f}_{dj}$ is a force in the Newtonian sense.

3.2. *Proposition II: The Diffusion Field for Nongaseous Systems*

For thermodynamic systems not in the gaseous state, we shall define the diffusion field for a constituent j still to be given by Eq. (3), provided that the quantity P_j signifies what may be called the *thermodynamic* or *internal pressure* of constituent j. This pressure is strictly described by the equation of (internal) state of constituent j. For nongaseous systems, the internal pressure is totally different from the *external* (measurable pressure), as may be observed for the case of a liquid in equilibrium with its vapor.

Clearly, for the special case of systems in the gaseous state, the internal and external pressures would be identically the same.

Justification of Proposition II has been discussed in Chapter 4.

3.3. *The Thermomotive Field*

When a particle* of constituent j is transported in a nonisothermal non-isobaric multicomponent system, its temperature must change, if it is to attain local equilibrium at other points of the system. Associated with the change in the particle temperature, positive or negative thermal work has to be done on the particle. As will be seen shortly, this work can be conveniently calculated by evaluating the line integral of what is to be defined as the thermomotive field.

To derive an expression for this field, consider a particle transported an infinitesimal distance $d\mathbf{1}$. If the particle temperature consequently rises by an amount dT, then the corresponding increase in the particle thermal energy dW_{Tj} will be $s_j \, dT$. Here s_j may be defined as the *transport specific heat* per particle of constituent j. The quantity s_j has been shown in Chapter 4 to be the entropy per particle. We may now write

$$dW_{Tj} = s_j \, dT = \mathbf{f}_{Tj} \cdot d\mathbf{1}, \tag{4}$$

and define $\mathbf{f}_{Tj}$ to be the *thermomotive field*.

To solve Eq. (4) for $\mathbf{f}_{Tj}$, consider first T which, if independent of time, is a function of the position coordinates x, y, and z. Therefore, dT may be expressed as

$$dT = (\partial T/\partial x) \, dx + (\partial T/\partial y) \, dy + (\partial T/\partial z) \, dz. \tag{5}$$

In view of Eqs. (4) and (5), we may write

$$\mathbf{f}_{Tj} \cdot d\mathbf{1} = s_j[\mathbf{i}(\partial T/\partial x) \cdot d\mathbf{1} + \mathbf{j}(\partial T/\partial y) \cdot d\mathbf{1} + \mathbf{k}(\partial T/\partial z) \cdot d\mathbf{1}], \tag{6}$$

where $\mathbf{i}$, $\mathbf{j}$, and $\mathbf{k}$ are unit vectors along the three Cartesian axes x, y, z, and $d\mathbf{1} = \mathbf{i} \, dx + \mathbf{j} \, dy + \mathbf{k} \, dz$.

From Eq. (6) it follows that $\mathbf{f}_{Tj} \cdot d\mathbf{1} = (s_j \, \nabla T) \cdot d\mathbf{1}$, that is

$$\mathbf{f}_{Tj} = s_j \, \nabla T. \tag{7}$$

It should be noticed from the preceding derivation that, unlike the diffusion field $\mathbf{f}_{dj}$, the thermomotive field is not associated with a Newtonian

---

* The use here of one particle is meant in the statistical sense. Specifically, this particle represents a sufficiently large number of particles in a sufficiently small surrounding in which the pressure, temperature, and other thermodynamic parameters may be considered uniform. Thus, whenever we say the particle temperature, it is meant to be that of the proper assembly of particles in a sufficiently small volume containing our (representative) particle. Accordingly, the work done per particle signifies the work done on a sufficiently-large number of particles divided by that number.

force. Rather, f_{Tj} represents a virtual force field. The line integral of that field between two points a and b at temperatures T_1 and T_2, respectively, merely represents the amount of heat necessary to raise the particle temperature from T_1 to T_2, as the particle changes position from a to b.

The resultant field f_{tj} of the diffusion and thermomotive fields has been derived in Chapter 4 directly by an entirely different method. The advantage of the independent derivations of f_{dj} and f_{Tj}, presented here, is that they explain in a simple and straightforward way the important conceptual aspects of these two fundamental physical quantities. However, the derivation in Chapter 4 has the advantage of being more complete, and more rigorous.

4. STATISTICAL MECHANICAL FORMULATION OF THE DIFFUSION FIELD

The concept of diffusion field developed in the preceding section will be investigated next from the point of view of statistical mechanics. Specifically, we shall consider systems which obey ideally* either the Fermi–Dirac, or the Bose–Einstein statistics. We shall further treat the case of electrons (ideal Fermi gas) accounting for relativistic effects.

For simplicity, the volume energy density of quantum states g will be assumed to be parabolic for all systems to be treated.

4.1. *Ideal Nonisothermal Fermi and Bose Systems*

We shall first consider the case of ideal Fermi gases, such as conduction electrons in metals and in semiconductors. The concentration n of particles in an ideal Fermi system, as explained in Chapter 5, may be expressed by:

$$n = \int_0^\infty g(\epsilon) F(\epsilon, \epsilon_f, T) \, d\epsilon, \tag{8}$$

$$F(\epsilon, \epsilon_f, T) = \{\exp[(\epsilon - \epsilon_f)/kT] + 1\}^{-1}, \tag{9}$$

$$g(\epsilon) = C\epsilon^{1/2}, \qquad C = (8\pi/h^3)(2m_e^3)^{1/2}. \tag{10}$$

Here F is the Fermi–Dirac distribution function, ϵ is the energy associated with any quantum state and is measured from the bottom of the quantum-mechanical energy band, which is the conduction band in the case of electrons, ϵ_f the energy difference between the Fermi level and the bottom of the quantum-mechanical energy band, m_e the particle effective mass, h Planck's constant, k Boltzmann's constant, and T the absolute temper-

---

* The term ideal is used here in the sense that the particles of the system have a standard (parabolic) energy band and the kinetic energy of the particles is entirely translational.

ature. The function $g(\epsilon)$, defined by Eqs. (10), is the volume energy density of quantum states.

According to Proposition II, the quantity P appearing in Eq. (3) can be calculated using the virial theorem (Wilson 1957). For an ideal Fermi system, P merely equals two-thirds of the average kinetic energy per unit volume. Thus, in view of Eqs. (9) and (10), if the effective mass, m_e, is constant throughout the system, then C will be constant and

$$P = \tfrac{2}{3}C \int_0^\infty \epsilon^{3/2} F(\epsilon, \epsilon_f, T) \; d\epsilon. \tag{11}$$

Therefore,

$$\nabla P = \tfrac{2}{3}C \; \nabla \int_0^\infty \epsilon^{3/2} F(\epsilon, \epsilon_f, T) \; d\epsilon. \tag{12}$$

Since the only position-dependent variables in the preceding integrand are ϵ_f and T, then the real-space operator ∇ will only operate on ϵ_f and T, rather than ϵ. Thus Eq. (12) may be written as

$$\nabla P = \tfrac{2}{3}C \int_0^\infty \epsilon^{3/2} [(\partial F/\partial \epsilon_f) \; \nabla \epsilon_f + (\partial F/\partial T) \; \nabla T] \; d\epsilon. \tag{13}$$

From Eq. (9), however, it follows that

$$\partial F/\partial \epsilon_f = -\partial F/\partial \epsilon, \qquad \partial F/\partial T = [(\epsilon_f - \epsilon)/T] \; \partial F/\partial \epsilon. \tag{14}$$

Substituting Eqs. (14) into Eq. (13) and integrating by parts, we get

$$\nabla P = C [\nabla \epsilon_f - \epsilon_f (\nabla T/T)] \int_0^\infty \epsilon^{1/2} F \; d\epsilon + \tfrac{5}{3}C (\nabla T/T) \int_0^\infty \epsilon^{3/2} F \; d\epsilon. \tag{15}$$

The diffusion field can now be found by dividing both sides of Eq. (15) by $(-n)$. Carrying out this step, and in view of Eqs. (8) and (10), we may write

$$\mathbf{f}_d = -\nabla \epsilon_f - [\tfrac{5}{3}\langle \epsilon \rangle - \epsilon_f](\nabla T/T), \tag{16}$$

where the quantity $\langle \epsilon \rangle$ may be interpreted as the average thermal kinetic energy per particle. Specifically, this quantity is given by

$$\langle \epsilon \rangle = \int_0^\infty \epsilon^{3/2} F(\epsilon, \epsilon_f) \; d\epsilon \Big/ \int_0^\infty \epsilon^{1/2} F(\epsilon, \epsilon_f) \; d\epsilon. \tag{17}$$

It should be noticed that ϵ_f is generally a function of the three position coordinates and T. Therefore, $\nabla \epsilon_f$, in Eq. (16), can be expanded into two terms; one involving $(\nabla \epsilon_f)_T$, and the other ∇T.

Under isothermal conditions, the diffusion field as expressed by Eq. (16) reduces to

$$\mathbf{f}_d = - \nabla \epsilon_f. \tag{18}$$

It should be remembered here that the quantity ϵ_f represents the difference between the Fermi level and the bottom of quantum-mechanical energy band at various points of the system.

By a similar procedure, it can be shown that for an ideal boson system,

$$\mathbf{f}_d = - \nabla \epsilon_b - [\tfrac{5}{3}\langle \epsilon \rangle - \epsilon_b](\nabla T/T), \tag{19}$$

where ϵ_b is the Bose level measured from the bottom of the energy band associated with the system quantum states, and $\langle \epsilon \rangle$ is calculated from an equation similar to (17) with the Fermi–Dirac function replaced by the Bose–Einstein function.

Equation (19) reduces to

$$\mathbf{f}_d = - \nabla \epsilon_b, \tag{20}$$

for an ideal isothermal boson system.

4.2. *Ideal Nonisothermal Classical Systems*

Equations (16) and (19) express the diffusion field for ideal fermion and boson systems, respectively, regardless of the degree of degeneracy of either one. In the classical limit, both equations reduce to a simple, useful form to be derived next.

To do so, consider Eqs. (9) and (11), which in the classical limit $(\epsilon_f \ll -kT)$, will lead to

$$P = \tfrac{2}{3}C \int_0^\infty \epsilon^{3/2} \exp[-(\epsilon - \epsilon_f)/kT] \, d\epsilon$$

$$= -\tfrac{2}{3}CkT \int_0^\infty \epsilon^{3/2} (\partial/\partial\epsilon) \{\exp[-(\epsilon - \epsilon_f)/kT]\} \, d\epsilon, \tag{21}$$

where P is the thermodynamic pressure of the gas, and ϵ_f the Fermi level measured from the bottom of the quantum-mechanical energy band of the system. Integrating Eq. (21) by parts, and in view of Eq. (8) modified for nondegenerate systems, we get

$$P = kTn. \tag{22}$$

Therefore, from Eqs. (3) and (22), it follows that

$$\mathbf{f}_d = - (k/n) \, \nabla(nT), \tag{23}$$

which represents the diffusion field for a classical system.

4.3. *Isothermal Relativistic Degenerate Electrons*

We next consider the diffusion field for the case of isothermal degenerate electrons under relativistic conditions. Degeneracy and relativistic effects may occur when the concentration and temperature are both extremely high such as may prevail on the stars (Chandrasekhar 1939).

To investigate this rather general case, consider the electron pressure P_n and the concentration n for relativistic degenerate electrons. Using Juttner's transformation (Juttner 1928), it can be shown (Chandrasekhar 1939) that

$$P_n = A \int_0^\infty \sinh^4 \theta \ F(\theta, \epsilon_f) \ d\theta, \tag{24}$$

$$n = [3A/m_{0e}c^2] \int_0^\infty \sinh^2 \theta \cosh \theta \ F(\theta, \epsilon_f) \ d\theta, \tag{25}$$

$$\beta = (1/kT), \qquad A = \tfrac{8}{3}(\pi c^5/h^3) m_{0e}{}^4, \tag{26}$$

$$F(\theta, \epsilon_f) = \{\exp[\beta m_{0e}c^2(\cosh \theta - 1) - \beta \epsilon_f] + 1\}^{-1}. \tag{27}$$

Here m_{0e} is the electron rest effective mass, and c the speed of light.

In view of Eqs. (3) and (24), under isothermal conditions, we have

$$\mathbf{f}_{dn} = - (A/n) (\nabla \epsilon_f) \int_0^\infty \sinh^4 \theta (\partial F/\partial \epsilon_f) \ d\theta. \tag{28}$$

From Eq. (27), it follows that

$$\frac{\partial F(\theta, \epsilon_f)}{\partial \epsilon_f} = \left(\frac{-1}{m_{0e}c^2 \sinh \theta}\right) \frac{\partial F(\theta, \epsilon_f)}{\partial \theta}. \tag{29}$$

Substituting Eq. (29) in Eq. (28), and integrating the result by parts, we get

$$\mathbf{f}_{dn} = - \left(\frac{3A}{m_{0e}c^2 n}\right) (\nabla \epsilon_f) \int_0^\infty \sinh^2 \theta \cosh \theta \ F(\theta, \epsilon_f) \ d\theta. \tag{30}$$

From Eqs. (25) and (30), it follows that

$$\mathbf{f}_{dn} = - \nabla \epsilon_f, \tag{31}$$

which is a fundamental relation holding generally for an isothermal degenerate electron gas with relativistic effects taken into account. Equation (31) is consistent with Eq. (18) derived earlier for the special case of an ideal isothermal nonrelativistic Fermi system.

5. ACTIVE AND PASSIVE FIELDS AND THEIR INTERACTIONS IN SYSTEMS CONTAINING ONLY SOLENOIDAL FLUXES

From the preceding two sections, it is apparent that associated with each constituent in a thermodynamic system we may define a diffusion field and a thermomotive field. These fields are supported by concentration gradients and/or temperature gradients. From their derivations, it can be readily seen that these two fields do not account for any electric, magnetic or gravitational effects. The object in this section is to specify the manner in which the diffusion and thermomotive fields interact near thermal equilibrium with other possible force fields in a system that may be caused by electric, magnetic and/or gravitational effects. We shall be confined in this section, however, to systems in which there are no creation or annihilation of any constituent. This will mean that for each constituent, the flux is solenoidal. Such a condition implies generally that there are no chemical reactions in the system. This condition would also mean that electrons and ions in a gaseous system, and electrons and holes in semiconductors are not involved in a net process of generation or recombination.

The case in which nonsolenoidal fluxes occur will be treated in Chapter 7. For that particular case, we shall be concerned with the interactions of a number of fields in an electron-hole system in which there is a net charge-carrier recombination.

Before treating the interaction problem between different fields acting on different constituents, it is necessary to discuss two fundamentally different properties of fields to be called *passive* and *active*. As will be seen shortly, these properties do not depend on the nature of the fields under consideration.

5.1. Passive Fields

Proposition III. Associated with each identifiable (actual) flux density $\mathfrak{J}_{ij}$ of a constituent j, there corresponds a force (per particle) field $\mathbf{f}_{isj}$ to be called *passive*. Sufficiently near thermal equilibrium, this *force field** at any point in the system is given by

$$\mathbf{f}_{isj} = (A_j/n_j)\,\mathfrak{J}_{ij}. \tag{32}$$

Here n_j is the concentration of constituent j, and A_j is a constant which depends on the constituent but not on the nature of $\mathbf{f}_{isj}$.

Corollary I. At thermal equilibrium, each identifiable passive force field $\mathbf{f}_{isj}$ vanishes individually, for each constituent j, everywhere in the system.

---

* Some of these force fields (forces per particle) are statistical in nature and others are not. For example, the diffusion field is statistical, whereas the electric force per particle is not so.

This corollary follows from Eq. (32) and Proposition I, which specifies that at thermal equilibrium each identifiable flux density $\mathcal{J}_{ij}$ would vanish for each constituent, at each point in the system.

Corollary II. Each identifiable passive force field must reverse direction whenever its corresponding flux is reversed.

This fundamental property follows at once from Eq. (32).

Aspect of Heat Dissipation. At any point in a system, the time rate of heat of evolution $(\partial Q_{isj}/\partial t)$, per unit volume, associated with a flux density $\mathcal{J}_{ij}$ is given by

$$\partial Q_{isj}/\partial t = \mathbf{f}_{isj} \cdot \mathcal{J}_{ij}, \tag{33}$$

where t signifies time. Equation (33) follows directly from Eq. (63) [Chapter 4]. From Eqs. (32) and (33), it follows that

$$\partial Q_{isj}/\partial t = (A_j/n_j) \mathcal{J}_{ij}^2 = (n_j/A_j) f_{isj}^2. \tag{34}$$

Further discussion of the aspects of heat dissipation follows in Subsection 5.4.

Corollary III. Nonvanishing identifiable fluxes and their corresponding passive force fields individually lead to positive heat dissipation, regardless of the direction of the fluxes and their corresponding passive force fields.

This corollary follows from Corollary II and Eq. (33). It also follows from Eq. (34).

Corollary IV. At thermal equilibrium, associated with each identifiable passive force field, there can be no evolution of heat at any point in a system.

This corollary follows from Proposition I, and Eq. (34).

5.2. *Active Fields*

Proposition IV. Active force fields are those which are established either (1) not entirely by an actual flux, or (2) altogether by other than an actual flux.

Corollary V. Every force field found in a system at thermal equilibrium is an active field, since by Corollary I, each passive force field individually vanishes at thermal equilibrium.

Examples of active fields include the diffusion field existing at the liquid-vapor boundary, and the diffusion and electrostatic force fields acting on each electron in the transition region between any two different conductors. In the first example, $\nabla P \neq 0$ at the liquid-vapor boundary, since the value of the internal pressure P in the liquid is completely different from that in the vapor. Here P is strictly determined from the equation of internal state as described in Section 3 and discussed in Chapter 4.

When a current is placed in a magnetic field, each electron on the average will be acted on by a Lorentz force f_l. This force, clearly, is not entirely generated by a flux. In fact, its direction is transverse to both the current and the magnetic field.

Corollary VI. At any point, an active field will not necessarily be reversed if the flux at the point is reversed.

This statement is a direct consequence of Proposition IV, since no physical (continuous) quantity can reverse sign without vanishing first.

As an example for Corollary VI, consider the liquid-vapor problem. If we have a net transport of particles from the liquid to the vapor, or *vice versa,* the direction of the concentration gradient of the particles in both cases will remain the same. Thus, the direction of the active diffusion field will likewise remain the same, regardless of the direction of flow of the particles.

Aspect of Work. If at a point a in a system, there is a flux density $\mathfrak{J}_j$ of constituent j, which is subject at a to an active force field f_{iaj} of a specific nature i, then the time rate $(\partial Q_{iaj}/\partial t)$ of doing work at a, per unit volume, on the nontransported particles by the transported particles is given by

$$\partial Q_{iaj}/\partial t = -f_{iaj} \cdot \mathfrak{J}_j. \tag{35}$$

Equation (35) follows immediately from Eq. (63) [Chapter 4].

Corollary VII. Depending upon the direction of $\mathfrak{J}_j$, the quantity $(\partial Q_{iaj}/\partial t)$ will be either positive or negative. This corollary follows from Corollary VI and Eq. (35).

Further discussion of this Corollary will follow in Subsection 5.4.

5.3. *Interaction of Active and Passive Fields*

In the preceding two subsections, we have defined passive and active fields on physical grounds, and we have seen how passive fields are specifically related to fluxes to which active fields have not been so far related. In this subsection, we shall attempt to relate active to passive fields under certain restrictions, which are still sufficiently general. We shall, however, first introduce the following useful concept.

Transport Work. In a system containing any number of solenoidal fluxes, we shall define the quantity

$$W_{ab} = \int_{C_1} f_{ij} \cdot d1, \tag{36}$$

where $d1$ is an infinitesimal increment of length, and W_{ab} the transport work associated with the force field f_{ij} between two points a and b along a specific path C_1. The field f_{ij} may be active or passive. Clearly, W_{ab} represents the statistical average work done on a particle of constituent j by the force field $\mathbf{f}_{ij}$, as the particle is transported from a to b along a specific path C_1.

It is now possible to state:

Proposition V. If in a system, each identifiable flux density $\mathcal{J}_{ij}$ of any constituent j is solenoidal, then around every closed loop C in the system, the line integral of the total active force field $\mathbf{f}_{taj}$ shall equal that of the total passive field $\mathbf{f}_{tsj}$, that is

$$\oint_C (\mathbf{f}_{taj} - \mathbf{f}_{tsj}) \cdot d\mathbf{l} = 0, \tag{37}$$

where

$$\mathbf{f}_{taj} = \sum_{i=1}^{N_{aj}} \mathbf{f}_{iaj}, \qquad \mathbf{f}_{tsj} = \sum_{i=1}^{N_{sj}} \mathbf{f}_{isj}. \tag{38}$$

Here N_{aj} and N_{sj} are the number of identifiable active and passive fields, respectively, acting on the constituent j. Equations (37) and (38) have been reasoned earlier in Chapter 4.

It should be noticed here that in the limit as thermal equilibrium is infinitesimally approached, there will be no creation or annihilation of any constituent in the system. Thus, consequences of Eq. (37) should be applicable to the important situation of thermal equilibrium. This matter will be specifically treated in Section 7.

5.4. *Distinguishability of Active and Passive Fields in Physical Systems*

We shall summarize the basic characteristics of active and passive fields, which make them completely distinguishable in physical systems. We shall further cite specific examples that illustrate some of their basic transport properties.

Passive fields, regardless of their nature, are defined to be those entirely generated by actual flux. Characteristically, every such field must vanish individually at thermal equilibrium, and must reverse direction whenever its corresponding flux is reversed. Regardless of the direction of flux, a passive field is necessarily associated with heat liberation, representing an increase in the internal energy of the host medium. This will mean that the transported particles must do work on the medium. Transport processes associated with passive fields include: (a) ohmic conduction in a uniform resistor, (b) the diffusion of minority carriers in the bulk regions of p-n junctions, and (c) viscous flow in gases and liquids. Clearly in all the preceding examples, reversing the direction of flux will be necessarily associated with reversing the direction of the following: in case (a) the electric field, in case (b) the diffusion field, accompanied by reversing the direction of the concentration gradient, and in case (c) the viscous forces.

By contrast, active fields are defined to be those which are established either not entirely by an actual flux, or altogether by other than an actual flux. Furthermore, such fields are those which will not necessarily vanish at thermal equilibrium, that is they will not be necessarily reversed by reversing the flux. Consequently, depending on the direction of the flux, positive or negative work will be done on the transported particles by the fields.

If these fields are *intrinsic*, that is originating from the region hosting the particles, then, depending on the direction of flow of these particles, the internal energy of the host region must either decrease or increase to account for the positive or negative work done on the transported particles, respectively. In some cases, the decrease or increase in the internal energy of the host region occurs in the form of absorbing or liberating heat, respectively. Such a particular phenomenon, for example, can be observed when particles are transported from the liquid to the vapor phase and when the direction of that transport is reversed. Notice in this case that, at the boundary, the particle concentration gradient and active diffusion field will not be reversed when the flow of the particles is reversed. Another interesting example is that of the well known Peltier effect (Peltier 1834). When a sufficiently small current flows in a specific direction through a junction between two different metals, the junction cools off. Reversing the current direction in this case necessarily causes the junction to heat up. Clearly, within the junction, there are an electrostatic and a diffusion field. Both are active, for they can be found at thermal equilibrium and neither one will be reversed when the junction current (of sufficiently small intensity) is reversed. A detailed treatment of the Peltier effect will be presented in Chapter 9.

Transport processes associated with active fields will be also referred to as active. An obvious example of intrinsic active processes include that associated with the emf of the lossless battery. Clearly in this case, reversing the battery current necessarily reverses the direction of change of the battery internal energy. In this particular case, the internal energy is in a chemical form, rather than in heat form as in the previous two examples. Notice in this case that reversing the battery current again will not necessarily reverse its voltage polarity.

An active field will be called *extrinsic*, if it originates from a source altogether outside the thermodynamic system. An example of such a field is the gravitational field exerted by a planet on the particles of a small isolated system. The gravitational force $\mathbf{f}_g$ per particle, by definition, is active, for it is established by other than flow. It should be observed in this case that reversing the particle flux at any point will not, of course, reverse $\mathbf{f}_g$. Hence, depending on the direction of flux, work will be done either on, or by the particles. Since the transfer of energy is not between the region hosting the particles and the transported particles, no change in the internal energy of the medium can result when particles are transported in a purely extrinsic field. Thus, in the earth atmosphere, as air flows, no heating or cooling will be expected as a result of the extrinsic gravitational force field f_g. However, the active intrinsic diffusion field f_d will cause cooling for rising air and heating for falling air. The passive viscous force fields, however, will lead to heating whether the gas rises or drops.

From Eq. (7), it is evident that the direction of the thermomotive field f_T in an electron system, for example, is determined by the direction of the temperature gradient which can be controlled by a source totally independent of carriers transported in that field. Thus, reversing the direction of carrier flow will not necessarily reverse the direction of the field. Consequently, f_T seems to be always active and never passive. Since it is intrinsic, then when carriers are transported in that field, work must be done either by, or on them, and the internal energy of the medium hosting the field must either increase or decrease, respectively. Heat will then be either liberated or absorbed in the medium. In Chapter 9, we shall see how, in the framework of the thermodynamic theory of generalized fields, the force fields f_d, f_T, and the electrostatic force field f_e interact to produce the Seebeck effect (Seebeck 1826). These three intrinsic force fields also lead to the Thomson effect (Thomson 1882).

If a current I_c flows perpendicular to a magnetic field **H**, then on a statistical basis each carrier will be acted on by a force f_l which will be transverse to both·I_c and **H**. The magnetic force field f_l per particle leads to the well known Hall effect (Hall 1879, 1880). Clearly f_l is an active field, since, for one thing, f_l is not proportional to a current parallel to it. Thus, one can reverse a current along f_l without reversing f_l.

6. PASSIVE NATURE OF STOKES'S, OHM'S AND FICK'S LAWS

In Section 5, passive fields have been defined and have been related to their corresponding fluxes by Eq. (32). In this section, we shall show that Eq. (32) leads to Stokes's, Ohm's, and Fick's laws. We shall further show that for charged gases, such as a degenerate electron gas, under certain restricted conditions, the Einstein diffusion–mobility relationship (Einstein 1905) follows from Eq. (32). One important implication of the results to be derived in this section is that Stokes's, Ohm's, and Fick's laws all indeed describe strictly passive (dissipative) processes. Thus, their use will be strictly confined to such processes only, and in no way they will be used to misrepresent active processes.

6.1. *Stokes's Law*

A flux density $\mathcal{J}_{vj}$ of constituent j is simply related to the velocity v_j of that constituent in a viscous fluid by: $\mathcal{J}_{vj} = n_j v_j$.* Here, n_j is the concentra-

---

* This equation can be derived in exactly the same way as that used for Eq. (26) [Chapter 3].

tion of the particles of constituent j. Substituting this equation into Eq. (32), we get

$$\mathbf{f}_{vsj} = A_j\mathbf{v}_j, \tag{39}$$

where $\mathbf{f}_{vsj}$ is the viscous (passive) force per particle and A_j is a constant. Equation (39) will be recognized to be essentially the same as Stokes's law (Stokes 1845, Jeans 1940), generally expressed by

$$\mathbf{f}_j = 6\pi\eta_j a_j\mathbf{v}_j, \tag{40}$$

where η_j is the viscosity of the particles of constituent j, and a_j is the particle radius.

6.2. *Electron Conduction and Ohm's Law*

For an electron system, it is more convenient to use the concept of current density $\mathbf{J}_n$ rather than flux density $\mathcal{J}_n$. Since $\mathbf{J}_n = -q\mathcal{J}_n$, Eq. (32) for electrons, if transported by a process of nature i, may be written as

$$-\mathbf{f}_{isn} = \mathbf{J}_{in}/\mu_n n. \tag{41}$$

Here μ_n and n are the electron mobility and concentration at any point, respectively, and q is the magnitude of the electron charge.

Ohmic conduction will be defined here to be that transport process strictly associated with an electric field $\mathbf{E}_s$. This field is of course passive. From the definition of an electric field, an electron subject to $\mathbf{E}_s$ will be acted on by a passive force $\mathbf{f}_{esn} = -q\mathbf{E}_s$. Substituting $\mathbf{f}_{esn}$ for $\mathbf{f}_{isn}$ in Eq. (41) and solving for the electron current density, we simply get

$$\mathbf{J}_{en} = q\mu_n n\mathbf{E}_s. \tag{42}$$

It should be noticed here that $\mathbf{E}_s$ will always reverse, whenever the drift electron current density $\mathbf{J}_{en}$, responsible for it, is reversed. This is a unique property of passive processes. Equation (42) will be recognized to express Ohm's law.

It is rather interesting to see how the distinction can be made between active and passive electric fields in a specific problem. This will be done particularly in the next chapter in connection with the active and passive processes within the transition region and in the bulk regions of a junction diode.

6.3. *Fick's Law*

We next show that for the specific case of isothermal electrons, if the diffusion field is substituted in the current-passive field generalized relationship, expressed by Eq. (41), Fick's law (Fick 1855) follows. Using that equation we derive, generally for degenerate electrons, an expression for the diffusion–mobility relationship.

To do so, consider first the case of nondegenerate electrons for which the diffusion field has been shown to be given by Eq. (23). Substituting this equation into Eq. (41), and solving under isothermal conditions for the diffusion current density $\mathbf{J}_{dn}$, we get

$$\mathbf{J}_{dn} = kT\mu_n \nabla n. \tag{43}$$

It can now be recognized that Eq. (43) essentially expresses Fick's law, which is generally written for electrons as

$$\mathbf{J}_{dn} = qD_n \nabla n, \tag{44}$$

where D_n is the diffusion constant for electrons.

Comparion of Eqs. (43) and (44) gives at once the Einstein diffusion–mobility relationship

$$D_n/\mu_n = kT/q, \tag{45}$$

originally derived (Einstein 1905) for ideal, classical isothermal gases.

To derive a more general relationship between D_n and μ_n for an isothermal degenerate electron gas, consider Eqs. (18) and (41) which, when solved for $\mathbf{J}_{dn}$, will give

$$\mathbf{J}_{dn} = \mu_n n \nabla \epsilon_f. \tag{46}$$

Comparing Eq. (46) with Fick's law, expressed by Eq. (44), and solving for the ratio (D_n/μ_n), we get

$$D_n/\mu_n = (n/q)(\nabla \epsilon_f/\nabla n). \tag{47}$$

From Eqs. (8) and (10), it follows that

$$\nabla n = C_n(\nabla \epsilon_f)(\partial/\partial \epsilon_f) \int_0^\infty \epsilon^{1/2} F(\epsilon, \epsilon_f, T) \, d\epsilon, \tag{48}$$

where $F(\epsilon, \epsilon_f, T)$ is as expressed by Eq. (9).

Introducing the variable transformations:

$$\eta = \epsilon/kT, \qquad \eta_f = \epsilon_f/kT, \tag{49}$$

and in view of Eqs. (47) and (48), we may write

$$D_n/\mu_n = (kT/q)\rho_d, \tag{50}$$

$$\rho_d = \left[\int_0^\infty \eta^{1/2} F(\eta, \eta_f) \, d\eta \right] \Big/ \left[(\partial/\partial \eta_f) \int_0^\infty \eta^{1/2} F(\eta, \eta_f) \, d\eta \right], \tag{51}$$

$$F(\eta, \eta_f) = [1 + \exp(\eta - \eta_f)]^{-1}. \tag{52}$$

The coefficient ρ_d represents the ratio of (D_n/μ_n) to (kT/q). Figure 2 shows the dependence of the factor ρ_d on the normalized value of the Fermi energy, $\eta_f = \epsilon_f/kT$. As observed in the figure, ρ_d tends asymptotically to

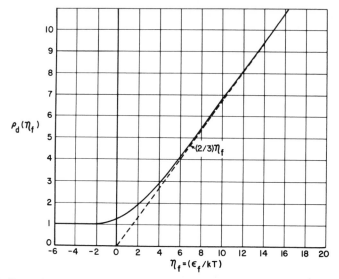

Fig. 2. Dependence on η_f of ratio ρ_d of (D/μ) to its classical value of (kT/q) for a fermion system. The Fermi energy is measured from the bottom of the (standard) energy band.

$(2/3)\eta_f$. Thus, for metals and highly degenerate n-type semiconductors, $(D_n/\mu_n) = (2/3)(\epsilon_f/q)$. As η_f increases negatively, ρ_d rapidly tends to 1, and correspondingly (D_n/μ_n) approaches its classical limit of (kT/q).

Based on the classical detailed balancing, an expression for (D_n/μ_n), equivalent to those described by Eqs. (50), (51), and (52), has been derived by Landsberg (1952). The significant difference, however, between the present derivation and that of Landsberg is the important supposition that the relationship between D_n and μ_n are physically meaningful only for passive processes and for one special case of active processes to be discussed in the next section. The present derivation further emphasizes the individuality of the diffusion field and its complete independence from, for example, an electric field.

It is interesting to note that from the present derivation it follows that Eq. (50) is valid in those ranges of nonequilibrium for which μ is linear. As we shall see in the next chapter, this conclusion is verified by experiment for current densities > 100 A/cm^2 in some semiconductor diodes.

7. SPECIAL AND GENERALIZED CONDITIONS OF THERMAL EQUILIBRIUM

The object in this section is to arrive at the fundamental conditions which active fields, regardless of their nature, must satisfy in any system at thermal equilibrium.

It has been concluded in Subsection 5.1 that an important consequence of the fundamental mechanism of detailed *self*-balancing, described in Section 2, is that at thermal equilibrium, each identifiable passive force field f_{isj} pertaining to any constituent j must vanish everywhere in any system. Consequently, at thermal equilibrium, Eq. (37) reduces to

$$\oint_C f_{taj} \cdot d1 = 0, \tag{53}$$

where f_{taj} is as given by Eq. (38), and C is any closed loop in the system. Equation (53) may be regarded as a necessary and sufficient condition for thermal equilibrium.

We shall next investigate the physical and mathematical implications of Eq. (53). In general, any active field is a function of position and may depend further on time t. For example, the gravitational force f_g per particle in a system placed on the surface of the earth will be caused by the static terrestial gravitational field and the time-varying field of the moon. Let us first consider the case for which

$$\partial f_{taj}/\partial t = 0. \tag{54}$$

In such a case, f_{taj} is only a function of position. In order to satisfy Eq. (53) for every closed loop C in the system, by Stokes's theorem (Kaplan 1952), we must have

$$\nabla \times f_{taj} = 0, \tag{55}$$

at every point in the system. Here f_{taj} is as given by Eq. (38).

It is now evident that Eqs. (54) and (55) constitute a set of conditions sufficient for thermal equilibrium. Clearly, Eq. (55) constitutes also a necessary condition. We shall next present the argument that Eq. (54) is additionally a necessary condition for thermal equilibrium.

To do so, suppose that f_{taj} is time-varying. Let us now imagine a statistical particle of constituent j to be transported between two points a and b in the system along a path C_1, then again transported from b to a along a different path C_2. If the trip along the closed loop C formed by C_1 and C_2 occurs instantaneously, then Eq. (53) will indeed be satisfied, because of Eq. (55). But instantaneous transport is physically meaningless here, for the particle must take whatever finite time around the closed loop C allowed by the finite flow velocity. To explain the effect of the time finiteness, let it be, for the sake of the argument, that the particle is transported along C_1 instantaneously at an instant t_1, and along C_2 also instantaneously, but at another instant t_2. Since f_{taj} is time-dependent, clearly the line integral at t_2 along C_2 cannot be equal and opposite to that along C_1 at t_1, for all values of t_1 and t_2, and for every two points in the system. Hence, Eq. (53) cannot possibly be satisfied, unless Eq. (54) is satisfied.

In view of the preceding discussion, we may state the following:

A necessary and sufficient condition for thermal equilibrium is that the resultant active field f_{taj}, associated with all the processes, is stationary and conservative everywhere in the system.

Let us now consider the individual active components fields f_{iaj} of the total field f_{taj}. In view of Eq. (38), it is evident that Eq. (55) has essentially four different kinds of mathematically possible solutions. The first is that two or more fields may be nonconservative individually, even though they are conservative collectively. This solution, however, is believed not to be particularly important.

Another possible solution is that the active fields would have the properties that

$$\sum f_{iaj} = 0, \tag{56}$$

for any two or more fields pertaining to a specific constituent j.

This solution is believed to be in some respects special, and as will be explained in Subsection 8.1, it characterizes all systems to be called *unconstrained.*

It is also possible that

$$f_{iaj} = 0, \tag{57}$$

for some or all values of i pertaining to a specific constituent j.

The fourth and most general kind of solutions is that

$$\nabla \times f_{1aj} = 0, \qquad \nabla \times f_{2aj} = 0, \qquad \cdots, \qquad \nabla \times f_{iaj} = 0. \tag{58}$$

Solutions of the types expressed by Eq. (57) characterize, for example, the (active) thermomotive field. From Eq. (7), it is apparent that this field must vanish at thermal equilibrium. Solutions typified by Eqs. (58) appear to be fulfilled in any natural system when it is at thermal equilibrium. These generalized conditions may be stated as follows: *at thermal equilibrium, each identifiable active force field pertaining to each constituent is stationary and conservative everywhere in the system.*

Clearly, if an active field vanishes, such as the thermomotive field, then it is only a special case of the general statement.

The preceding *generalized conditions of thermal equilibrium* will be further discussed in Section 9 from a number of points of view. Specifically, these will concern those of electromagnetism, gravitation, statistical mechanics, circuit theory and the first and second laws of thermodynamics.

8. THERMAL EQUILIBRIUM IN TWO PHYSICAL SYSTEMS CONTAINING ACTIVE FIELDS

The preceding sections were mainly concerned with presenting some general aspects of the theory of generalized fields. In this section we shall specifically apply this theory to two simple particular problems.

8.1. *Atmospheric Thermal Equilibrium*

Consider the atmosphere of a spherical planet of radius R. Let this atmosphere be an ideal, classical gas of one constituent, which is at thermal equilibrium. If we ignore gravitational effects of all other stars and planets, then at any point a in the gas, at a distance r from the center of the planet, there are only two active force fields. One of these fields, f_{ga}, is gravitational in nature. The other one is the active diffusion field f_{da}. This gaseous system may be called *unconstrained* in the sense that its concentration n_g has to adjust itself at various points so that the sum of all of its active fields would vanish; that is

$$f_{da} + f_{ga} = 0, \tag{59}$$

and there are no constraints in the system to dictate otherwise.

At any radius r, greater than the planet radius R, the two active force fields may be expressed by

$$f_{ga} = -a_r m g_0 (R/r)^2, \qquad f_{da} = -(kT/n_g) \, \nabla n_g. \tag{60}$$

Here a_r is a unit radial vector, g_0 the gravitational acceleration on the surface of the planet, and m is the mass per particle. The last equation follows from Eq. (23).

In the spherical coordinate system, with no dependence of n_g on other than r, $\nabla n_g = a_r (\partial n_g / \partial r)$. Using this relation and substituting Eqs. (60) into (59), we get a differential equation whose approximate solution will be

$$n_g(z) \simeq n_{g0} \exp(-mg_0 z/kT), \tag{61}$$

where $z = (r - R)$, may be interpreted to be the altitude at any point. The quantity n_{g0} here represents the concentration of the gas at $z = 0$.

It is interesting to compare the conditions of thermal equilibrium for this particular system with those discussed in Section 7. Equation (59), of course, is the same as Eq. (56). The latter should hold for all unconstrained systems, such as those consisting of only one phase.

Perhaps the most interesting aspect to discuss for the present problem concerns the generalized conditions of thermal equilibrium, derived in Section 7 generally for any system. For our present problem, it follows from Eq. (60) that

$$\nabla \times f_{da} = -kT \, \nabla \times \nabla(\ln n_g) = 0, \tag{62}$$

and

$$\nabla \times f_{ga} = -mg_0 R^2 \, \nabla \times a_r(1/r^2) = mg_0 R^2 \, \nabla \times \nabla(1/r) = 0. \tag{63}$$

Clearly, we also have

$$\partial f_{da}/\partial t = 0, \qquad \partial f_{ga}/\partial t = 0. \tag{64}$$

Thus, for the present problem, under thermal equilibrium conditions, each identifiable active field is stationary and conservative. Clearly, Eqs. (62), (63), and (64) verify Eqs. (54) and (58) arrived at generally for any system.

It is important here to remember that Eqs. (58) are fundamentally based on the mechanism of detailed *self*-balancing, which requires that each identifiable passive force field and flux to vanish at thermal equilibrium and whatever fields existing under such conditions must be active. The active force fields f_{ga} and f_{da} that exist at thermal equilibrium give rise to what correspond to emfs in circuit theory. Specifically, if a statistical particle is actually transported between any two points a and b in the atmosphere along a specific path C_1, then the (active) work done W_{ab} on it by, for example, f_{ga} alone, will be:

$$W_{ab} = \int_{C_1} f_{ga} \cdot d\mathbf{l}.$$

The quantity W_{ab} corresponds to an emf in circuit theory.

Now, because f_{ga} is stationary and conservative, it follows that regardless of the transport velocity of the statistical particle, the (active) work done on it around any closed loop in the system under the action of f_{ga} alone must vanish. Again this corresponds in circuit theory to a multi-mesh network for which the emf around every closed loop in the system is zero. Clearly, the electric current in that network must be zero everywhere. Thus, by analogy the flux induced by the active force field f_{ga} alone is zero. A similar statement can be made for f_{da}. This will mean that at thermal equilibrium, each one of the active force fields f_{ga} and f_{da} is in *self*-balance.

8.2. *Liquid-Vapor Coexistence at Thermal Equilibrium*

We next consider two aspects of thermal equilibrium of a liquid and its vapor. First, we derive an approximate equation for the vapor pressure of the liquid based in part on the concept of active diffusion field. This will be followed by discussing the mechanism of detailed *self*-balancing and the analogy between an electric circuit and the liquid-vapor system.

The Vapor Pressure. It is a consequence of the Clausius–Clapeyron equation that (Prigogine and Defay 1954) the vapor pressure P_v for a liquid may be expressed by

$$dP_v/dT = Q_L/T[V_v - V_l], \tag{65}$$

where Q_L is the latent heat of evaporation per mole, and V_v and V_l are, respectively, the volumes of the vapor and of the liquid per mole.

Neglecting V_l compared with V_v, and dividing both the numerator and denominator of the right-hand side of Eq. (65) by Avogadro's number, we get

$$dP_v/dT \simeq (W_L/T) n_v, \tag{66}$$

where n_v is the number of vapor particles per unit volume, and W_L the latent heat of evaporation per particle.

If there is a net transport of particles from the liquid to the vapor, then each transported particle statistically will be acted on by an active diffusion field f_{da}, which will contribute an amount of transport work W_L per particle. As explained in Subsection 5.4, f_{da} is intrinsic, that is originating in the regions hosting the transported particles. Hence, by the principle of conservation of energy, the amount of work W_L done on the particle by the system must lead to a decrease in the internal energy of the region hosting f_{da}. This region is the liquid-vapor interface. The decrease in the internal energy of that region will be in the form of heat absorption amounting to the latent heat of evaporation. Clearly, if the flux of particles is reversed in this case, f_{da} will not be reversed. Consequently, W_L will be negative giving rise to heat liberation, which is essentially the latent heat of condensation.

We may, therefore, express W_L by

$$W_L = \int_{l_i}^{l_v} f_{da} \cdot d\mathbf{1}, \tag{67}$$

where the integration is carried on a path beginning at l_i in the liquid and ending at any point l_v in the vapor.

According to Proposition II, stated in Subsection 3.2., f_{da} is given by Eq. (3), in which P represents the equation of internal state at any point in the system. If we consider the equation of internal state to be approximately that of a system in which the thermal kinetic energy is entirely translational, then

$$P \simeq knT. \tag{68}$$

Therefore, for the vapor

$$dP_v/dT = kT(dn_v/dT) + kn_v. \tag{69}$$

From Eqs. (3), (67) and (68), we have

$$W_L \simeq -kT \ln(n_v/n_i), \tag{70}$$

where n_v and n_i are the concentration of particles in the vapor and liquid phases, respectively. Substituting Eqs. (69) and (70) into (66) leads to

$$-\frac{dT}{T} \simeq \frac{dn_v}{n_v[1 + \ln(n_v/n_i)]} = \frac{d[\ln(n_v/n_i)]}{[1 + \ln(n_v/n_i)]}. \tag{71}$$

Notice that in Eq. (71), the temperature dependence of n_i has been neglected, so that n_i is considered essentially a constant.

Integrating both sides of Eq. (71), we get

$$\ln(T_0/T) \simeq \ln[1+\ln(n_v/n_l)], \tag{72}$$

where T_0 is an arbitrary constant.

From Eq. (68), it follows that for the vapor, $n_v = P_v/kT$. Substituting this relation into Eq. (72) and solving for the vapor pressure P_v, we have

$$\ln P_v \simeq \ln A + \ln T + (T_0/T) - 1, \qquad A = kn_l. \tag{73}$$

Figure 3 compares Eq. (73), for mercury in the temperature range

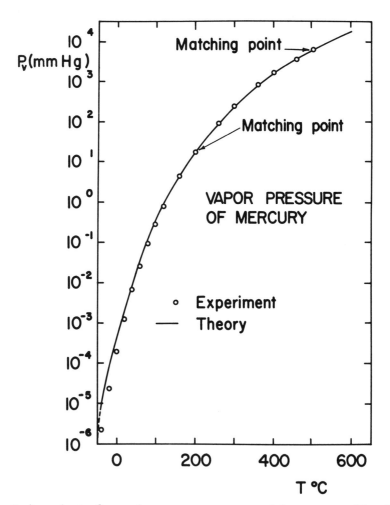

Fig. 3. Approximate theory of vapor pressure compared for mercury with values reported by Douglas, Ball, and Ginnings (1951).

$-38.88°$ to $500°C$, with those values compiled by Douglas, Ball, and Ginnings (1951).

In principle, there is only one arbitrary constant T_0, resulting from integrating Eq. (71), to be evaluated from the experiment, since A depends upon n_l. The latter should be determined by independent means. This, however, is not quite the case here. Equation (68) is, of course, fairly accurate for the vapor of mercury, which is a monatomic gas. However, Eq. (68) must be expected to depart considerably from the actual value of the internal pressure for mercury in the liquid phase. But $A = (kn_l)$ was primarily contributed by the use of Eq. (68), at a point in the liquid, in the process of evaluating the line integral of $\mathbf{f}_{da}$. Therefore, this constant cannot be expected to be equal to that determined from the experiment. Using $n_l = 4.1 \times 10^{22}/cm^3$, gives $\ln A = 15.6$, where A is in dyne/cm^2-$°K$. Calculated in the same units from the data of Douglas $et\ al$, $\ln A = 18.68$. If these data are experimentally accurate, then the discrepancy, as explained earlier, would be caused, at least in part, by the inaccuracy of Eq. (68) for the liquid phase.

Corresponding to the units used in Fig. 3, the two constants used for plotting the theoretical curve are: $\ln A = 11.5$ (A in mm Hg/$°K$), and $T_0 = -6.53 \times 10^3\ °K$.

The Detailed Self-Balancing. The state of thermal equilibrium in the liquid-vapor system illustrated in Fig. 4(a) may be represented as shown in Fig. 4(b). It will be recalled that W_L as expressed by Eq. (70) may be represented by an emf in the sense used in circuit theory. Figure 4(b) shows a (large) number of emf sources of equal emfs and all are connected in parallel. In this example, notice that the emf around every closed loop in the system is zero. Therefore, the electric current is zero at every point in

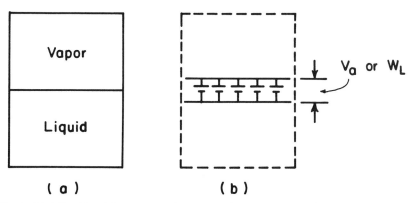

Fig. 4. (a) A liquid and its vapor at thermal equilibrium; and (b) the equivalent electric circuit representation.

the system. By analogy, the active diffusion field f_{da} cannot drive any flux anywhere, because it is stationary and conservative and will lead to what corresponds to a vanishing emf around every closed loop in the system.

We may additionally consider the active gravitational force f_{ga} per particle. As explained in the previous subsection, f_{ga} cannot drive any flux anywhere in the system for it is also stationary and conservative everywhere. Therefore, the diffusion field and the gravitational force per particle must each be in self balance, at thermal equilibrium.

9. DISCUSSION

This section will discuss some fundamental aspects of the theory of generalized fields from the points of view of a few established laws of nature.

9.1. *The Generalized Conditions of Thermal Equilibrium*

As discussed in Section 7, one possible fundamental consequence of Proposition I (Section 2), Corollary II and Proposition V (Subsections 5.1 and 5.3), is that at thermal equilibrium, each identifiable active force field (per particle) is stationary and conservative. We shall verify this conclusion by discussing some general cases.

Without loss of generality, consider conduction electrons in any solid body containing any number of interfaces between its different constituent materials. Let the equilibrium concentration gradients of the electrons at the interfaces be equal to any finite values. Examples of such a solid body include thermocouples, and semiconductor p–n junctions with shorted terminals.

It is well known from experience that the electrons in any one of the preceding systems will be at thermal equilibrium, if the system is isothermal, even if it is placed in a static magnetic and/or gravitational field, no matter how intense these fields may be.

In any one of these electron systems, we can identify generally four fields: (1) an electrostatic field $\mathbf{E}$, built in the various solid interfaces; (2) a magnetostatic field $\mathbf{H}$ caused by any magnet placed in the proximity of the electron system; (3) a diffusion field f_d also built in the interfaces; and (4) a gravitational field leading to a force f_g per particle. From Proposition I (Section 2) and Corollary V (Subsection 5.2), it follows that each one of the preceding four fields are entirely active at thermal equilibrium. It is particularly interesting to observe that, under the preceding conditions, Maxwell's equations of classical electromagnetism (Maxwell 1873, Jordan 1950) predict that

$$\nabla \times \mathbf{E}_a = 0, \quad \text{and} \quad \nabla \times \mathbf{H}_a = 0. \tag{74}$$

That

$$\nabla \times \mathbf{f}_{ga} = 0 \tag{75}$$

is a direct consequence of Newton's fundamental law of gravity (Newton 1687). Finally, under thermal equilibrium conditions, according to Eq. (18), $\mathbf{f}_{da} = -\nabla \epsilon_f$. Thus,

$$\nabla \times \mathbf{f}_{da} = 0. \tag{76}$$

The validity of Eq. (18) has been shown in Subsection 4.3 to hold for electrons even when quantum-mechanical and relativistic conditions are important. Such conditions would prevail under intensely high temperatures and for extremely high concentrations, as are believed to be found on the stars (Chandrashekhar 1939). Thus, even under such general conditions, Eq. (76) will be satisfied at thermal equilibrium.

In case the system consists of magnetic mobile particles rather than electrons, then the magnetic force $\mathbf{f}_{ma}$ per particle will have the property that $\nabla \times \mathbf{f}_{ma} = 0$. This result follows from one of Eqs. (74), since $\mathbf{f}_{ma} = q_m \mathbf{H}_a$, where q_m is the magnetic charge per particle.

With the exception of some trivial cases, it is believed that the preceding fundamental conclusions can be verified generally for any thermodynamic system whatever, even when the particles are nonideal. These *generalized conditions of thermal equilibrium* are entirely compatible with the mechanism of detailed *self*-balancing described in Section 2.

9.2. Circuit Theory

In Subsection 6.2, it has been shown that Eq. (42) leads to Ohm's law (Ohm 1825, 1826). We shall next see that other laws of circuit theory follow from the theory of generalized fields.

Kirchhoff's Laws. In Circuit theory, the concern usually is for no carriers other than electrons and there are no net electron generation or annihilation. Thus, the electron current density is solenoidal everywhere in any system. This will mean that the algebraic sum of all the currents flowing towards and out of any one node must vanish. This is, of course, a statement of Kirchhoff's current law (Kirchhoff 1847). This fundamental current law merely expresses the conservation of charge, a condition satisfied in the present theory by representing mesh currents by statistical particles which are transported around closed loops in the system, when the flux densities are solenoidal.

Consider next the one-loop circuit shown in Fig. 5. Notice in that example that the clockwise line integral of $(\mathbf{f}_{sn}/-q)$ through the resistor R is merely the (passive) voltage V_s. Here $\mathbf{f}_{sn}$ is the passive electrostatic force per electron. Also the clockwise closed loop line integral of $(\mathbf{f}_{an}/-q)$ through the entire closed loop is $(V_{a1} - V_{a2})$. The quantity $\mathbf{f}_{an}$ represents

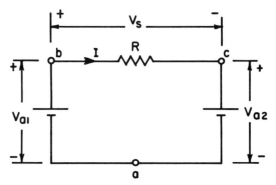

Fig. 5. A one-loop electric circuit containing two active voltage (emf) sources and a resistor hosting a passive electric field.

the active force per electron at any point in any one of the two emf sources. Thus, the interpretation of Eq. (37) in this case is that: $V_{a1} - V_{a2} - V_s = 0$. The passive voltage can be immediately shown to be given by: $V_s = RI$, which is an expression of Ohm's law.

Consequently, for a multi-mesh system, Proposition V, expressed by Eqs. (37) and (38), reduces to the following: around every closed loop in the system, the sum of all the (active) voltages across all the emf sources less the sum of all the (passive) voltages across the resistors must vanish. Clearly, the preceding statement is that of Kirchhoff's voltage law (Kirchhoff 1847).

Thermal Equilibrium and Nonequilibrium. We shall define the state of thermal equilibrium for the electrons in a multi-mesh electric network to be one for which the current vanishes everywhere in the system. This definition, of course, does not rule out the presence of emf sources in the system.

In our simple example of Fig. 5, if $I \neq 0$, then the active voltages (emfs) V_{a1} and V_{a2} will be unequal. This will mean that the line integral of $(\mathbf{f}_{an}/-q)$ between a and b through the source V_{a1} will not equal that between a and b through the source V_{a2}. The active voltages, therefore, calculated between the two points a and b depend on the path. Here, of course, the passive voltage V_s is not counted. Thus, under such conditions, the emf sources introduce a nonconservative active process in the electron system. Electrons in this case, according to Eqs. (37) and (41) are necessarily in nonequilibrium, that is $I \neq 0$, a conclusion predicted at once by circuit theory, whenever $V_{a1} \neq V_{a2}$.

If, however, $I = 0$, the passive voltage V_s must vanish. Thus, the sum of the active voltages around the closed loop must vanish, that is the active voltage between any two points in the system will not depend on the path.

The emf sources, therefore, constitute a conservative active process in the system. This conclusion, of course, can be generalized to any multi-mesh electric network. Thus, the generalized conditions of thermal equilibrium, derived in Section 7 are once more satisfied.

9.3. *The First and Second Laws of Thermodynamics*

The first law of thermodynamics has been applied in the present theory in a number of instances, which include: (1) determining the time rate of energy conversion per unit volume associated with passive and active fields [see Eqs. (33), (34), and (35)]; (2) postulating that around every closed loop in a system containing only solenoidal fluxes, the work done per particle of a given constituent associated with all the active force fields equals that associated with all the passive force fields [see Eq. (37)].

It is a fundamental consequence of Proposition I that at thermal equilibrium, associated with each identifiable passive field, there can be no net evolution or absorption of heat at any point (see Corollary IV, Subsection 5.1). Furthermore, from Eq. (37), based on the first law of thermodynamics, at thermal equilibrium, generally each active force field pertaining to any one constituent is stationary and conservative, at each point in the system. This means that under the action of each identifiable active force field, the work done on each constituent around any closed loop must vanish. Thus, at thermal equilibrium, there can be no heat liberation or absorption in the system, or in any part thereof. Consequently, in the system as a whole, and in any part thereof, at thermal equilibrium, the entropy remains constant. However, upon introducing a nonconservative active field, such as an emf source or an electromagnetic field, thermal equilibrium will necessarily be upset.

Suppose now that nonequilibrium is maintained in the system for a finite length of time, after which the state of thermal equilibrium is recovered. From the point of view of our thermodynamic theory, the entropy of the system *as a whole* will be uniquely defined *only* during the initial and final states of thermal equilibrium, *but not during the intermediate nonequilibrium states*. If the entropies of the entire system, corresponding to the initial and final states of thermal equilibrium, are S_1 and S_2, respectively, then it is necessary that

$$S_2 > S_1. \tag{77}$$

Inequality (77), and its important conditions, represent the only manner in which the second law is interpreted in the framework of the thermodynamic theory of generalized fields.

By contrast, in classical thermodynamics entropy has been assumed to exist during nonequilibrium states. As stated in Chapter 4, serious objections to such an assumption have been raised by a number of prominent thermodynamicists (see, for example, the important statements of Meixner quoted in Chapter 4, pp. 61–62.)

10. SUMMARY AND CONCLUSION

On the basis of the mechanism of detailed *self*-balancing, we have presented a theory to account for thermal equilibrium, and nonequilibrium. For simplicity, the treatment has been confined to steady-state conditions in systems containing only solenoidal fluxes.

According to the present theory, the state of thermal equilibrium in a system is characterized by the important properties that: each identifiable passive force field vanishes individually, and generally each identifiable active force field is stationary and conservative. These results are applicable to each identifiable constituent. Accordingly, nonequilibrium will inevitably be established in a system, if one or more active fields in the system become nonconservative and/or time-varying. The present conclusions concerning thermal equilibrium have been verified from the standpoints of a number of fundamental laws of nature.

As has been shown for particle fluxes, it seems possible to decompose thermal fluxes into identifiable components, each of which should vanish at thermal equilibrium.

The more general illustration of the present theory for nonequilibrium is left to Chapters 7 and 9. In the former, the fundamental theoretical aspects developed here will be applied to the problem of electrical conduction in a broad class of semiconductor interfaces. A number of the fundamental theoretical aspects will be discussed including the introduction by the present theory of significant quantities of transport energy. Most importantly, theory will be shown to accurately account for extensive electrical measurements involving current variations which extend in some cases to over ten orders of magnitude. The studies have been made at different temperatures between 4.2° and 800°K, and for semiconductor materials with energy gaps ranging between 0.17–2.8 eV. Corresponding to that energy-gap range, at 77°K, the crucial concentration of minority charge carriers would lie in a range extending roughly over a 10^{168}-to-1 ratio. This ratio increases more drastically at 4.2°K. Under all these strongly different conditions, the present thermodynamic theory has led to a unified theory of conduction. On the other hand, only some of the experimental characteristics to be presented, under relatively restricted conditions, had been explained earlier by numerous different empirical qualitative and quantitative theories based on different hypotheses *ad hoc*.

Considerations in this chapter have been made strictly from the point of view of the real space. It will be shown in Chapter 8 that the real space is only part of a four-dimensional hyperspace. This hyperspace consists of the three position coordinates of the real space and a fourth independent axis of temperature.

PROBLEMS

1. Show that, from a mathematical point of view, the quantity $\nabla \epsilon_f$ occurring in Eq. (16) can be expanded into

$$\nabla \epsilon_f = (\nabla \epsilon_f)_T + (d\epsilon_f/dT)_{x,y,z} \, \nabla T.$$

2. Derive an expression for f_d in an isothermal nondegenerate electron gas for which the electron concentration n is uniform, but the electron effective mass m_e is such that $\nabla m_e \neq 0$. [The conditions described in this problem can be physically realized in what are known as heterojunctions in semiconductors, to be discussed in the next chapter.]
   [Ans. $f_d = -\nabla \epsilon_f - \langle \epsilon \rangle (\nabla m_e)/m_e$.]

3. Solve Problem 2, assuming that the system is isothermal, but $\nabla n \neq 0$, and $\nabla m_e \neq 0$.

4. Solve Problem 2, assuming generally that $\nabla T \neq 0$, $\nabla m_e \neq 0$, and $\nabla n \neq 0$.

5. Using the Sommerfeld–Bethe approximation, derive an expression for (D/μ) in metals.

6. An electron gas has $\epsilon_f = 75 \times 10^{-3}$ electron volt at 300°K. Calculate for that gas the ratio (D/μ).

REFERENCES

Bose, S. N. 1924, Z. Phys. **26**, 178.
Chandrasekhar, S. 1939, An Introduction to the Study of Stellar Structure, Chap. 10, p. 357, The University of Chicago Press.
Einstein, A. 1905, Ann. Physik **17**, 549.
—— 1924, S. B. Preuss. Akad. Wiss., 261.
Dirac, P. A. M. 1926, Proc. Roy. Soc. **A112**, 661.
Douglas, T. B., Ball, A. F., and Ginnings, D. C. 1951, J. Research Natl. Bur. Std. **46**, 334.
Fermi, E. 1926, Z. Phys. **36**, 902.
Fick, A. 1855, Pogg. Ann. **94**, 59.
Hall, E. H. 1879, Am. J. Math. **2**, 287.
—— 1880, Am. J. Science **19**, 200.
Jeans, J. H. 1940, An Introduction to the Kinetic Theory of Gases, p. 164, The University Press, Cambridge.
Jordan, E. C. 1950, Electromagnetic Waves and Radiating Systems, Chap. 4, p. 94, Prentice-Hall.
Juttner, F. 1928, Z. Phys. **47**, 542.
Kaplan, W. 1952, Advanced Calculus, p. 275, Addison-Wesley.
Kirchhoff, G. 1847, Pogg. Ann. Phys. **72**, 497.
Landsberg, P. T. 1952, Proc. Roy. Soc. **A213**, 226.
Maxwell, J. C. 1873, A Treatise on Electricity and Magnetism, vol. 2, Clarendon Press.

Melehy, M. A. 1964, Nature **202**, 864.

—— 1965a, Nature **205**, 456; *ibid*. **206**, 875.

—— 1965b, Proc. IEEE **53**, 536.

—— 1966a, Report on the MIT Ann. Phys. Elec. Conf. **26**, 402.

—— 1966b, Nature **209**, 670.

—— 1970, Proceedings of the Pittsburgh, Pennsylvania 1969 International Symposium on "A Critical Review of the Foundations of Thermodynamics," pp. 345–376; edited by E. B. Stuart, Benjamin Gal-Or, and A. J. Brainard, Mono Book Corp., Baltimore.

Newton, I. 1687, Philosophiae Naturalis Principia Mathematica (London: Jessu Societatis Regiae ac Typis Josephi Streater), English Translation by Andrew Motte 1729. Revised by Florian Cajori, 1934 (Berkeley; University of California).

Ohm, G. S. 1825, Pogg. Ann. **4**, 79.

—— 1826, *ibid*. **6**, 459.

—— 1826, *ibid*. **7**, 45.

Peltier, J. C. 1834, Ann. Chim. Phys. **56**, 371.

Prigogine, I. and Defay, R. 1954, Chemical Thermodynamics, English Translation by D. H. Everett; p. 193, Longmans Green.

Seebeck, T. J. 1826, Ann. Phys. Pogg. **6**, 1, 133, 253.

Stokes, G. G. 1845, Phil. Mag. **29**, 60.

Thomson, W. (Lord Kelvin) 1882, Mathematical and Physical Papers, vol. 1, The University Press, Cambridge.

Wilson, A. H. 1957, Thermodynamics and Statistical Mechanics, pp. 221–223, The University Press, Cambridge.

Chapter 7

UNIFIED THEORY OF ELECTRICAL CONDUCTION IN $p\text{-}n$ JUNCTIONS, HETEROJUNCTIONS AND SCHOTTKY DIODES*

1. INTRODUCTION

This chapter will be concerned with applying the thermodynamic theory of generalized fields, presented in Chapter 6, to the specific problem of steady-state, forward electrical conduction in a broad class of semiconductor crystals involving interfaces. This class consists of what is generally referred to as $p\text{-}n$ junctions, heterojunctions, and Schottky diodes.

Conduction in such semiconductor diodes is generally carried by two oppositely charged constituents: electrons and holes. Under nonequilibrium conditions, there will be in these diodes a net generation, or recombination of electron-hole pairs. Therefore, we shall be concerned with the interaction of active and passive fields—pertaining to electrons and to holes—under the conditions for which the individual electron and hole currents are non-solenoidal. This particular situation has not been considered in Chapter 6. We shall further illustrate in a concrete manner, a number of fundamental theoretical aspects, which have only been discussed in a general sense in Chapter 6. These aspects include: (1) the complete distinguishability of active and passive fields, for each constituent; (2) the mechanism of detailed *self*-balancing; and (3) the introduction of new significant quantities of transport energy.

It can be expected, therefore, that the present thermodynamic theory would lead to fundamentally new results for certain types of systems. For charged systems, for example, consequences of the present theory become more significant for higher particle concentration gradients. Thus, it is particularly interesting to analyze—on the basis of the present and classical thermodynamic formulations—a problem such as that of conduction in semiconductor junction diodes and test the consequences by experiment. Electrons and holes in these diodes happen to have unusually large concentration gradients which can be profoundly changed by changing the ambient temperature.

In this chapter, we shall compare theory—based on the classical and present thermodynamic frameworks—and experiment at temperatures

---

* The content of this chapter was presented, for the most part, at the Pittsburgh, Pennsylvania 1969 International Symposium on "A Critical Review of Thermodynamics." Publication has followed in the Symposium Proceedings (Melehy 1970a).

ranging from 4.2° to 800°K for samples made of semiconductor materials with energy gaps ranging from 0.17 to 2.8 eV. At 77°K, this energy gap range will require that, at thermal equilibrium, the concentration of minority electrons on one side of the junction, for example, would lie in a range extending roughly over a 10^{168}-to-1 ratio. This ratio increases more dramatically at 4.2°K. On the other side of the junction, however, the concentration of electrons is relatively high—typically about 10^{17} to $10^{19}/$ cm^3—and is very nearly temperature independent above, say, 75°K. Since the junction might roughly be about 400 Å, the electron concentration gradient within the junction will be extremely high and very strongly dependent upon the ambient temperature. Likewise will be the hole concentration gradient.

Despite the dramatic variation of the electron and hole concentrations, and concentration gradients, described above, applying the present thermodynamic theory to the three types of semiconductor junction diodes has led to a unified theory (Melehy 1967, 1968, 1969, 1970a, b, 1971). Without empiricism, the latter has accounted for extensive electrical measurements involving current variations extending in some cases over more than 10 orders of magnitude. Under relatively restricted conditions, only a small portion of these measurements had been explained earlier empirically, qualitatively, and quantitatively by numerous different theories, most of which are based on different hypotheses *ad hoc*. Some of these theories are: for *p-n* junctions, (1) on Ge (Shockley 1949, Hall 1952); (2) a few theories on Si are summarized by Sah (1962); (3) on GaAs (Rediker and Quist 1963, Dumin and Pearson 1965); (4) for various heterojunctions (Anderson 1962, Perlman and Feucht 1964, Rediker *et al.* 1964, Riben and Feucht 1966, Donnelly and Milnes 1966); and for metal-semiconductor junctions including Schottky diodes (Schottky 1938, 1939, Bardeen 1947, Macdonald 1962, Stratton 1962, Kahng 1963, Padovani and Sumner 1965, Padovani and Stratton 1966).

2. SEMICONDUCTOR JUNCTION DIODES UNDER THERMAL EQUILIBRIUM AND FORWARD-BIAS CONDITIONS

This section will describe briefly some preliminary aspects concerning *p-n* junctions, heterojunctions and Schottky diodes. We shall hereinafter refer collectively to these three different semiconductor diodes as junction diodes.

2.1. *p-n Junctions*

A *p-n* junction consists of a single semiconductor crystal. This crystal consists of two regions separated by a narrow transition region, which may be roughly of the order of 400 Å wide. The concentration of electrons n_n

in the n region must be much higher than the thermal-equilibrium concentration p_n of minority holes in that region. In the p region, however, the concentration of holes p_p is much higher than the thermal-equilibrium concentration n_p of electrons in that region.

If the concentrations of majority carriers (electrons or holes) in a p-n junction are sufficiently small so that the Maxwell-Boltzmann Statistics apply, then the p-n junction is said to be nondegenerate. Otherwise it is called degenerate. For the first case, it has been shown in Chapter 5 that, at thermal equilibrium, in any one crystal

$$p_p n_p = n_n p_n = n_i{}^2 = p_i{}^2 = BT^3 \exp\left(-q\epsilon_g/kT\right)/\text{cm}^6, \qquad B = 2.33 \times 10^{31}, \quad (1)$$

where n_i and p_i are the concentrations of electrons and holes, respectively, in the crystal if it were intrinsic, ϵ_g the energy gap in electron volts, q the magnitude of the electron charge, k is Boltzmann's constant, and T is the crystal absolute temperature in degrees Kelvin. If the free, and effective electron masses in the crystal are not equal, then the constant B has to be modified slightly.

For a Si semiconductor crystal, for example, $\epsilon_g = 1.11$ eV. At $T = 300°K$ (room temperature), $kT/q \simeq 0.025$ eV. Thus, from Eq. (1), $n_i{}^2 \simeq 10^{20}/\text{cm}^6$, and if $n_n = 10^{18}/\text{cm}^3$, then $p_n = 10^2/\text{cm}^3$. At $T = 523°K$, however, $n_i{}^2 \simeq 4 \times 10^{29}/\text{cm}^6$ and $p_n \simeq 4 \times 10^{11}/\text{cm}^3$.

2.2. *The Continuity Equation for Excess Minority Carriers in p-n Junctions*

As has just been explained, at thermal equilibrium, $p_p \gg p_n$ and $n_n \gg n_p$. If now the p-n junction is forward biased by an emf source as shown in Fig. 1, then the abundant holes on the p side will be injected through the transition region to the n region, where they will drastically modify the concentration of minority holes at the n-region boundary from its thermal-equilibrium value p_n to a new higher nonequilibrium value p_e. Consequently, holes will progressively diffuse and recombine in the n region. Likewise, electrons will be injected into the p region, where they will diffuse and recombine with the majority holes. It is then of fundamental concern to determine the equation which describes the variation of minority-carrier concentrations in the bulk regions as they relate to the current densities and the process of electron-hole recombination. The equation to be sought is generally called the *continuity equation* for minority carriers.

Let us first consider injected holes in an n-type semiconductor. Imagine an elementary volume dV near the junction and within the n region. In that infinitesimal volume, if the concentration of holes p changes in time, it must be due to the following processes: (1) a time-rate of generation G of holes per unit volume; (2) a time-rate of recombination R of holes per unit volume; and a net time-rate of outward flow of holes through all the surfaces of the volume dV. From the discussions in Section 3.2 [Chapter 2]

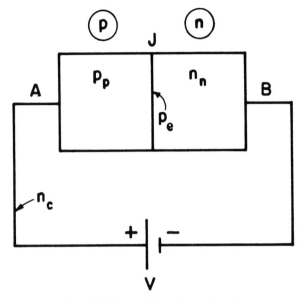

Fig. 1. A forward biased p–n junction.

on the divergence, it will be recalled that the net time-rate of outward hole flow is merely $(\nabla \cdot \boldsymbol{\jmath}_p)\, dV$. Here $\boldsymbol{\jmath}_p$ is the hole flux density.

The three processes contributing to the time variation of hole concentration must be interrelated by

$$(\partial p/\partial t)\, dV = [G - R - (\nabla \cdot \boldsymbol{\jmath}_p)]\, dV. \tag{2}$$

Let us next evaluate the quantity $(G - R)$. In the elementary volume dV, we may express the concentration of holes p, and that of electrons n, in terms of their thermal-equilibrium values by

$$p = p_n + \delta p, \tag{3}$$

$$n = n_n + \delta n. \tag{4}$$

The process of electron-hole recombination results because there exists a finite probability per unit time for each conduction electron to be in a favorable position to recombine with a hole. The more concentrated the electrons and the holes are, the more will be their rate of recombination per unit volume. Accordingly, it may be assumed that

$$R = (rpn), \tag{5}$$

where r is a constant of proportionality to be determined later.

Let us now consider the generation process. Electrons and holes to be generated cannot anticipate the existing concentrations of conduction electrons and holes. Rather, they are only sensitive to the conditions of thermal equilibrium. They further foresee that the crystal is very nearly intrinsic. For, its pure atomic composition has only been modified minutely by donor impurities. Thus, the rate of generation G of holes within dV (per unit volume) will be proportional to the intrinsic concentration p_i of holes and of electrons n_i. We may, therefore, write

$$G = (g p_i n_i), \tag{6}$$

where g is a constant of proportionality.

If we now assume that the constants g and r do not depend on the concentrations p and n, we can then relate g to r. If the crystal is at thermal equilibrium, then the rate of generation G must equal the rate of recombination R. But in the n-type crystal, at thermal equilibrium, $p = p_n$, and $n = n_n$. Equations (5) and (6), therefore, lead to

$$r p_n n_n = g p_i n_i. \tag{7}$$

From Eqs. (1) and (7), it follows at once that

$$g = r. \tag{8}$$

Equation (8) will only hold, if the majority carriers are nondegenerate. For, otherwise, Eqs. (1) would not be valid.

If electrons and holes in the n region are in a state of nonequilibrium, then in view of Eqs. (3)–(6), and (8), we may write

$$
\begin{aligned}
G - R &= -r\left[(p_n + \delta p)(n_n + \delta n) - n_i^2\right] \\
&= -r\left[n_n p_n + n_n\,\delta p + p_n\,\delta n + \delta p\,\delta n - n_i^2\right] \\
&= -r\left[n_n\,\delta p + p_n\,\delta n + \delta p\,\delta n\right].
\end{aligned}
\tag{9}
$$

In all situations of interest in this chapter, $p_n \ll n_n$ and $\delta p \ll n_n$. Since the charge neutrality condition holds in the bulk n region, then $\delta p = \delta n$. Therefore, Eq. (9) reduces approximately to

$$G - R \simeq -r n_n\,\delta p. \tag{10}$$

Hence, Eq. (2) can be rewritten as

$$\partial p / \partial t = -\nabla \cdot \mathbf{\mathcal{J}}_p - r n_n\,\delta p. \tag{11}$$

The quantity $(r n_n)$ is a constant, and has further the dimension of $(\text{time})^{-1}$. Generally, $(r n_n)$ is defined to be the inverse of what is called the lifetime τ_p of minority holes. In terms of τ_p and the hole current density $\mathbf{J}_p$, which equals $(\mathbf{\mathcal{J}}_p / q)$, Eq. (11) will be

$$\partial p / \partial t = -(1/q)\nabla \cdot \mathbf{J}_p - (p - p_n)/\tau_p. \tag{12}$$

Equation (12) represents the continuity relation for minority holes. By a similar procedure, it can be shown that the continuity equation for minority electrons (in the p region) will be

$$\partial n/\partial t = (1/q) \, \nabla \cdot \mathbf{J}_n - (n - n_p)/\tau_n. \tag{13}$$

Here τ_n is defined as the lifetime of minority electrons.

Equations (12) and (13) were first derived by Shockley (1949, 1950).

2.3. *Time-Independent, One-Dimensional Solution of the Continuity Equation for Minority-Carrier Densities*

Having obtained the continuity equations for minority carriers, it is then possible to determine how they are distributed in the neighborhood of the junction where they are injected. In all the cases to be studied in this chapter, electrical conduction in the diodes will be in response to a dc voltage. We shall, therefore, be only concerned with the time-independent solutions of the continuity equations for which $\partial p/\partial t = 0$ and $\partial n/\partial t = 0$.

Under such conditions, and in one dimension, the continuity equation for holes reduces to

$$(1/q) \, (dJ_p/dx) = -(p - p_n)/\tau_p, \tag{14}$$

where x is the distance between points in the n region and the junction.

As explained in Chapter 6, the transport of minority carriers in the bulk regions is purely passive. Thus, if minority carriers are subject to only passive diffusion, then as shown in Subsection 6.3 [Chapter 6], we may apply Fick's law to determine the diffusion current density. For minority holes, the diffusion current density J_{dp} will be

$$J_{dp} = -qD_p \, dp/dx. \tag{15}$$

Since J_p in our case is the same as J_{dp}, then from Eqs. (14) and (15), it follows that

$$d^2p/dx^2 = (p - p_n)/L_p^2, \tag{16}$$

or

$$d^2(p - p_n)/dx^2 = (p - p_n)/L_p^2, \tag{17}$$

where L_p is defined as the diffusion length and is given by

$$L_p^2 = D_p \tau_p. \tag{18}$$

Equation (17) has the general solution:

$$p - p_n = A_0 \exp(-x/L_p) + B_0 \exp(x/L_p), \tag{19}$$

where A_0 and B_0 are arbitrary constants. The second term in Eq. (19) increases indefinitely as x increases. Therefore, this term is physically meaningless, and B_0 must vanish. Equation (19), hence, reduces to

$$p-p_n=A_0 \exp(-x/L_p). \tag{20}$$

The arbitrary constant A_0 can be determined by imposing the boundary condition that at $x=0$, $p=p_e$, where p_e is the boundary value of the density of injected minority holes, under forward biasing. When these values are substituted in Eq. (20), we get

$$A_0=p_e-p_n. \tag{21}$$

From Eqs. (20) and (21), it follows that

$$p(x) = (p_e-p_n) \exp(-x/L_p)+p_n. \tag{22}$$

Equation (22) was first derived by Shockley (1949).

An equation similar to Eq. (22) may be written for minority electrons in the p region. In all the cases to be studied here, we shall assume that the injected minority hole current is much greater than the injected minority electron current. This is usually the case when $p_n \gg n_p$; that is, from Eq. (1), $p_p \gg n_n$. Under such conditions, the terminal current I equals the diffusion hole current evaluated at $x=0$. Therefore, from Eq. (22) and one similar to Eq. (44) [Chapter 6], we have

$$I = (qD_pA/L_p)(p_e-p_n). \tag{23}$$

Here, D_p is the diffusion constant for holes, and A the crystal cross-sectional area.

2.4. *Heterojunctions and Schottky Diodes*

Heterojunctions generally are supposed to consist of one crystal made of two different semiconductors separated by the junction. Therefore, we shall assume that upon forward biasing a p-n heterojunction, minority carriers will be injected. Subsequently, they will recombine and diffuse in the bulk regions, as do minority carriers in p-n junctions.

The theory of diffusion of minority carriers in heterojunctions was suggested by Kroemer (1957) and, Anderson (1962). Although this theory appears to be the oldest one considered, it was later virtually abandoned, because its analysis by classical methods had yielded results departing appreciably from experiment. This departure will be seen in Fig. 10.

For the Schottky diodes, we shall assume that between the metal and the n region of the semiconductor, there is an inversion layer which is actually p type. The existence of this layer has been discussed earlier (Bardeen and Brattain 1949, Simpson and Armstrong 1953). Thus, upon forward biasing, we shall assume that holes will be injected from the inversion p layer into the n region where they will progressively recombine and diffuse.

Under such conditions, the mechanism of conduction will be identical with that of p-n junctions.

3. INTERACTION OF ACTIVE AND PASSIVE FIELDS IN THE PRESENCE OF ELECTRON-HOLE RECOMBINATION

We have discussed in Chapter 6 how active and passive fields would interact if the fluxes were solenoidal. In our present problem, there is a net electron-hole recombination in the bulk n and p regions. To determine how the interactions between the different active and passive fields occur in this problem, consider again Fig. 1, which represents a p-n junction connected to an emf source. The current I fed by a battery to a p-n junction diode will be carried at various points of the loop by electrons and/or holes. Although the total electron and hole currents through any cross section in the loop must be constant, the electron and hole current components of I vary generally from point to point. If we now imagine that I may be represented by a fictitious *composite* carrier which is transported around a complete loop in a given time, we must be aware of the fact that this effective carrier at some points of the loop may be an electron or a hole and at other points may be partly an electron and partly a hole. It is, therefore, evident that around one complete mesh C, the law of conservation of energy, when imposed on this composite carrier, will lead to

$$\oint_C dW_{ta} - \oint_C dW_{ts} = 0, \qquad (24)$$

where,

$$dW_{ta} = dW_{tan} + dW_{tap}, \qquad dW_{ts} = dW_{tsn} + dW_{tsp}. \qquad (25)$$

Here dW_{tan} and dW_{tap} are the electron and hole components of dW_{ta}, which represents the infinitesimal increment of work done on a composite carrier by all the active force fields as the carrier is transported an infinitesimal distance $d\mathbf{l}$ along any closed loop C in the system. For passive force fields, the corresponding infinitesimal increments of work are dW_{tsn}, dW_{tsp} and dW_{ts}, respectively.

It is now possible to relate the differentials dW_{ta} and dW_{ts} to the force fields $\mathbf{f}_{ta}$ and $\mathbf{f}_{ts}$. To do so, consider a current density which is totally along the x direction, and which is generally divided between electrons and holes. Suppose that as the holes flow along the x direction, they progressively recombine with electrons. To be general, assume that the holes and electrons are subject to any number of active and passive fields. Let any one of these fields be designated by $\mathbf{f}_{ip}$ for holes, and $\mathbf{f}_{in}$ for electrons. It is the purpose now to calculate dW_i representing the infinitesimal increment of work, dW_{ip} and dW_{in}, done on a composite carrier by $\mathbf{f}_{ip}$ and $\mathbf{f}_{in}$, respectively, as the carrier is transported a distance dx.

If the holes were not to recombine, dW_{ip} would simply be: $\mathbf{f}_{ip}\cdot d\mathbf{l}$. When a hole recombines, however, it will no longer exist to be acted on by $\mathbf{f}_{ip}$, and it will not, therefore, contribute to dW_{ip}.

To calculate dW_{ip}, accounting only for those holes which have not recombined, consider a point a at a distance x from a reference plane. At a, there will be $[J_p(x)/q]$ holes crossing a transverse unit area per second. Statistically, each hole will be subject to f_{ip}. Thus, the work done per second on all holes crossing a unit area while the carriers are displaced from x to $x+dx$ will be: $[f_{ip}(x)\,dx\,J_p(x)/q]$. Since $[J(x)/q]$ electrons and holes—that is, composite carriers—must cross the unit area per second, then from the definition of dW_{ip}, we may write

$$dW_{ip} = (f_{ip}\,dx)[J_p(x)/J(x)]. \tag{26}$$

Correspondingly, for electrons,

$$dW_{in} = -(f_{in}\,dx)[J_n(x)/J(x)]. \tag{27}$$

The minus sign in Eq. (27) is to account for the fact that dW_{in} is referred to a positive composite carrier representing J, while J_n is an electron current. In the preceding example, it should be remembered that

$$J(x) = J_p(x) + J_n(x), \tag{28}$$

and $\mathbf{f}_{ip}$ and $\mathbf{f}_{in}$ can be active or passive.

It is interesting to observe that in the event that there is no net carrier recombination and J is entirely carried by holes, then from Eqs. (26) and (22), $dW_{ip} = \mathbf{f}_{ip}\cdot d\mathbf{x}$, as stated in Subsection 5.3 of Chapter 6. Furthermore, $dW_{in} = 0$. The latter results will be, for example, applicable to holes in the transition region of a p-n junction, if there is no net electron-hole recombination in that region and the injection is entirely carried by holes.

If an electron-hole system has no net carrier generation or recombination anywhere, one can therefore see that the "fictitious" composite carrier can be chosen to be either an electron and a vanishingly small fraction of a hole, or a hole and a vanishingly small fraction of an electron. Thus, applying the law of conservation of energy around closed loops to each one of the two possible types of composite carriers will lead at once to Eq. (37) [Chapter 6].

4. WORK DONE ON A COMPOSITE CARRIER BY SEVEN DIFFERENT ACTIVE AND PASSIVE FIELDS IN THE JUNCTION DIODES

This section will be concerned with calculating the work done on a composite carrier by all the active and passive force fields in the electron-hole system, as the composite carrier is transported along a closed loop enclosing any one of the three different kinds of junction diodes.

4.1. *Work Done by the Active Diffusion Field in the Junction*

At every point in the transition region, the electrons and holes have concentration gradients, which support an electron and hole diffusion fields, respectively. These force fields are active, simply because they are caused entirely by the atomic structure in the transition region, rather than by flow. We shall next derive an expression for the work done W_{daj} on a composite carrier by the diffusion field, as the carrier is transported through the junction. We shall assume that the injection is entirely carried by electrons. If the injection is totally carried by holes, the corresponding answer for W_{daj} can be found by analogy.

As assumed earlier, if there is no net carrier generation or recombination in the transition region, the total current density in the region $J(y')$ equals the electron current density $J_n(y')$, while the hole current density $J_p(y')=0$; here, y' being the axial distance between any point a within the transition region, and the n-region boundary.

In view of Eqs. (25)–(27), W_{daj}, referred to a negative composite carrier, may be expressed in electron volts as

$$W_{daj}=q^{-1}\int_0^w \mathbf{f}_{dan}\cdot d\mathbf{y}'. \tag{29}$$

Here, w is the width of the transition region, which in this theory is assumed to be constant at any one temperature.

Under isothermal conditions, according to Eq. (18) [Chapter 6], $\mathbf{f}_{dan}=-\nabla\epsilon_f$. Substituting $\mathbf{f}_{dan}$ into Eq. (29), we get

$$W_{daj}=-q^{-1}\int_0^w (\nabla\epsilon_f)\cdot d\mathbf{y}'=q^{-1}[\epsilon_f(n_n)-\epsilon_f(n_e)]. \tag{30}$$

The quantities $\epsilon_f(n_n)$ and $\epsilon_f(n_e)$ represent the energy difference between the Fermi level or quasi Fermi level and the bottom of the conduction bands in the n region and at the p-region boundary, respectively.

At thermal equilibrium, $n_e=n_p$ and Eq. (30) reduces to

$$\phi_0=q^{-1}[\epsilon_f(n_n)-\epsilon_f(n_p)], \tag{31}$$

where ϕ_0 may be defined to be the limit of W_{daj} as the conditions of thermal equilibrium are approached.

Under the condition that minority electrons are nondegenerate, according to Eq. (32) [Chapter 5], (also Shockley 1950), the Fermi energy $\epsilon_f(n_p)$, corresponding to the electron concentration, n_p, will be given by

$$\epsilon_f(n_p)=-kT\ln(N_c/n_p), \tag{32}$$

where N_c is a constant at any one temperature. Thus from the definition of quasi* Fermi energy, corresponding to an electron concentration, n_e, we have

$$\epsilon_f(n_e) = -kT \ln(N_c/n_e). \tag{33}$$

From Eqs. (30)-(33), it follows that in electron volts

$$W_{daj} = W_{dan} = \phi_0 - (kT/q)\ln(n_e/n_p). \tag{34}$$

By a similar procedure, it can be shown that if the injection is entirely carried by holes, then the work done by the hole (active) diffusion field on a positive composite carrier as the carrier is transported through the junction is given by

$$W_{daj} = W_{dap} = \phi_0 - (kT/q)\ln(p_e/p_n). \tag{35}$$

Here, p_e is the boundary value of the concentration of minority holes, and p_n the thermal equilibrium value of p_e. The amount W_{daj} is expressed in electron volts.

For Eqs. (34) and (35) to be valid, it should be remembered that minority carriers are nondegenerate and the crystal is isothermal. Majority carriers, however, can be generally degenerate.

4.2. Work Done by the Active Electrostatic Field in the Junction

When carriers, such as holes, are transported in the forward direction through the transition region, then they will be subject to an opposing active electrostatic force field, $\mathbf{f}_{ea}$. This field is entirely supported by a space charge which is caused by the lack of atomic symmetry in the transition region, rather than by a flow. Because there is no carrier recombination, it follows from Eq. (26) that the line integral of $\mathbf{f}_{ea}$ through the junction will represent the statistical work done W_{eap} on a hole as the particle is transported through the transition region. This hole, in the absence of recombination, constitutes a composite carrier. For this carrier, the quantity corresponding to W_{eap} is W_{eaj}. In electron volts W_{eaj} may be simply related to the active electrostatic voltage, built in the junction, by

$$W_{eaj} = W_{eap} = -\psi = -(\psi_0 + \delta\psi). \tag{36}$$

Here, ψ represents the active electrostatic voltage built in the junction, and $\delta\psi$ is the increase in ψ above its thermal equilibrium value ψ_0. This deviation in ψ is caused by the injection of minority carriers and the consequent change in the space charge distribution through the transition region.

As will be shown in Subsection 5.2, the quantity ψ_0 will have no effect whatever on the V-I characteristics of the diodes. It will be seen, however, that the quantity $\delta\psi$ is strongly a function of current bias, junction type,

---

* The quasi Fermi energy is the Fermi energy of a fermion system in a state of nonequilibrium.

temperature, crystal energy gap and other material physical constants. We shall next derive an expression for this important quantity for all the three different types of p-n diodes.

For simplicity, we shall be confined in this chapter to the case for which $p_p \gg n_n$. This particular assumption corresponds to most common diodes, and in any event, the rest of the cases can be found by inspection (Melehy 1968) from the one considered here. For our particular case, as is well known, the injection will be almost entirely carried by holes. More importantly, $\delta\psi$ will be most predominantly supported by the change in hole rather than electron concentration in the junction.

Consider now any point a, within the transition region. Let the distance between a and the p-region boundary be y. At a the internal electrostatic voltage, $\psi = \psi_0 + \delta\psi$, can be related to the space charge density by Poisson's equation which may be written as*

$$(d^2/dy^2)(\psi_0 + \delta\psi) = -(q/\kappa)(p_1 - n + N_d - N_a). \tag{37}$$

Here κ is the dielectric constant at the junction, and p_1, n, N_d and N_a are, respectively, the concentrations of holes, electrons, and ionized donor and acceptor atoms in the transition region.

At thermal equilibrium, however, the distributions N_d, and N_a remain the same, assuming that w remains constant, and the change in n will be negligibly small. Furthermore, by definition, $\delta\psi$ must vanish. Thus, under such conditions, Eq. (37) reduces to

$$d^2\psi_0/dy^2 \simeq -(q/\kappa)(p_0 - n + N_d - N_a). \tag{38}$$

Here, p_0 is the thermal equilibrium distribution of hole concentration in the transition region.

Subtracting Eq. (38) from (37), we get

$$d^2(\delta\psi)/dy^2 \simeq -(q/\kappa)(p_1 - p_0). \tag{39}$$

Let it be assumed that the distribution of hole concentration in the junction is exponential so that

$$p_1 = p_p \exp(-a_1 y), \qquad p_0 = p_p \exp(-a_0 y), \tag{40}$$

where a_1 and a_0 are arbitrary constants determined from the following boundary conditions:

$$p_e = p_p \exp(-a_1 w), \qquad p_n = p_p \exp(-a_0 w). \tag{41}$$

Here, w is the width of the transition region, which according to the present theory, is considered constant at any one temperature.

---

* Equation (37) is one-dimensional. It follows from Maxwell's third equation [Eq. (66), Chapter 3] and Eq. (18) [Chapter 3].

Solving for a_1 and a_0, we get

$$a_1 = w^{-1} \ln (p_p/p_e), \qquad a_0 = w^{-1} \ln (p_p/p_n). \qquad (42)$$

If $p_p \gg p_e$, as is usually the case, the negative portion of the dipole charge associated with $(p_1 - p_0)$, will be much thinner than the positive portion. Thus, $\delta\psi$ will be almost entirely contributed by the positive portion of the dipole charge, which is toward the n-region boundary. Introducing this approximation will simplify considerably solving Eq. (39) for $\delta\psi$, which may be determined by substituting Eqs. (40) into (39) and integrating twice. Carrying out the steps, we get

$$\delta\psi \simeq (qp_p/\kappa)\{ (a_1^{-2} - a_0^{-2}) + [a_0^{-2} + (w/a_0)] \exp(-a_0 w)$$
$$- [a_1^{-2} + (w/a_1)] \exp(-a_1 w)\}. \qquad (43)$$

The first arbitrary constant encountered in solving the differential equation has been evaluated by imposing the boundary condition that the active electric field vanishes at the n-region boundary, that is, $d\delta\psi(w)/dy = 0$. The second arbitrary constant drops out, since the second integral is a definite one evaluated between the limits of $y = 0$ and $y = w$.

For all the cases of interest in this chapter, $p_p \gg p_e$, and $p_p \gg p_n$. Thus, from Eqs. (42) and (43), we get

$$\delta\psi \simeq \delta\psi^*[\ln^{-2}(p_p/p_e) - \ln^{-2}(p_p/p_n)], \qquad \delta\psi^* = qp_p w^2/\kappa. \qquad (44)$$

Equation (44) is a solution of Eq. (39), for which it has been assumed that $p_p \gg n_n$. Similar solutions can be obtained if $p_p \ll n_n$. Such conditions are usually satisfied for most common p-n junctions. In case that n_n and p_p are comparable to each other, such as is the case for some heterojunctions, it can be shown (Melehy 1968, 1971) that Eq. (44) should be modified to another more accurate form.

4.3. Work Done by the Passive Electrostatic Field in the Junction

We shall next calculate the amount of work W_{esj} done on a composite carrier by the passive electrostatic field, as the carrier is transported through the junction. Because it is assumed that there is no carrier recombination in the junction, W_{esj} will simply be the line integral of the passive electrostatic force f_{esp} per hole. Since the injection is entirely by holes, we may write on the basis of an equation similar to Eq. (41) [Chapter 6]:

$$f_{esp} = \frac{I}{A\mu_p p_1(y)} = \frac{I \exp(a_1 y)}{A\mu_p p_p}, \qquad (45)$$

where y is the distance between a point a within the junction and the p-region boundary, a_1 is as given by Eq. (42), and A is the crystal cross-sectional area.

Therefore, in electron volts

$$W_{esj} = \frac{I}{q\mu_p p_p A} \int_0^w \exp(a_1 y) \, dy. \tag{46}$$

From Eqs. (42) and (46), it follows that

$$W_{esj} \sim \left(\frac{w}{L_p}\right)\left(\frac{D_p}{\mu_p}\right)\left(\frac{I}{I'}\right) \ln^{-1}\left(\frac{p_p}{p_e}\right), \qquad I' = \frac{qD_p p_e A}{L_p}. \tag{47}$$

From Eqs. (71), to be derived in Section 5, it follows that

$$I' = I + I^*, \tag{48}$$

where I^* is the reverse-saturation current of a diode.

If the holes in the transition region are nondegenerate, then according to an equation similar to (45) [Chapter 6], $D_p/\mu_p = kT/q$. For all the diodes studied in this chapter, $w/L_p \ll 1$, and $\ln^{-1}(p_p/p_e) \ll 1$. From Eq. (48), it can also be seen that: $0 \leq (I/I') < 1$, for $I \geq 0$. Thus, Eq. (47) leads to

$$0 \leq W_{esj} \ll kT/q, \qquad \text{for } I \geq 0. \tag{49}$$

It is evident that the quantity W_{esj} is much smaller than W_{daj} and W_{eaj} derived earlier. Hence, W_{esj} should remain negligible, even if the carriers were degenerate. We shall, therefore, neglect W_{esj} in the derivation of the V-I relationship to be presented in Section 5.

4.4. *Work Done by the Passive Diffusion Field in the n Region*

In the last three subsections, we have calculated three components of the work done on a composite carrier transported through the junction. In the three subsections to follow, we shall calculate three more components of work associated with fields hosted in the bulk p and n regions.

In this particular subsection, we shall derive an expression for the amount of work W_{dsb} done by the passive diffusion of minority carriers on a composite carrier, as the carrier is transported through the entire n-type base region. To do so, consider Eq. (26) which, for the diffusion current density $J_{dp}(x)$ of minority holes, may be written as

$$dW_{dsb} = (f_{dsp} \, dx)[J_{dp}(x)/J]. \tag{50}$$

Here x is the distance between points in the n region and the junction, and J is the total current density at any point. Clearly, J is constant.

From Eq. (22) and one similar to Eq. (44) [Chapter 6], it follows that

$$J_{dp}(x) = J \exp(-x/L_p), \tag{51}$$

$$J = J_{dp}(0) = (qD_p/L_p)(p_e - p_n). \tag{52}$$

From an equation similar to Eq. (23) [Chapter 6], it follows that the passive diffusion field f_{dsp} for isothermal holes may be expressed as

$$f_{dsp} = - (kT/p) \, \nabla p. \tag{53}$$

In view of Eqs. (50), (51) and (53), W_{dsb} may be expressed in electron volts as

$$W_{dsb} = - \left(\frac{kT}{q}\right) \int_{p_e}^{p_n} \frac{\exp(-x/L_p)}{p} \, dp. \tag{54}$$

The upper limit of p_n is a good approximation, assuming that the length of the n region is several times the diffusion length L_p for holes.
Solving Eq. (22) for $\exp(-x/L_p)$, we get

$$\exp(-x/L_p) = [p(x) - p_n]/(p_e - p_n). \tag{55}$$

Substituting Eq. (55) into (54) and carrying out the integration, it follows that

$$W_{dsb} = (kT/q)r_p, \qquad r_p = 1 - [p_n/(p_e - p_n)] \ln(p_e/p_n). \tag{56}$$

The quantity W_{dsb} can be shown to be important at relatively low current densities and under reverse bias conditions.

4.5. *Work Done by the Passive Electrostatic Field in the Bulk Regions*

We shall assume that the length l_n of the n region is much longer than the diffusion length for minority holes L_p. For simplicity, we shall also assume that the length l_p of the p region is much longer than the diffusion length for minority electrons L_n. Accordingly in most of the bulk regions, there will be no net carrier recombination. Thus, a total current density, I/A will generate a passive electrostatic force field f_{esn} per electron in the n region, and f_{esp} per hole in the p region. From Eq. (41) [Chapter 6] and one similar to it for holes, these force fields may be expressed as

$$f_{esn} = -I/\mu_n n_n A, \qquad f_{esp} = I/\mu_p p_p A. \tag{57}$$

Since there is no net carrier recombination in most of the bulk regions, then in electron volts

$$W_{esb} \simeq q^{-1} \left[- \int_{0}^{l_n} f_{esn} \, dx + \int_{-l_p}^{0} f_{esp} \, dx \right]. \tag{58}$$

Substituting Eqs. (57) into (58), we get

$$W_{esb} \simeq IR_b, \qquad R_b = R_{bn} + R_{bp}, \qquad R_{bn} = l_n/A\sigma_n, \qquad R_{bp} = l_p/A\sigma_p,$$

$$\sigma_n = q\mu_n n_n, \qquad \sigma_p = q\mu_p p_p. \tag{59}$$

It will be recognized here that σ_n and σ_p are simply the bulk electrical conductivities in the n and p regions, respectively, at points sufficiently far from the junction. Therefore, R_{bn} and R_{bp} are simply the bulk ohmic resistances of the n and p regions, respectively.

4.6. *Work Done by the Majority-Electron Active Diffusion Field*

The condition of charge neutrality in the bulk requires that the concentration of majority carriers should increase from its thermal-equilibrium, uniform value of n_n to

$$n(x) = n_n + p(x) - p_n. \tag{60}$$

Thus, at any point in the n region, at an axial distance x from the junction, majority carriers have generally a concentration gradient given by

$$\partial n/\partial x = \partial p/\partial x, \tag{61}$$

which supports an electron diffusion field $\mathbf{f}_{dan}$. This field is an active one, since its main cause is the charge neutrality, rather than diffusion obeying Fick's law.

For simplicity, we shall assume that majority carriers are nondegenerate. Thus, from Eq. (23) [Chapter 6] and Eqs. (60), and (61), it follows that for isothermal electrons

$$\mathbf{f}_{dan} = -(kT/n)\,\partial n/\partial x \simeq -(kT/n_n)\,\partial p/\partial x. \tag{62}$$

The approximation that $n(x) \simeq n_n$, used in Eq. (62), follows from the assumption that $n_n \gg p_e$.

Since $[J_{dp}(x) + J_{rn}(x) = J]$, then in view of Eq. (51), we may express the density of electron recombination current $J_{rn}(x)$ by

$$J_{rn}(x) = J[1 - \exp(-x/L_p)]. \tag{63}$$

We shall next calculate the amount of work W_{dab} done on a composite carrier by $\mathbf{f}_{dan}$ as the carrier is transported through the entire bulk n region. In view of Eq. (27), W_{dab} in electron volts may be expressed as

$$W_{dab} = -q^{-1} \int_0^\infty \mathbf{f}_{dan}(J_{rn}/J)\,dx. \tag{64}$$

Using Eq. (22), the field f_{dan}, described by Eq. (62), can be expressed in terms of x. Substituting this result and Eq. (63) into Eq. (64), and carrying out a few steps, we get

$$W_{dab} = -(kT/2q)[(p_e - p_n)/n_n]. \tag{65}$$

Since $(p_e - p_n) \ll n_n$, then W_{dab} is a vanishingly small quantity, and should remain negligible, even if the majority carriers were degenerate. Thus, we shall neglect its contribution in the derivation of the V-I theoretical relationship to be presented in the next section.

5. THEORY OF FORWARD CONDUCTION

The purpose of this section is to derive a general expression for the forward voltage applied to a junction diode in terms of its current. To do so, it will be necessary to evaluate first the boundary values of the concentration of injected minority holes p_e.

5.1. *Boundary Values of the Concentration of Injected Minority Carriers*

It has been shown in the last section that the various components of work done on a composite carrier (transported through the diode crystal) by five of seven active and passive fields depend in varying degrees upon the concentration p_e. Evaluation of this quantity will be necessary to determine the voltage–current relationship for various diodes.

In order to evaluate p_e, consider a diode connected to a lossless battery of which the emf is V, as shown in Fig. 1. Let all the system be isothermal. According to Section 3, and Eqs. (24) and (25), if a positive composite carrier is transported around a closed loop enclosing the emf source and the battery, then the work done on the carrier by all the active force fields must equal that done by the passive force fields. For simplicity, let us assume here that the junction is a perfect hole emitter. In this case, neglecting W_{esj} and W_{dab}, we may simply write

$$V + \phi_c + \psi_c + W_{daj} + W_{eaj} - W_{dsb} - W_{esb} = 0. \tag{66}$$

Here, ϕ_c, ψ_c designate the work done on a composite carrier as the carrier is transported through the two nonrectifying contacts of the diode. Specifically, ϕ_c and ψ_c are associated with the active diffusion and electrostatic fields, respectively, in these metal-semiconductor interfaces.

In view of Eqs. (35), (36), (56), and (59), Eq. (66) may be written as

$$V + \phi_c + \psi_c + \phi_0 - (kT/q) \ln (p_e/p_n) - (\psi_0 + \delta\psi) - r_p(kT/q) - R_b I = 0. \tag{67}$$

If the contacts are ideally nonrectifying, a current through them cannot cause injection of carriers on either side of the ohmic junctions. Consequently, the distribution of the concentration of electrons and/or holes within the contacts will remain constant at thermal equilibrium and otherwise. Correspondingly ϕ_c and ψ_c remain always constant. At thermal equilibrium, however, $V = 0$, $I = 0$, and $p_e = p_n$. Furthermore, under such conditions, from Eqs. (44) and (56), it follows that $\delta\psi = 0$, and $r_p = 0$. Therefore, at thermal equilibrium, Eq. (67) reduces to

$$\phi_c + \psi_c + \phi_0 - \psi_0 = 0, \tag{68}$$

which expresses a relation between four purely active quantities.

Subtracting Eq. (68) from (67), and solving for p_e, we get

$$p_e = p_n \exp[(V - r_p V_T - \delta\psi - R_b I)/V_T], \qquad V_T = (kT/q). \tag{69}$$

5.2. *Voltage–Current Dependence*

We shall derive next a theoretical *V-I* relationship. To do so, consider Eq. (69), which when solved for *V*, gives

$$V = (kT/q)[\ln(p_e/p_n) + r_p] + \delta\psi + R_b I. \tag{70}$$

Solving Eq. (52) for p_e, we get

$$p_e = p_n(1+\alpha), \qquad \alpha = I/I^*, \qquad I^* = qD_p p_n A/L_p. \tag{71}$$

From Eqs. (56) and (71), we get

$$r_p = 1 - \alpha^{-1}\ln(1+\alpha). \tag{72}$$

Figs. 2 to 14. Theory and experiment are compared for twelve different *p–n* junctions, heterojunctions, and Schottky diodes, all of which are forward biased, and one additionally is reverse biased. All the theoretical characteristics are based on the conduction processes used by Shockley (1949), and either the classical thermodynamic framework (dashed lines), or that of the theory of generalized fields (solid lines). Dotted curves represent the present theory not accounting for the bulk ohmic resistance, R_b. Additional information is indicated under each figure separately, and in Section 7.

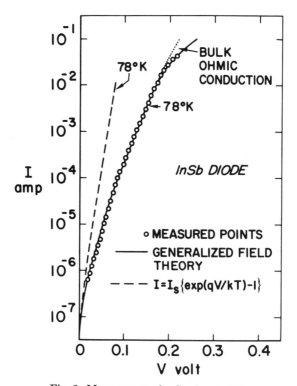

Fig. 2. Measurements by Stocker (1961).

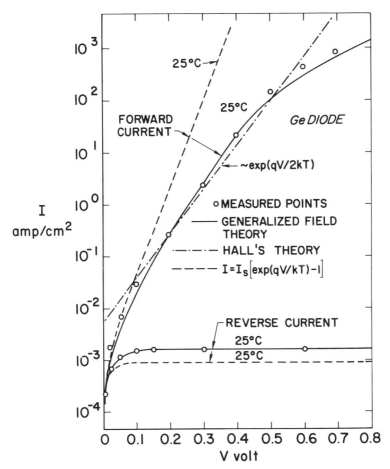

Fig. 3. Measurements conducted by Hall (1952). Hall's theory may also be found in the same reference. The slight excess of experimental currents over the (solid) theoretical curve for current densities greater than 100 amps/cm² is believed to be caused by heating of the sample above its initial value of 25°C. For a possible explanation of the small departure between theory and experiment at low forward current densities, see the subcaption of Fig. 9.

Thus, in view of Eqs. (70)–(72), the voltage V applied to a junction diode may be expressed by

$$V = \left(\frac{kT}{q}\right) \ln\left(1 + \frac{I}{I^*}\right) + \left(\frac{kT}{q}\right)\left[1 - \left(\frac{I^*}{I}\right)\ln\left(1 + \frac{I}{I^*}\right)\right] + \delta\psi + R_b I, \quad (73a)$$

where

$$\delta\psi = \delta\psi^*[\ln^{-2}(p_p/p_e) - \ln^{-2}(p_p/p_n)], \qquad \delta\psi^* = qp_p w^2/\kappa, \quad (73b)$$

$$p_e = p_n[1 + (I/I^*)], \qquad I^* = qD_p p_n A/L_p, \quad (73c)$$

and R_b is the diode bulk resistance. The preceding expressions for $\delta\psi$ and p_e are the same as those of Eqs. (44) and (71), respectively.

Equation (73a) represents a new V-I relationship for nontunneling p-n junctions, heterojunctions and Schottky diodes. The equation is based on the new concepts of the thermodynamic theory of generalized fields (TTGF). Specifically, the first voltage term in Eq. (73a) is due to the active diffusion field in the junction, the second is due to the passive diffusion field for minority carriers, the third is due to the active electrostatic field in the junction, and the fourth is due to the passive electrostatic field acting on the majority carriers in the two bulk regions. The latter voltage is merely what is known as the ohmic voltage drop. The voltage associated with the passive electrostatic field in the junction and the active diffusion field for majority carriers have been ignored in Eq. (73a).

Considering the same conduction processes and the classical thermodynamic framework, it has been shown by Shockley (1949) that for p-n

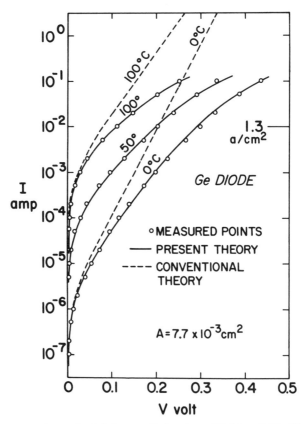

Fig. 4. Measurements conducted in our Laboratory (Melehy 1967). Diode made by General Electric Co. (type 1N 91).

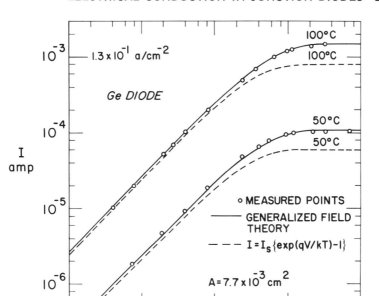

Fig. 5. Measurements conducted in our Laboratory (Melehy 1967). Diode made by General Electric Co. (type 1N 91).

junctions

$$I = I_s[\exp(qV/kT) - 1]. \tag{74}$$

Here I_s is generally known as the reverse saturation current.

Solving Eq. (74) for V, and accounting for the bulk ohmic resistance, we have

$$V = (kT/q) \ln[1 + (I/I_s)] + R_b I. \tag{75}$$

Comparing Eqs. (73a) and (75), one clearly observes that the TTGF has led to the same voltage (transport energy) terms as the classical thermodynamic framework, and, in addition, two other significant ones. The physical interpretations of the common logarithmic term, however, are different in the two theories. In Eq. (75) this term is thought of to be associated with an electrostatic process, whereas in the TTGF, it is associated with the active diffusion field.

6. CONDUCTION ZONES OF A JUNCTION DIODE

In this section we shall compare the magnitudes of different nonohmic voltage components appearing in the general diode equation at what are considered to be different injection levels, and near the reverse saturation.

Relevance of these results to experiment on various diodes will be discussed in Section 7. The voltage components to be compared in Eq. (73a) are:

$$V_1 = V_T \ln (1+\alpha), \tag{76}$$

$$V_2 = V_T[1 - (1/\alpha) \ln (1+\alpha)], \tag{77}$$

$$\delta\psi = \delta\psi^*[\ln^{-2} (p_p/p_e) - \ln^{-2} (p_p/p_n)]. \tag{78}$$

6.1. *Medium Injection Levels*

In view of Eqs. (71), the quantity $\ln^{-2} (p_p/p_e)$ in Eq. (78) may be written as

$$\ln^{-2} (p_p/p_e) = 1/\ln^2[p_p/p_n (1+\alpha)]$$

$$= \{\ln^{-2} (p_p/p_n)\}/\{1 - [\ln (1+\alpha)]/\ln (p_p/p_n)\}^2. \tag{79}$$

If, however,

$$2 \ln (1+\alpha) \ll \ln (p_p/p_n), \tag{80}$$

then the denominator of Eq. (79) will be approximately linear in $\ln (1+\alpha)$, and Eq. (79) may then be written as

$$\ln^{-2} (p_p/p_e) \simeq \{1 + 2[\ln (1+\alpha)]/\ln (p_p/p_n)\} \ln^{-2} (p_p/p_n). \tag{81}$$

From Eqs. (78) and (81), it follows that

$$\delta\psi \simeq 2\delta\psi^*[\ln^{-3} (p_p/p_n)][\ln (1+\alpha)], \tag{82}$$

provided that condition (80) is satisfied.

We may now define medium injection levels to be those levels for which $\alpha \gg 1$ and condition (80) is satisfied. At such levels $V_2 \simeq V_T$ and V_1 and $\delta\psi$ will both be proportional to $\ln \alpha$, that is $\ln (I/I^*)$. Thus, if the bulk ohmic voltage drop is negligible, V will be linearly dependent on $\ln I$.

At such injection levels, V_1 and $\delta\psi$ can be the more important components of voltage since V_2 attains a maximum value of V_T.

6.2. *Very-Low- and Low-Injection Levels*

Very-low-injection levels may be considered to correspond to

$$\alpha = (I/I^*) \ll 1. \tag{83}$$

When condition (83) is satisfied, then it can be shown that

$$V_1 \simeq \alpha V_T, \qquad V_2 \simeq (\alpha/2) V_T, \tag{84}$$

$$\delta\psi \simeq 2\alpha\delta\psi^* \ln^{-3} (p_p/p_n). \tag{85}$$

Equation (85) follows from Eq. (80), which is satisfied whenever Eq. (83) is satisfied.

Under such conditions V_1, V_2, and $\delta\psi$ can be all equally important and they are all linearly dependent on I.

Low injection levels may be defined to be those levels for which $\alpha \simeq 1$. Under such conditions the dependence of $\ln I$ on V is nonlinear and V increases faster than $\ln I$.

6.3. *High-Injection Levels*

High-injection levels may be defined to be those for which condition (80) is appreciably violated, that is

$$2 \ln (1+\alpha) \geq \ln (p_p/p_n). \tag{86}$$

Under such conditions, and even when $\alpha \gg 1$, $\delta\psi$ will be a nonlinear function of $\ln I$, and the former will more rapidly increase than the latter. Thus, $\delta\psi$ can be the more important component of voltage in this high-injection region.

6.4. *Reverse-Bias Conditions*

As the reverse saturation is approached, α tends to -1, and $\mid \ln (1+\alpha) \mid \gg 1$. Thus, from Eqs. (76) and (77), it follows that

$$V_2 \simeq V_T \ln (1+\alpha) = V_1. \tag{87}$$

Under such conditions, however, p_e tends rapidly to zero, and from Eq. (78) it follows that

$$\delta\psi \simeq -\delta\psi^* \ln^{-2} (p_p/p_n). \tag{88}$$

It is, therefore, apparent that V_1 and V_2 become equally important, whereas $\delta\psi$ for most cases becomes small compared to other terms.

Results just discussed are, of course, only applicable if the carrier generation is negligible in the junction.

7. COMPARISON OF THEORY AND EXPERIMENT

7.1. *The V-I Characteristic Curves*

Theoretical and experimental voltage-current (V-I) characteristics are compared in Figs. 2 to 14 for twelve different types of p-n junctions, heterojunctions and Schottky diodes. All the theoretical characteristics are based on Shockley's (1949) conduction mechanisms and either the classical thermodynamic framework (dashed lines), or that of the thermodynamic theory of generalized fields (solid lines).

The characteristics based on the classical theory are plotted, in almost all cases, at the highest and lowest temperatures used for the experiments. The fitting points are all at the lowest measured points, or extrapolations thereof. In all cases for which the fitting points lie at sufficiently small voltages the characteristics based on the classical theory and the TTGF provide accurate comparison between the two theories. More specifically, at any forward current, in such cases, the difference between the voltages predicted by the TTGF and classical theories represent the transport energy

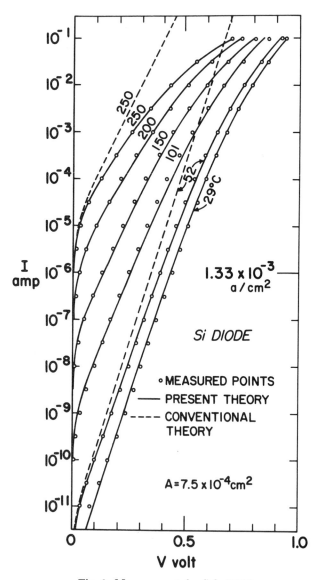

Fig. 6. Measurements by Sah (1962).

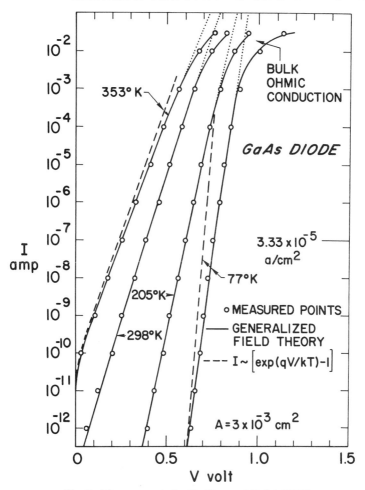

Fig. 7. Measurements by Rediker and Quist (1963).

quantities $(W_{dsb} + \delta\psi)$. Examples of such cases include the forward characteristics of the Ge and Si diodes at all temperatures studied as may be
observed in Figs. 4 and 6. In the other cases for which the classical theory
and experimental curves are fitted at relatively high voltages, the characteristics based on the TTGF and classical theory provide comparison for
only the slopes of these curves. Examples of such cases include all curves
measured at 77°K, and below that temperature.

For some samples, at sufficiently high currents, the voltage drop across
the bulk ohmic resistance R_b is appreciable. To show in the various figures
whether this ohmic (passive) voltage drop is significant, dotted curves have
been used to represent the TTGF not accounting for the (IR_b) voltage drop.

As an illustration, Table I contains a list of physical constants pertaining to the Ge and Si diodes whose V-I characteristics are shown in Figs. 4, 5, and 6. These constants have been used in making the calculations based on the thermodynamic theory of generalized fields. Sources from which some of the constants were obtained, and other details pertinent to calculating the theoretical curves of various diodes, may be found in two references (Melehy 1968, 1970b). Briefly, the two constants I^* and $\delta\psi^*$ are calculated from each experimental curve. The rest of the constants are found by other, well-known means. In the first reference, more experimental measurements are compared with the TTGF.

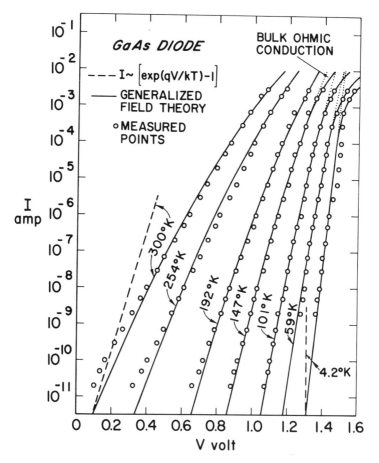

Fig. 8. Measurements conducted by Dumin and Pearson (1965). For a possible explanation of the slight excess of experimental currents over the theoretical curves, see the subcaption of Fig. 9.

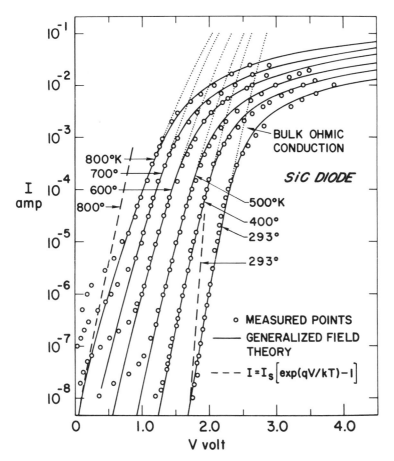

Fig. 9. Measurements by Violin and Kholuyanov (1964). It was pointed out by van Opdorp (1970) that the excess of experimental currents over the theoretical curves, observed in this figure for the SiC diode, was probably due to surface leakage. In the grown-silicon carbide diodes made at Philips Laboratories, Eindhoven, the Netherlands, this leakage current was also observed and was completely removed by electrolytic etching of the samples.

7.2. *The Various Regions of Injection Levels*

As may be clearly observed in many figures, the V-I characteristics involve large portions of what have been defined in Subsection 6.1, as the medium-injection regions. Such regions are those in which V is a linear function of $\ln I$. The medium-injection region occurs for a diode whenever $I \gg I^*$ and $\ln(p_p/p_n) \gg 2 \ln(I/I^*)$. But p_n decreases for wider-gap semiconductors, with higher doping levels and at lower temperatures. Likewise, the medium-injection range expands for wider-gap semiconductors, with higher doping levels and at lower temperatures. Such behavior can be seen in many figures, including Figs. 4, 6, 7, and 8.

The very-low-injection region is characterized [Subsection 6.2] for a diode by: $I \ll I^*$, whereas the low-injection region is defined to be that for which $I \simeq I^*$. In such regions, the forward diode voltage is relatively small—of the order of V_T. These regions disappear—as I becomes immeasurably small—if I^*, that is, p_n is sufficiently small. Thus, the disappearance of the very-low- and low-injection regions takes place for wider-gap materials, with higher doping levels, and at lower temperatures. Examples include the characteristics shown in Figs. 7, 8, 9, and 10.

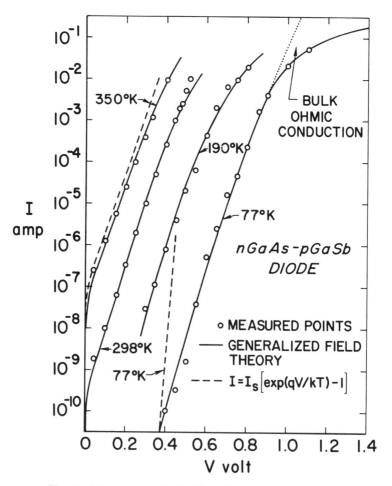

Fig. 10. Measurements by Rediker, Stopek, and Ward (1964).

TABLE I

Physical constants used for calculating, on the basis of the thermodynamic theory of generalized fields, the V-I characteristics of the Ge diodes (Figs. 4 and 5) and Si diode (Fig. 6). The quantity $V_T = kT/q = 28$ mV, at $T = 325°$K.

$T(°C)$	p_n (cm^{-3})	n_p (cm^{-3})	I^*(A) or (A/cm^2)	$\delta\psi^*$(V)	R_B (ohm)
	Alloyed Ge p-n junction of Figs. 4 and 5 (Melehy 1967). $p_p = 5 \times 10^{18}$ cm^{-3}, n_n (28°C) $= 9.13 \times 10^{13}$ cm^{-3}.				
0	2.74×10^{11}	ins	3.00×10^{-6} A	7.68	ins
50	3.79×10^{13}	ins	1.10×10^{-4}	3.93	ins
100	5.55×10^{14}	ins	1.50×10^{-3}	2.90	ins
	Alloyed Si p-n junction of Fig. 6 (Sah 1962). $p_p = 3.75 \times 10^{20}$ cm^{-3} †, n_n (28°C) $= 8.00 \times 10^{14}$ cm^{-3}.				
29	2.18×10^5	ins	7.50×10^{-13} A	2.350×10^1	ins
52	6.72×10^6	ins	8.00×10^{-12}	1.750×10^1	ins
101	3.12×10^9	ins	1.80×10^{-9}	1.500×10^1	ins
150	5.00×10^{11}	ins	8.00×10^{-8}	1.100×10^1	ins
200	1.83×10^{13}	ins	2.00×10^{-6}	1.040×10^1	ins
250	5.00×10^{14}	ins	2.10×10^{-5}	8.16	ins

ins—Too small to be significant.

† Value of doping level not stated in the reference, thus determined by searching for the best fit.

The high-injection regions are those in which the nonohmic portion of V is a nonlinear function of $\ln I$. These regions set in at lower values of (I/I^*) when the diodes have also lower values of $\ln(p_p/p_n)$, such as may be noticed for Ge Fig. 4, at 0°C and more so above that temperature. Also, depending on the doping levels, in Si diodes (Fig. 6), the high-injection region occurs at 300°K and increasingly so at higher temperatures. Generally, this region expands for diodes with narrower-gap semiconductors, with weaker doping levels and at higher temperatures. Examples in which this region can be seen include Figs. 3, 4, and 6.

8. DISCUSSION

8.1. *Newly Introduced Quantities of Transport Energy*

In analyzing the problem of electrical conduction in p-n junctions, Shockley (1949) has assumed that, upon forward biasing, minority carriers would be injected through the junction. Subsequently they would progressively diffuse and recombine in the bulk. Shockley's derived V-I relationship is equivalent to Eq. (75), which involves only one nonohmic voltage term. Since, by definition, voltage represents the work done per unit charge, Eq. (75) essentially involves *only* one nonohmic (transport) energy term despite the fact that in Shockley's analysis three fundamental nonohmic transport processes were considered: the diffusion and drift processes in the junction and the diffusion of minority carriers in the bulk. The reason why only one energy term was obtained, rather than three, lies in the fact that classically diffusion seems to be considered to be a flux but not associated with a force field of its own which leads to transport work.

In the TTGF, a concentration gradient, even under isothermal conditions,

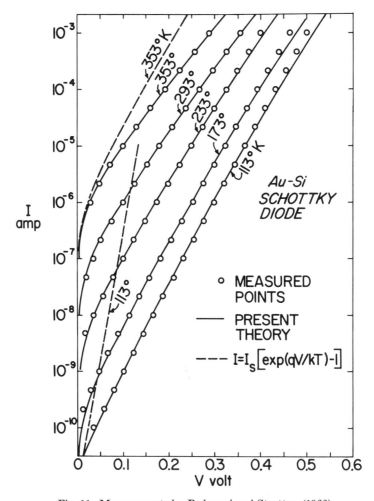

Fig. 11. Measurements by Padovani and Stratton (1966).

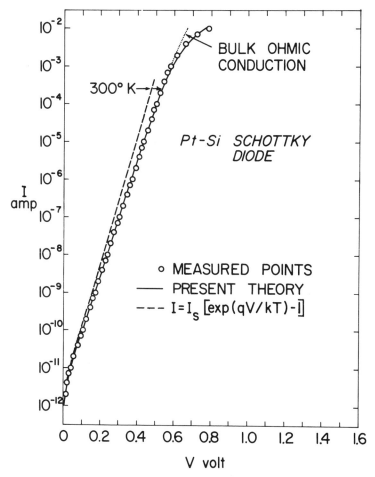

Fig. 12. Measurements by Lepselter and Sze (1968).

is generally associated with a diffusion field, which is an independent physical quantity much like the gravitational or the electrostatic field. Thus, it leads to transport energy over and above what other fields contribute.

8.2. *Mechanism of Detailed Self-Balancing*

According to Eq. (73a), the voltage applied to a junction diode essentially supports a current through five significant transport processes, contributing to four transport energy terms. Two other small transport energy terms have been neglected. In the limit as thermal equilibrium is infinitesimally approached, each one of the seven transport energy terms is the closed-loop line integral of an identifiable active or passive force field.

According to the present thermodynamic theory, at thermal equilibrium, each identifiable passive field vanishes individually, and generally each identifiable active field is stationary and conservative. Thus, each identifiable transport energy term must individually vanish at thermal equilibrium. This statement can now be verified by considering each one of the voltage terms in Eq. (73a), and allowing that $\alpha = (I/I^*) = 0$, and by considering Eqs. (47), (59), and (65). For the latter, notice that from Eq. (71), at thermal equilibrium, $p_e = p_n$. Notice also that, in Eq. (59), IR_b consists of two identifiable components: IR_{bn} (pertaining to electrons) and IR_{bp} (pertaining to holes), each of which must vanish individually at thermal equilibrium.

Therefore, the conduction theory presented in this chapter verifies Proposition I stated in Chapter 6. Furthermore, this theory provides an interesting means for checking some important consequences of the thermo-

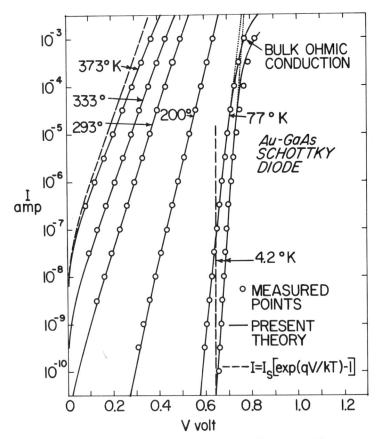

Fig. 13. Measurements by Padovani and Sumner (1965).

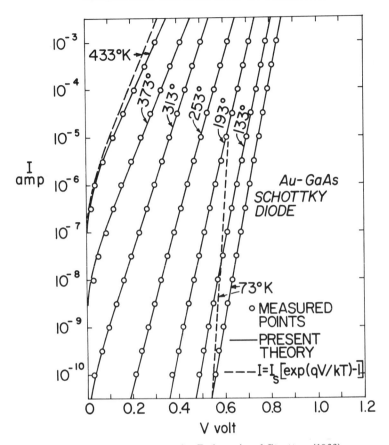

Fig. 14. Measurements by Padovani and Stratton (1966).

dynamic theory of generalized fields directly by experiment under extremely different conditions.

PROBLEMS

1. A homogeneous, highly extrinsic $(n_n \gg p_n)$ n-type crystal is exposed to uniform steady light. After the steady-state has been reached, the concentration of holes attained a new equilibrium p_0. At an instant $t = t_0 = 0$, the light was suddenly removed. Assuming that the minority-carrier lifetime is constant, and there is no concentration gradient, derive an expression for p as a function of time t.

2. At a time $t = 0$, there is a distribution of holes injected in the n region of a p-n junction. At the boundary, for which $x = 0$, this initial concentration of holes per unit area is N_p.

(a) Show that neglecting the drift, and during periods much shorter than the minority-carrier lifetime, the concentration of holes p is given by

$$p(x, t) = (A/t^{1/2}) \exp[-(\alpha x^2/t)],$$

where A and α are arbitrary constants.

(b) Evaluate the constants α and A in terms of D_p and N_p. [Ans. $\alpha = (4D_p)^{-1}$, $A = N_p(\pi D_p)^{-1/2}$.]

3. Show that if the current of a junction diode starts with a large forward value and continues to decrease linearly in time, then the most general (steady-state) solution of continuity equation for minority holes will be given by

$$p(x, t) = p_n + a_p[x - 2(D_p/L_p)(t-t_p)] \exp(-x/L_p),$$

where a_p and t_p are arbitrary constants, x is the distance between any point in the n region and the junction, and t is time.

Hint. Reason that the most general solution for p must be of the form: $p(x, t) = f(x) + g(x)t + C$, where $f(x)$ and $g(x)$ are functions of x only, and C is a constant. Substituting $p(x, t)$, as expressed above, into the continuity equation, makes it possible to extract two ordinary differential equations, which can be solved to determine $g(x)$ and $f(x)$. For a detailed solution, see Melehy and Shockley (1961).

4. Derive Eq. (43) by solving Eq. (39).

5. Show that Eq. (43) reduces to Eq. (44), if $p_p \gg p_n$ and $p_p \gg p_e$.

6. From Eqs. (50), (51), and (53), derive Eq. (54). Show, then, that from the latter, Eqs. (56) follow.

7. Going through the detailed steps, verify that Eqs. (59) follow from Eq. (58).

8. On the basis of Eqs. (70)–(72), derive Eq. (73a).

9. Show that if the midinjection range of a junction diode is extrapolated in the $(\ln I)$-V plane, it will pass through the point whose coordinates are $(V_T, \ln I^*)$.

REFERENCES

Anderson, R. L. 1962, Solid-State Electronics **5**, 341.
Bardeen, J. 1947, Phys. Rev. **71**, 717.
Bardeen, J. and Brattain, W. H. 1949, Phys. Rev. **75**, 1208.
Donnelly, J. P. and Milnes, A. G. 1966, Proc. IEE **113**, 1468.
Dumin, D. J. and Pearson, G. L. 1965, J. Appl. Phys. **36**, 3418.
Hall, R. N. 1952, Proc. IRE **40**, 1512.
Kahng, D. 1963, Solid-State Electronics **6**, 281.

Kroemer, H. 1957, Proc. IRE **45**, 1535.

Lepselter, M. P. and Sze, S. M. 1968, Bell System Tech. J. **47**, 195.

Macdonald, J. R. 1962, Solid-State Electronics **5**, 11.

Melehy, M. A. and Shockley, W. 1961, IRE Trans. Electron Dev., ED-8, pp. 135–139.

Melehy, M. A. 1967, Proc. National Electronics Conf. **23**, pp. 347–352.

—— 1968, Intern. J. Electronics **24**, pp. 41–68.

—— 1969, Bull. Am. Phys. Soc. **14**, 317.

—— 1970a, Proceedings of the Pittsburgh, Pennsylvania, 1969 International Symposium on, "A Critical Review of Thermodynamics," pp. 377–405; edited by E. B. Stuart, Benjamin Gal-Or, and A. J. Brainard, Mono Book Corp., Baltimore.

—— 1970b, Intern. J. Electronics **29**, pp. 525–532.

—— 1971, Proceedings of the Budapest, Hungary, 1970 International Conference on the Physics and Chemistry of Semiconductor Heterojunctions and Layer Structures, vol. **1**, pp. 297–307, Akadémiai Kiadó, Budapest.

van Opdorp, C. 1970, A comment on Fig. 9 [which appeared also in Melehy (1971)], submitted for publication in the Proceedings of the Budapest, Hungary, 1970 International Conference on the Physics and Chemistry of Semiconductor Heterojunctions and Layer Structures, but was inadvertently omitted.

Padovani, F. A. and Stratton, R. 1966, Solid-State Electronics **9**, 695.

Padovani, F. A. and Sumner, G. G. 1965, J. Appl. Phys. **36**, 3744.

Perlman, S. S. and Feucht, D. L. 1964, Solid-State Electronics **7**, 911.

Rediker, R. H. and Quist, T. M. 1963, Solid-State Electronics **6**, 657.

Rediker, R. H., Stopek, S. and Ward, J. H. R. 1964, Solid-State Electronics **7**, 621.

Riben, A. R. and Feucht, D. L. 1966, Intern. J. Electronics **20**, 583.

Sah, C. T. 1962, IRE Trans. Elec. Dev. ED-**9**, 94.

Schottky, W. 1938, Naturwissenschaften **26**, 843.

—— 1939, Phys. Z. **113**, 367.

Shockley, W. 1949, Bell System Tech. J. **28**, 435.

—— 1950, Electrons and Holes in Semiconductors, D. Van Nostrand; p. 295.

Simpson, J. H. and Armstrong, H. L. 1953, J. Appl. Phys. **24**, 25.

Stocker, H. J. 1961, J. Appl. Phys. **32**, 322.

Stratton, R. 1962, Phys. Rev. **125**, 67.

Violin, E. E. and Kholuyanov, G. F. 1964, Fizika Tverd. Tela **6**, 593; English translation 1964, Soviet Phys.—Solid State **6**, 465.

Chapter 8

CONSERVATION OF TRANSPORT ENERGY IN THE TEMPERATURE-POSITION HYPERSPACE

1. INTRODUCTION

In Chapters 4, 6, and 7, we have seen how precise a distinction can be made between active and passive force fields in a thermodynamic system. We have further seen that, sufficiently close to thermal equilibrium, passive force fields and particle flux densities are linearly related as prescribed by Proposition III. This proposition has been shown to lead to Ohm's, Fick's and Stokes's *dissipative* laws. Proposition III, however, is totally inapplicable to active fields. Consequently, Ohm's, Fick's, Stokes's and other dissipative laws cannot possibly be applied to active processes. Therefore, at any point a in a system, the particle flux densities cannot be determined from active force fields alone at point a. This *indeterminateness*, inherently associated with active fields, manifests itself, for example, in the simple case of a lossless battery (source of a purely active process) connected to a *black box*, containing an unknown electric network. Obviously, in this case the battery current I_B (electron flux) cannot be predicted from the battery (active) voltage alone, since complete information must additionally be known about what is in the black box before I_B can be determined. It is this indeterminateness associated with active voltages (emfs) in circuit theory that made it necessary, and provided the opportunity, for the use of Kirchhoff's voltage law, in addition to Ohm's law. Kirchhoff's voltage law, however, is but an expression of the conservation of transport energy around every closed loop in the network. Broadly speaking, these loops pertain to the *real* (three-dimensional position) *space*. It is the collective use of Ohm's law and Kirchhoff's law that, for solenoidal current densities, have brought about complete determinateness in solving the problems of circuit theory.

Correspondingly, in the framework of the Thermodynamic Theory of Generalized Fields (TTGF), it is the distinction between active and passive fields that has created the necessity, and provided the opportunity, for the use of Proposition V. This proposition has prescribed that active and passive fields shall interact in such a way as to conserve the transport energy around every closed loop in the real space occupied by a system. Subsequently, we have seen that in the framework of the TTGF, Proposition V crucially leads to the conclusion that: for *all* thermodynamic systems, the state of thermal equilibrium is uniquely characterized by the newly-formulated mechanism of detailed *self*-balancing, discussed at length in Chapters 4, 6, and 7.

By analogy with circuit theory, one may raise the fundamental question as to whether Proposition III (passive field-flux relationship) and Proposition V (conservation of energy in the real space) have completely removed all indeterminateness in thermodynamic systems, as they have in the special case of circuit theory? This question can be answered, at least in part, by a careful consideration of the mechanism of detailed *self*-balancing. This mechanism specifies that at thermal equilibrium, each identifiable force field pertaining to each constituent balances itself. Thus, to an observer, *only conscious* of the real space, it will seem that each identifiable force field and particle flux is entirely decoupled from all other force fields and fluxes at thermal equilibrium. Since nature cannot be so chaotic as to allow this total decoupling of all force fields and fluxes at thermal equilibrium, it is then an obvious matter that the real space cannot possibly be the most general space in which all processes and their associated fields interact. Rather, there should exist some hyperspace of which the real space is a part. In that hyperspace, all force fields in a system would remain completely coupled, *even* at thermal equilibrium. Such a hyperspace should, therefore, remove any indeterminateness hitherto unremoved by considerations of the real space.

In this chapter, we shall show that this hyperspace consists of the real space and a fourth independent axis of temperature. On the basis that the net transport energy is conserved around every closed loop in this *temperature-position hyperspace*, we shall derive what is to be called the *hyperspace (conservation of energy) equation*. Boundary conditions for the hyperspace equation will be determined at the absolute zero from fundamental thermodynamic properties satisfied generally at that temperature. A number of fundamental consequences of the new generalized hyperspace equation and its boundary conditions will be discussed in this and the two chapters to follow.

2. VARIATION OF THE TRANSPORT ENERGY FUNCTION ON THE TEMPERATURE AXIS

In Chapter 4, the concept of intrinsic or thermodynamic transport energy function ν has been defined. It has been pointed out that ν would not account for electric, magnetic, and gravitational effects, if any are present in a system. It has further been shown that if particles are transported and, in so doing, experience changes dT and dP in their temperature and internal pressure, respectively, then these changes involve imparting an amount of (transport) energy $d\nu$ per particle given by

$$d\nu = s \, dT - (1/n) \, dP. \tag{1}$$

Here, s and n are the entropy per particle and particle concentration, respectively.

The changes dT and dP can, of course, be achieved in two fundamentally different ways. The first, and more obvious way, would be to let the particles be transported a distance dl in a nonisothermal system involving a concentration gradient. This procedure has led to the fundamental concepts of diffusion and thermomotive fields, discussed in general in Chapters 4 and 6. The diffusion field has further been extensively treated in Chapter 7.

Another feasible and equally important way for changing infinitesimally T and P would be by letting the (statistical) particle remain stationary in the real space, but the temperature in the appropriately small volume V surrounding it is made to change by an amount $d\tilde{T}$. In this way we shall say that the particle has been *displaced* or *transported* on the one-dimensional temperature axis. The temperature change can, of course, be done by some external heat source. Consequently, a change in P within V will occur.

For particles displaced $d\tilde{T}$ on the temperature axis, but not in the real space, Eq. (1) may be rewritten as

$$dv = [s - (1/n)(dP/dT)_{x,y,z}] d\tilde{T}. \tag{2}$$

In a nonisothermal system, the temperature is, of course, generally dependent on position. Therefore, we may represent T functionally by

$$T = T(x, y, z, \tau), \tag{3}$$

where τ is a parameter independent of the position coordinates x, y, z.

It is possible then to write

$$d\tilde{T} = (\partial T/\partial \tau)_{x,y,z} d\tau. \tag{4}$$

The differential $d\tilde{T}$ is an infinitesimal increment along an independent temperature axis. This axis together with the three coordinates of the real space constitute the temperature-position hyperspace to be referred to briefly as the *thermodynamic hyperspace*, or simply the *hyperspace*.

3. INTERACTION OF ACTIVE AND PASSIVE FIELDS IN THE THERMODYNAMIC HYPERSPACE

3.1. *Formulation of Proposition VI*

In order to properly determine how the transport energy is conserved around every closed loop in the thermodynamic hyperspace, consider the following example.

Figure 1 represents any one-constituent system in which the particle flux density is solenoidal. Let a and b be any two points in the system. Let

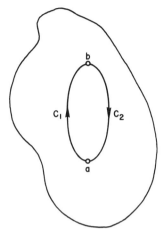

Fig. 1.

C_1 and C_2 be two different paths (in the real space) between points a and b. Suppose that the initial temperature throughout the system is T_1 which, for simplicity, is uniform. We shall next describe four different steps involving the transport around a closed loop in the hyperspace of a small number of particles. Each one of these steps requires transferring to the system a certain amount of heat from an external source in order to maintain the assumed conditions satisfied.

Imagine that, first, the N particles are transported on C_1 from a to b, while the temperature everywhere is kept at its initial value of T_1; second, the temperature of the system, including the N particles, is raised from T_1 to T_2; third, the N particles are transported from point b to a on C_2, while the system temperature is kept equal to T_2; and fourth, the temperature of the entire system is brought back to the initial value of T_1. Going through the four steps just described, the N particles have actually swept a closed loop in the thermodynamic hyperspace.

If we now assume that all the four transport steps have occurred quasi-statically (all passive fields are vanishingly small), it is an obvious matter that the net amount of heat added to the system in order that the N particles would be transported around a hyperspatial closed loop must be zero. It is also obvious that our conclusion would still be valid, even if we have instead of four abrupt steps a number, as large as we please, of infinitesimally small steps. In the latter case, the hyperspatial closed loop can be a smooth curve.

If the transported particles attain local thermodynamic equilibrium at all points as they sweep the hyperspatial loop, we may consider that the generalized work done on a (statistical) particle, transported through any region (hosting the intrinsic force fields) is equal to the decrease in the internal energy of the nontransported particles in that region. This conclusion can be further extended to nonisothermal systems and those systems containing dissipation, that is, passive fields. Generally, the temperature in the system is varied such that

$$T(x, y, z, \tau) = [T_0(x, y, z) + \tau] u(T_0 + \tau), \tag{5}$$

and
$$
\left.
\begin{aligned}
u(T_0 + \tau) &= 1, \quad \text{for } (T_0 + \tau) \geq 0, \\
u(T_0 + \tau) &= 0, \quad \text{for } (T_0 + \tau) < 0.
\end{aligned}
\right\} \tag{6}
$$

Here τ is an independent parameter which represents a displacement along the one-dimensional temperature space for the entire system.

Equations (5) and (6) actually *define* the *restrictive* manner in which the temperature at various points in a system can be made to depart from an initial nonuniform temperature distribution $T_0(x, y, z)$ so that closed loops in the thermodynamic hyperspace can be generated. A simple representation of Eqs. (5) and (6) is shown in Fig. 2 for a system having only one real-space axis.

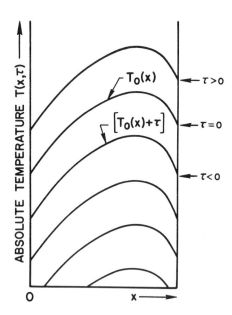

Fig. 2. Temperature profile $T(x, \tau) = [T_0(x) + \tau] u(T_0 + \tau)$ at various values of the independent temperature parameter τ for a one-dimensional system in the real space. For this nonisothermal system, the family of curves represents the manner in which the two-dimensional thermodynamic space is generated.

In view of the preceding discussions, we may state the following:

Proposition VI. In a nonisothermal multicomponent system, containing no other than solenoidal particle fluxes, if we imagine a hypothetical statistical particle of a specific constituent j transported around any closed loop ξ in the thermodynamic hyperspace, then under steady-state conditions the generalized work (transport energy) done around ξ by all the active processes must equal that done by all the passive processes. These processes may generally include intrinsic and extrinsic force fields pertaining to constituent j.

The condition of solenoidal particle fluxes should be maintained, even when the independent temperature axis $\tilde{T}$ of the hyperspace is being swept.

3.2. *The Hyperspace Conservation of Energy Equation*

The purpose in this subsection is to determine the mathematical consequences of Proposition VI. To do so, consider in a nonisothermal system any two points $A\,(x_0,\,y_0,\,z_0)$ and $B\,(x_0+\Delta x,\,y_0+\Delta y,\,z_0+\Delta z)$ which are arbitrarily close to each other and lie on an arbitrary path C in the real space. Let the temperature at points A and B be T_0 and $(T_0+\Delta T)$, respectively. Let l_0 and $(l_0+\Delta l)$ be lengths measured on C from a reference point also on C, to the points A and B, respectively. For this system let us introduce the parameter τ pertaining to the independent temperature axis $\tilde{T}$. Consider then the arbitrarily small hyperspatial closed loop formed by the small changes Δl, in length, and $\delta \tilde{T}$, in temperature. If we plot Δl parallel to the plane of the paper, we can then represent simply, yet generally, this small hyperspatial closed loop, as shown in Fig. 3.

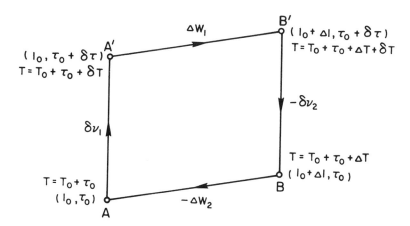

Fig. 3. Two-dimensional representation of an arbitrarily small hyperspatial closed loop.

When we now say that a hypothetical particle is transported clockwise around the closed loop, as represented in Fig. 3, the following is actually meant: First, the particle begins at any point in the real space, such as A, whose hyperspace coordinates are x_0, y_0, z_0, τ_0. While the particle is fixed in position, the initial temperature distribution $T(x_0, y_0, z_0, \tau_0)$ of the system is increased to an arbitrarily close value $T(x_0, y_0, z_0, \tau_0 + \delta\tau)$. Correspondingly, the particle, whose initial temperature is $(T_0 + \tau_0)$, moves on to another hyperspace point A' whose temperature is $(T_0 + \tau_0 + \delta\tilde{T})$. Second, the particle is then transported in the hyperspace from A' to B', that is, it is moved in the real space from A to B. The temperature at B' is $(T_0 + \tau_0 + \Delta T + \delta\tilde{T})$ and the hyperspace coordinates of that point are: $x_0 + \Delta x$, $y_0 + \Delta y$, $z_0 + \Delta z$, $\tau_0 + \delta\tau$. Third, the temperature distribution of the system is brought down from $T(x_0 + \Delta x, y_0 + \Delta y, z_0 + \Delta z, \tau_0 + \delta\tau)$ to $T(x_0 + \Delta x, y_0 + \Delta y, z_0 + \Delta z, \tau_0)$, and the particle, while fixed in the real space, is moved from B' to B. Correspondingly, the particle temperature drops from $(T_0 + \tau_0 + \Delta T + \delta\tilde{T})$ to $(T_0 + \tau_0 + \Delta T)$. Finally, the particle is moved from B to A with its temperature changed from $(T_0 + \tau_0 + \Delta T)$ to $(T_0 + \tau_0)$. The hyperspace closed loop is, therefore, completely swept.

We shall calculate next various components of the generalized transport work done on a particle sweeping the four segments of the hyperspatial closed loop, as represented in Fig. 3. In view of Eq. (2), the quantities of transport work $(\delta\nu_1)$ and $(-\delta\nu_2)$, corresponding to the segments AA' and $B'B$, respectively, will be given by

$$\delta\nu_1 \simeq \delta\tilde{T}[s - (1/n)(dP/d\tilde{T})]_{l_0, \tau_0}, \tag{7}$$

$$\delta\nu_2 \simeq \delta\tilde{T}[s - (1/n)(dP/d\tilde{T})]_{l_0 + \Delta l, \tau_0}$$
$$= \delta\tilde{T}\{[s - (1/n)(dP/d\tilde{T})] + \nabla[s - (1/n)(dP/d\tilde{T})] \cdot \Delta l\}_{l_0, \tau_0} + \cdots, \tag{8}$$

where $(d/d\tilde{T})$ signifies that a derivative is evaluated while holding the position coordinates x, y, z fixed. In Eq. (8), the terms left out of the Taylor's series expansion are of higher order than significant.

From Eq. (5), we may write

$$d/d\tilde{T} = (d/dT)_{x,y,z} = \partial/\partial\tau. \tag{9}$$

In view of Eqs. (4) and (5), the small increment $\delta\tilde{T}$ appearing in Eqs. (7) and (8), will simply be

$$\delta\tilde{T} = \delta\tau. \tag{10}$$

The components of generalized work ΔW_1 and $(-\Delta W_2)$ done on a particle transported on the segments $A'B'$ and BA, respectively, will be given by

$$\Delta W_1 \simeq \Delta l \cdot (f_{ta} - f_{ts})_{l_0, \tau_0 + \delta\tau}$$
$$= \Delta l \cdot \{(f_{ta} - f_{ts}) + [\partial(f_{ta} - f_{ts})/\partial\tau]\delta\tau\}_{l_0, \tau_0} + \cdots, \tag{11}$$

$$\Delta W_2 \simeq \Delta l \cdot (f_{ta} - f_{ts})_{l_0, \tau_0}, \tag{12}$$

where $\mathbf{f}_{ta}$ and $\mathbf{f}_{ts}$ designate the resultant of all active and passive force fields, respectively, at any point in the system. In Eq. (11), the quantities left out of the Taylor's series expansion give rise to terms of higher order than significant.

According to Proposition VI,

$$\delta\nu_1 - \delta\nu_2 + \Delta W_1 - \Delta W_2 = 0. \tag{13}$$

From Eqs. (7), (8), and (10)–(13), it follows that in the limit as Δl and $\delta\tau$ both tend to zero, we get for constituent j, in a multicomponent system,

$$d(\mathbf{f}_{taj} - \mathbf{f}_{tsj})/d\tilde{T} = \nabla[s_j - (1/n_j)(dP/d\tilde{T})]. \tag{14}$$

We shall call Eq. (14) the *hyperspace conservation of energy equation* or, simply, the *hyperspace equation*.

It is interesting to observe that the extrinsic force field, associated with a static gravitational field, has no dependence on temperature. Hence, it completely drops out of the hyperspace equation.

Equation (14) was first derived in 1969. The result was stated without proof (Melehy 1970) for systems at thermal equilibrium. In its present form, the hyperspace equation has been cited (Melehy 1971), again without derivation, in connection with the theory of p–n junctions in semiconductor and metal–semiconductor interfaces.

In general, the scalar function on the right-hand side of Eq. (14) can have a rather complicated functional dependence on parameters that depend on position. It may, therefore, be useful to state explicitly the meaning of the gradient in such cases. Suppose, for example, that this scalar function is Θ and that

$$\Theta = \Theta(\zeta, T), \quad \zeta = \zeta(x, y, z, T), \quad T = T(x, y, z, \tau). \tag{15}$$

As shown in Chapter 2,

$$\nabla\Theta = (\partial\Theta/\partial\zeta)_T[(\nabla\zeta)_T + (\partial\zeta/\partial T)_{x,y,z}(\nabla T)] + (\partial\Theta/\partial T)_\zeta \nabla T, \tag{16}$$

where $(\nabla\zeta)_T$ represents the gradient of ζ holding T constant, and the parameter τ is, of course, held constant for all the preceding *del* operations.

For degenerate gases, the quantity ζ corresponds to the Fermi or Bose energies, depending on whether the system consists of fermions or bosons, respectively.

4. HYPERSPACE BOUNDARY CONDITIONS

It may be expected that solving the hyperspace equation would in some cases involve integration on the independent temperature axis $\tilde{T}$ of the thermodynamic hyperspace. This step leads to an arbitrary function of position. Evaluation of such a function requires specifying values of the active and passive force fields in the system at any one temperature. In this section, we shall determine these *hyperspace boundary conditions* at the absolute zero.

It is well known that at the absolute zero, the specific heat vanishes for any system. Examples include solids, as follows from Einstein's and Debye's theories* (Einstein 1906, 1911; Debye 1912) and ideal boson and fermion gases.* We may, therefore, state that for any system generally

$$\lim_{T \to 0} c = 0. \tag{17}$$

Here c is the specific heat per unit volume. Equation (17) may be said to be more broadly a consequence of the third law of thermodynamics (Nernst 1912).

The absolute zero is further characterized by other thermodynamic properties of which we consider one expressed by the following premise.

Proposition VII. There exist no transport processes (of finite intensities) which can produce in a system an infinite time rate of change of temperature, even at the absolute zero.

4.1. *Systems With No Active Fields*

Consider a multicomponent system which contains any number of passive fields, but no intrinsic active ones. Let the system be in a state of non-equilibrium so that the flux density $\mathfrak{g}_{ij}$, associated with process i and constituent j, is nonvanishing. According to Eqs. (33) and (34) of Chapter 6, at any point in a system, the time rate of evolution of heat $(\partial Q_{isj}/\partial t)$ per unit volume associated with a passive force field $\mathbf{f}_{isj}$, pertaining to a process i and a constituent j, is given by

$$\partial Q_{isj}/\partial t = \mathbf{f}_{isj} \cdot \mathfrak{g}_{ij} = (n_j/A_j)f_{isj}{}^2. \tag{18}$$

Here t signifies time, n_j is the concentration of particles of constituent j, and A_j is a finite phenomenological coefficient pertaining to constituent j.

The law of conservation of energy requires that

$$c \, (\partial T/\partial t) = \sum_{i=1, j=1}^{N_i, N_j} (\partial Q_{isj}/\partial t) = \sum_{i=1, j=1}^{N_i, N_j} \mathbf{f}_{isj} \cdot \mathfrak{g}_{ij}, \tag{19}$$

where N_i and N_j are the number of processes and constituents, respectively.

---

* Einstein's and Debye's theories of specific heat for solids may be found in a number of references, including Seitz (1940), p. 103. The specific heat for ideal bosons and fermions, not accounting for the change in concentration due to thermal expansivity α_T, may be found in ter Haar (1966), pp. 126 and 133. Accounting for α_T in pertinent cases, such as for conduction electrons in metals, will make the specific heat, c, approach zero even faster as T tends to $0°$K.

In view of Eqs. (17), (18), and (19) and Proposition VII, we have

$$\lim_{T \to 0} \sum_{i=1, j=1}^{N_i, N_j} \mathbf{f}_{isj} \cdot \mathcal{J}_{ij} = \lim_{T \to 0} \sum_{i=1, j=1}^{N_i, N_j} (n_j/A_j) f_{isj}^2 = 0. \tag{20}$$

It is evident that, for all values of i and j, every one of the terms summed is nonnegative. Since n_j and A_j are all positive quantities, then from Eq. (20), it follows that

$$\lim_{T \to 0} \mathbf{f}_{isj} = 0, \quad \text{for all } i\text{'s and } j\text{'s.} \tag{21}$$

Thus, for any multicomponent system, in the limit as the temperature of the system hypothetically approaches the absolute zero, each distinguishable passive field, pertaining to each constituent, vanishes individually.

The preceding result, applied, for example, to electrons in solid crystals, implies the following: at the absolute zero, uniform crystals would be either perfect electrical insulators, or perfect conductors; but nothing in between. Further discussions of these interesting results and their relevance to the phenomena of superconductivity and superfluidity will be done in Chapter 10.

4.2. Systems Containing Active Fields

In the previous subsection, it has been reasoned why passive fields would vanish individually at the absolute zero in any system containing no intrinsic active fields. In this subsection, we shall arrive at the conclusion that the existence of intrinsic active fields in a system would not alter, for passive fields, these thermodynamic-hyperspace boundary conditions. Furthermore, we shall show that at the absolute zero, the total active field pertaining to each constituent in a multicomponent system must vanish.

At the absolute zero, even if the particles under consideration are gaseous, each particle flux density must be solenoidal. For, generally no generation of constituents, or recombination between them is possible at the absolute zero. Thus, at that temperature every constituent must decouple from all other constituents. Nevertheless, all intrinsic active fields pertaining to any one constituent must be coupled, at the absolute zero, in a particular way thence providing important hyperspace boundary conditions. We shall next determine these boundary conditions for active fields by two independent means.

Absolute-zero boundary condition consequential to Proposition VII. Let us first assume that at the absolute zero, passive fields are forbidden, even in the presence of active fields. If at any point a in a one-component system the resultant of all intrinsic active fields is $\mathbf{f}_{ta}$ and the particle flux density is $\mathcal{J}$, then according to Eq. (35), Chapter 6, the time rate of increase of internal energy $(\partial Q_{ta}/\partial t)$ per unit volume of the nontransported particles, associated with $\mathbf{f}_{ta}$ and $\mathcal{J}$, is given by

$$\partial Q_{ta}/\partial t = -\mathbf{f}_{ta} \cdot \mathcal{J}. \tag{22}$$

As explained in Chapter 6 (Subsection 5.2.), if $\mathcal{J}$ is sufficiently small, then reversing it will not reverse or change appreciably the magnitude of $\mathbf{f}_{ta}$. If $\mathbf{f}_{ta}$ were not to vanish, then consider the case for which the direction of $\mathcal{J}$ is opposite to that of $\mathbf{f}_{ta}$. In this case $\partial Q_{ta}/\partial t$ could not be negative, and, as explained in Subsection 4.1., we may write

$$c(\partial T/\partial t) = -\mathbf{f}_{ta} \cdot \mathcal{J}. \tag{23}$$

Equation (23) and Proposition VII directly lead to

$$\lim_{T \to 0} \mathbf{f}_{ta} = 0, \tag{24}$$

since $\mathcal{J}$ is not necessarily zero.

As explained earlier, at the absolute zero, intrinsic active fields pertaining to different constituents must be completely unrelated. Despite this fact, to maintain at the absolute zero, Proposition VII satisfied at every point in a multicomponent system, then Eq. (24) must be satisfied for each constituent j individually; that is

$$\lim_{T \to 0} \mathbf{f}_{taj} = 0. \tag{25}$$

It should be noticed that Eq. (25) is quite compatible with the mechanism of detailed *self*-balancing, since even at the absolute zero, Eq. (37) of Chapter 6 holds. The situation here becomes analogous to that of the atmospheric thermal equilibrium (Chapter 6) and other unconstrained systems.

Impossible heat extraction at 0°K. Equation (24) can be arrived at for a one-component system by another argument. If $\mathbf{f}_{ta}$ is not vanishing, let us imagine that the particle flux density $\mathcal{J}$ is established in the same direction as $\mathbf{f}_{ta}$. This would imply that the internal energy of the nontransported particles could be lowered below its absolute minimum attained at the absolure zero. If the internal energy in a system is all thermal—not in the form of a stored charge on a capacitor, for example—the preceding consequence would mean that a nonvanishing $\mathbf{f}_{ta}$ would make it possible to pump heat out of a system, or any part thereof, while the system is at the absolute zero. Such consequences, of course, are impossible. Therefore, we may conclude that, for the system under consideration, the condition expressed by Eq. (24) is invariably satisfied.

4.3. *Passive Fields at 0°K in the Presence of Active Fields*

We consider next whether the presence of active fields in a system would alter the hyperspace boundary conditions for passive fields, arrived at in Subsection 4.1.

In that subsection, we have seen that in the absence of intrinsic active fields, passive fields are to vanish individually at the absolute zero. This actually means that dissipative mechanisms are thermodynamically forbidden at the absolute zero. Thus, for example, for conduction electrons, the mobility μ_n has to be infinite. If we now imagine that active fields have been introduced in the system, then such fields could not modify μ_n by other than a finite factor. Thus, in this case μ_n will still be infinite. Correspondingly, passive fields must remain, at the absolute zero, individually vanishing under nonequilibrium conditions, even in the presence of active fields.

The preceding fundamental conclusion will have interesting verifying consequences relevant to the well known phenomena of superconductivity and superfluidity. These topics will be discussed in Chapter 10.

4.4. *Proposition V: A Consequence of Proposition VI and the Hyperspace Boundary Conditions*

Proposition V, stated in Chapter 6, has specified that active and passive fields shall interact in any system in such a way as to conserve the transport energy around every closed, real-space loop in the system. Proposition VI has further defined the manner in which the transport energy for these fields is conserved in the thermodynamic hyperspace. In any multicomponent system in which each particle flux density is solenoidal, Proposition V may be expressed for constituent j as

$$\nabla \times (\mathbf{f}_{taj} - \mathbf{f}_{tsj}) = 0. \tag{26}$$

Under the same conditions, Proposition VI has been shown earlier in this chapter to lead to

$$d(\mathbf{f}_{taj} - \mathbf{f}_{tsj})/d\tilde{T} = \partial(\mathbf{f}_{taj} - \mathbf{f}_{tsj})/\partial\tau = \nabla\Theta, \tag{27}$$

where the scalar function

$$\Theta = s - (1/n)(dP/d\tilde{T}). \tag{28}$$

We next show that Eq. (26) follows from Eq. (27), and the hyperspace boundary conditions at the absolute zero. To do so, consider Eq. (27). Taking the curl of both sides of this equation, we get

$$\nabla \times [\partial(\mathbf{f}_{taj} - \mathbf{f}_{tsj})/\partial\tau] = (\partial/\partial\tau)[\nabla \times (\mathbf{f}_{taj} - \mathbf{f}_{tsj})]$$

$$= \nabla \times \nabla\Theta. \tag{29}$$

Using Eq. (5), the reader may verify the interchangeability of the operations $(\nabla \times)$ and $(\partial/\partial\tau)$.

Since the curl of any gradient is zero, it follows from Eq. (29) that

$$(\partial/\partial\tau)[\nabla \times (\mathbf{f}_{taj}-\mathbf{f}_{tsj})]=0. \tag{30}$$

The most general solution of Eq. (30) will be

$$\nabla \times (\mathbf{f}_{taj}-\mathbf{f}_{tsj}) = G(x, y, z), \tag{31}$$

where G is an arbitrary function of position only.

To evaluate the arbitrary function $G(x, y, z)$, for any system, we must invoke the hyperspace boundary conditions. At the absolute zero,

$$\mathbf{f}_{taj}=0, \qquad \mathbf{f}_{tsj}=0. \tag{32}$$

Hence, Eq. (31) reduces to

$$G(x, y, z)=0. \tag{33}$$

Consequently,

$$\nabla \times (\mathbf{f}_{taj}-\mathbf{f}_{tsj})=0. \tag{34}$$

We may, therefore, state the fundamental conclusion that:

The conservation of transport energy in the real space (Proposition V) constitutes a direct consequence of the conservation of energy in the thermodynamic hyperspace (Proposition VI), and the boundary conditions of this hyperspace at the absolute zero.

As shown in Chapter 6 (Section 7), in the framework of the thermodynamic theory of generalized fields, Proposition V leads to the mechanism of detailed *self*-balancing at thermal equilibrium. Thus, from the relationship just established between Propositions V and VI, we may state:

Corollary VIII. The conservation of transport energy in the thermodynamic hyperspace, together with the hyperspace boundary conditions at the absolute zero, collectively guarantee that, in any system whatever, the mechanism of detailed *self*-balancing is satisfied everywhere in the system at thermal equilibrium.

5. ALLOWABLE NUMBER OF DISTINGUISHABLE INTRINSIC ACTIVE FIELDS IN ANY SYSTEM AT 0°K

At any point a in a one-component system, passive fields vanish individually, while the intrinsic active fields vanish collectively.

An immediate consequence of this result is that at $0°K$ *it is thermody-namically forbidden to have a single nonvanishing intrinsic active field any-where* in a system. The nonexistence of such fields at any, or all points of a system represents, of course, an allowable situation. Alternatives of this special case is to have two or more such fields. In Chapter 10, we shall dis-cuss relevance of these results to the phenomena of superconductivity and superfluidity. Next, however, we shall consider two simple examples.

If the system under consideration consists of conduction electrons in the interface between two dissimilar metals, clearly then one sees that at $0°K$ the diffusion field $\mathbf{f}_{da} \neq 0$. We observe here that $\mathbf{f}_{da} \neq \mathbf{f}_{ta}$, for $\mathbf{f}_{ta} = 0$. There-fore, to satisfy the hyperspace boundary conditions, it is necessary that there shall be at least one more distinguishable intrinsic force field $\mathbf{f}_{ia}$ such that, at $0°K$, $\mathbf{f}_{da} + \mathbf{f}_{ia} = \mathbf{f}_{ta} = 0$. The active force field $\mathbf{f}_{ia}$ happens to be, as is well known, associated with an electric field.

Let us consider another example: a solid–vapor system. In the limit as T tends to $0°K$, conceivably $\mathbf{f}_{da} = 0$ in the interface. Thus, $\mathbf{f}_{ta} = \mathbf{f}_{da}$, and the boundary condition is satisfied without the necessity of an additional field. The interface can, therefore, above the absolute zero have a minimum of one force field, which is $\mathbf{f}_{da}$.

We may, therefore, conclude that if, at $0°K$, the active diffusion field $\mathbf{f}_{da}$ vanishes at a given point a in a system, then it is permissible that $\mathbf{f}_{da}$ can be the only active force field at a. On the other hand, if, at $0°K$, $\mathbf{f}_{da} \neq 0$ at point a, then it is necessary that at least another distinguishable active field shall be there at point a, in addition to $\mathbf{f}_{da}$.

6. INSUFFICIENCY OF REAL-SPACE CONSIDERATIONS

We shall next discuss some interesting aspects which concern the lack of complete determinateness of the line integral for all the active fields in a system, if only the real space is considered. For simplicity, we shall assume that systems under consideration are at thermal equilibrium.

Consider, for example, conduction electrons in the junction between two dissimilar metals, or those in the transition region in a p–n junction. It can be easily shown that [see Eq. (18), Chapter 6] the line integral W_{da} of the active diffusion field $\mathbf{f}_{da}$ through the junction is merely equal to the difference between the Fermi energies evaluated at two points a and b on opposite sides of the junction. These Fermi energies, however, are totally dependent on the electron concentration at points a and b, and not on how the electron concentration varies through the junction. Therefore, W_{da} is totally determinate. However, the line integral W_{ea} of the active electro-static force field $\mathbf{f}_{ea} = -q\mathbf{E}$ is indeterminate, since, from Poisson's equation, $\mathbf{E}$ depends on the unknown space charge distribution and width of the junction. In this simple example, we have two active fields, one of which is indeterminate through real-space considerations.

Consider another example: the liquid-vapor system at thermal equilibrium. In the interface, we only have the active diffusion field. Its line integral through the interface, again, depends on the particle concentrations at points on opposite sides of the liquid-vapor interface. While the concentration on the liquid side, ignoring thermal expansion, is fixed, on the vapor side the concentration is indeterminate from real-space considerations.

To illustrate more concretely how the hyperspace equation removes the indeterminacies of the real-space, the Seebeck and Peltier effects will be treated in considerable detail in the next chapter.

7. DISCUSSION

7.1. *The Hyperspace Equation*

The strong distinction made between active and passive processes is uniquely a characteristic of the thermodynamic theory of generalized fields. This distinction has created the necessity, and provided the opportunity for using two independent equations to describe the transport of particles in a system. Correspondingly, in the classical thermodynamic framework, no more than one equation can possibly be constructed to describe the transport of such particles. In the theory of generalized fields, one of the two equations leads to Ohm's, Fick's, Stokes's, and other strictly dissipative laws. This matter has been treated in detail in Chapter 6. The second equation expresses the conservation of transport energy for active and passive processes in the (temperature-position) hyperspace.

In this chapter, we have shown that the conservation of transport energy in the hyperspace, together with the hyperspace boundary conditions at the absolute zero, lead to the conservation of transport energy in the real space. The latter, in turn, crucially leads to the mechanism of detailed *self*-balancing characterizing thermal equilibrium, for any system whatsoever, in the framework of the theory of generalized fields. This mechanism provides a new and generalized interpretation of the zeroth law of thermodynamics.

It is interesting to note that for the particular case of electric networks, the conservation of transport energy in the real space reduces to Kirchhoff's voltage law.

7.2. *The Four Principles of Thermodynamics*

The hyperspace equation represents a novel generalized interpretation of the first law of thermodynamics. This law guarantees the conservation of energy in all of its forms, including those new quantities of transport energy introduced in the theory of generalized fields. These energy quantities are calculated around a novel temperature-position hyperspatial closed loop. Solution of the hyperspace equation cannot be accomplished without invoking the boundary conditions of the hyperspace at the absolute zero. *These boundary conditions are relevant to third law of thermodynamics.*

The hyperspace equation further leads to the mechanism of detailed *self*-balancing which specifies in a new and generalized way the important state of thermal equilibrium. In addition, this equation contains the entropy, which is defined strictly according to *Clausius equality*.

8. CONCLUSION

On the basis of the preceding discussion, it may be concluded that the hyperspace equation is based on the four thermodynamic principles. The mechanism of detailed *self*-balancing, which characterizes thermal equilibrium, and the first, and second laws, however, are all interpreted in a novel manner different from that done in classical thermodynamics. The use of this equation, therefore, automatically invokes the four thermodynamic principles simultaneously. This result is not without philosophical implications. The simplest space, not accounting for relativistic effects, in which the interaction in any thermodynamic system takes place, is four-dimensional. In that hyperspace, the four thermodynamic principles are crucially relevant and none is superfluous, even in thermal equilibrium.

By contrast, it is inherent in the classical thermodynamic framework that at thermal equilibrium, the so-called generalized potential is constant. This interpretation of the mechanism of detailed balancing confines the interactions in any system simply to the real space. Consequently, the third law is made virtually superfluous.

PROBLEMS

1. Show that the operations $(\nabla \times)$ and $(\partial/\partial\tau)$ are interchangeable so that

$$\partial(\nabla \times \mathbf{f})/\partial\tau = \nabla \times (\partial\mathbf{f}/\partial\tau),$$

where

$$\mathbf{f} = \mathbf{f}(x, y, z, \tau),$$

and τ is the independent temperature parameter of the hyperspace.

2. Show that one of the boundary conditions of the hyperspace requires that for any electron system whatsoever, at $T = 0°\mathrm{K}$, $\mu = \infty$, and $D = \infty$, where μ and D are the mobility and diffusion constant for electrons, respectively. *Hint:* Consider Eqs. (41), (50), and (51) of Chapter 6. For Eq. (50), use the limit for D/μ as T tends to $0°\mathrm{K}$.

3. The third law of thermodynamics requires that, at $0°K$, $dP/d\tilde{T}=0$. Verify this result for electrons in metals from a quantum and statistical mechanical points of view assuming that: (a) the electrons have a standard band; and (b) the metal has a thermal expansivity α_T in the close neighborhood of the absolute zero given by $\alpha_T = a_0 T^3$. Here, a_0 is a constant.

4. From the result obtained for Problem 3 and definition of s, evaluate $d(\mathbf{f}_{ta}-\mathbf{f}_{ts})/d\tilde{T}$ at the absolute zero. Can the answer be general?

5. Using assumptions (a) and (b) of Problem 3, show that for conduction electrons in a metal, the specific heat c per particle vanishes at $0°K$.

6. Using assumptions (a) and (b) of Problem 3, evaluate for conduction electrons in a metal, $ds/d\tilde{T}$, at $T=0°K$.

7. Using assumptions (a) and (b) of Problem 3, and the answer for Problem 6, evaluate for conduction electrons: $d^2(\mathbf{f}_{ta}-\mathbf{f}_{ts})/d\tilde{T}^2$, at $0°K$.

REFERENCES

Debye, P. 1912, Ann. Physik **39**, 789.
Einstein, A. 1906, Ann. Physik **22**, 180, 800.
—— 1911, *Ibid.* **34**, 170.
ter Haar, D. 1966, Elements of Thermostatistics, pp. 126 and 133, Holt, Rinehart and Winston.
Melehy, M. A. 1970, Proceedings of the 1969 Pittsburgh, Pennsylvania International Symposium on "A Critical Review of Thermodynamics," edited by E. B. Stuart, B. Gal-Or, and A. J. Brainard, p. 365, Mono Book Corp.
—— 1971, Proceedings of the Budapest, Hungary, 1970 International Conference on the Physics and Chemistry of Semiconductor Heterojunctions and Layer Structures, vol. 1, pp. 297–307, Akadémiai Kiadó, Budapest.
Nernst, W. 1912, S. B. Preuss. Akad. Wiss., p. 134.
Seitz, F. 1940, The Modern Theory of Solids, p. 103, McGraw-Hill.

Chapter 9

HYPERSPACE EQUATION AND ITS FUNDAMENTAL SOLUTIONS APPLIED TO THE SEEBECK AND PELTIER EFFECTS

1. INTRODUCTION

In the preceding chapter, the hyperspace equation was derived, and its relevant boundary conditions determined. It has been shown that, subject to the boundary conditions at the absolute zero, one fundamental solution of the hyperspace equation represents the conservation of transport energy in the real space. Specifically, this solution expresses the relation that, in that space, the closed-loop line integral of the total active force field, $\mathbf{f}_{ta}$, equals that of the total passive force field, $\mathbf{f}_{ts}$. This result is applicable to each constituent in a multicomponent system, provided that the particle flux density for each constituent is solenoidal. Accordingly, the solution, just described, does not specify the value of the closed-loop line integral of either $\mathbf{f}_{ta}$, or $\mathbf{f}_{ts}$.

In this chapter, we shall determine, under the same restrictions—of solenoidal particle flux densities—a new fundamental general solution of the hyperspace equation. This *second* solution will make it possible to evaluate the real-space, closed-loop line integral of $\mathbf{f}_{ta}$.

For simplicity, the hyperspace equation, and its two solutions, relevant boundary conditions and other properties, will be discussed as applied to the Seebeck and Peltier effects. Generalizations of the results to other systems will then become an obvious matter.

The Seebeck effect is a well-known phenomenon, observed whenever two different junctions of a metallic thermocouple are placed at points of different temperatures. Under such conditions, an active voltage (electromotive force) is invariably induced across the terminals of the thermocouple. This effect was first observed by Seebeck (1826).* The same effect takes place generally between any two dissimilar materials, such as different semiconductors.

The Peltier effect is another interesting thermoelectric phenomenon. When an electric current is passed through the junction between two different metals, depending on the direction of current, the junction either cools off, or heats up. This effect was discovered by Peltier (1834). The

---

* In that paper, the effect was interpreted to be thermomagnetic. Later, in view of Ampère's law, it has become apparent that the effect is thermoelectric.

Peltier effect can be observed in junctions formed between almost any two different materials.

Using classical thermodynamics and other equivalent methods, the Seebeck and Peltier effects in metals have been treated by many authors, including Thomson (1882), and Bridgeman (1934).* More recently, the thermoelectric effects have been studied in semiconductors by numerous workers,† including Herring (1953, 1954) and Frederikse (1953).

In this chapter, we shall be concerned with deriving, in general terms, expressions for the Seebeck voltage, Υ, and what is known as the Peltier coefficient, Π. We shall further calculate Υ and Π for those metals for which the electron energy band may be assumed to be of a standard type.

2. THE PELTIER EFFECT IN GENERAL

Consider any two different solids, A and B, brought together to form a contact (Fig. 1). Let the concentration of conduction electrons be uniform within the bulk of each solid. Suppose now that the electron concentrations

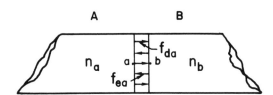

Fig. 1. The transition region between two different metals A and B.

n_a and n_b in solid A and B, respectively, are such that $n_a > n_b$. At various points of the *transition region*, lying between the two solids, we must then have an electron concentration gradient.

If we now assume that the entire assembly is isothermal, then in the transition region a concentration gradient will support only an active diffusion field $\mathbf{f}_{da}$. This force field will have a direction from point a to b, and according to Eq. (18), of Chapter 6, will be given by

$$\mathbf{f}_{da} = -\nabla \epsilon_f. \tag{1}$$

Here ϵ_f is the Fermi energy at various points in the transition region.

If we consider for the moment that the solids, A and B, are metals, then, at the absolute zero, n_a and n_b will be finite and unequal. Consequently,

---

* A complete treatment of the Seebeck and Peltier effects, using the classical method of Boltzmann's equation, may be found in Blatt (1957, 1968) and Ziman (1960).

† Extensive information concerning thermoelectricity in semiconductors may be found in a number of books, including Ioffe (1957), Egli (1958), and Goldsmid (1960).

$\mathbf{f}_{da}$ will likewise be finite at 0°K. As explained in Chapter 8, the hyperspace boundary conditions at the absolute zero make it forbidden that at this temperature a single, nonvanishing, intrinsic, active force field can exist anywhere in a system. In the transition region, it is, therefore, imperative that another intrinsic active force field will exist. This force field is electrostatic in nature and will be, of course, supported by a space charge. The force $\mathbf{f}_{ea}$ per electron, associated with the electrostatic field, will be such that

$$\mathbf{f}_{da} + \mathbf{f}_{ea} = 0, \qquad \text{at } T = 0. \tag{2}$$

As we shall see shortly, Eq. (2) does not hold necessarily at temperatures higher than the absolute zero.

Imagine now that an electric current is established between solids A and B such that electrons are continuously being transported from left to right. Let the applied current be sufficiently small so that passive fields in the junction and the bulk are negligibly small. As an electron crosses the junction, on the average, it will be acted on by the intrinsic, active fields $\mathbf{f}_{da}$ and $\mathbf{f}_{ea}$. Correspondingly, an amount of work, $q\Pi_{AB}$, will be done on it. If Π_{AB} is positive, then the conservation of energy requires that the internal energy of the junction will drop by an amount $q\Pi_{AB}$. The junction, therefore, cools off. Clearly, the reversal of the junction current will not reverse either of $\mathbf{f}_{da}$ or $\mathbf{f}_{ea}$. Hence, the electron must do work on the junction as it crosses through. The junction, therefore, inevitably heats up.

The amount of work, Π_{AB}, done on an electron crossing the junction in the direction of $\mathbf{f}_{da}$ (Fig. 1) in electron volts will simply be

$$\Pi_{AB} = q^{-1} \int_a^b (\mathbf{f}_{da} + \mathbf{f}_{ea}) \cdot d\mathbf{l}. \tag{3}$$

We now observe that the time rate, $\dot{Q}$, of the Peltier heat extracted from a junction, as a current I is passed from metal B to A, will be

$$\dot{Q} = (I/q) \int_a^b (\mathbf{f}_{da} + \mathbf{f}_{ea}) \cdot d\mathbf{l}. \tag{4}$$

For, (I/q) represents the number of electrons crossing the junction, per second, from left to right. But, by definition,

$$\dot{Q}/I = \text{the Peltier coefficient (eV).} \tag{5}$$

Therefore, Π_{AB}, as expressed by Eq. (3), is the Peltier coefficient. Since $\mathbf{f}_{da}$ is defined by Eq. (1), then

$$\Pi_{AB} = q^{-1} \left\{ [\epsilon_f(A) - \epsilon_f(B)] + \int_a^b \mathbf{f}_{ea} \cdot d\mathbf{l} \right\}, \tag{6}$$

where $\epsilon_f(A)$ and $\epsilon_f(B)$ are the Fermi energies in regions A and B, respectively, when the temperature of the assembly is T.

It is interesting to observe that in Eq. (6) both $\epsilon_f(A)$ and $\epsilon_f(B)$ can be completely determined from the electron concentrations, electron effective masses, etc. On the other hand, the integral term cannot be determined through any considerations of the real space. For, according to the laws of electrostatics, we must be given the space charge distribution in the junction and the junction width. We have neither.

We now proceed to determine Π_{AB} by invoking the conservation of energy in the thermodynamic hyperspace and the hyperspace boundary conditions at the absolute zero. Since we have ignored passive effects in the junction, the hyperspace equation reduces to

$$\int_a^b (d/d\tilde{T}) \, (\mathbf{f}_{da}+\mathbf{f}_{ea}) \cdot d\mathbf{l} = \int_a^b \nabla[s-n^{-1}(dP/d\tilde{T})] \cdot d\mathbf{l}. \tag{7}$$

Here, s is the entropy per electron, n and P are the electron concentration and internal pressure, respectively, and T is the absolute temperature. Since differentiation on the independent temperature axis of the hyperspace and integration in the real space are two interchangeable operations, then Eq. (7) may be rewritten as

$$(d/d\tilde{T}) \int_a^b (\mathbf{f}_{da}+\mathbf{f}_{ea}) \cdot d\mathbf{l} = \int_a^b \nabla[s-n^{-1}(dP/d\tilde{T})] \cdot d\mathbf{l}. \tag{8}$$

Now integrating—in the real space—through the junction from point a to b, we get

$$(d/d\tilde{T}) \Pi_{AB} = (1/q) [s-n^{-1}(dP/d\tilde{T})]_a^b. \tag{9}$$

We shall next evaluate the quantity $(dP/d\tilde{T})$ statistical-mechanically, assuming a parabolic volume-energy density $g(\epsilon)$ of quantum states. For an energy level ϵ, this density function is given by

$$g(\epsilon) = C_n\epsilon^{1/2}, \tag{10}$$

where C_n is a constant, if the electron effective mass is constant throughout the system.

As discussed in Chapter 6, even for a degenerate electron gas, the internal pressure P will be expressed as

$$P = \tfrac{2}{3}C_n \int_0^\infty \epsilon^{3/2} F \, d\epsilon, \tag{11}$$

where F is the Fermi–Dirac distribution function, given by

$$F = \{1+ \exp[(\epsilon-\epsilon_f)/kT]\}^{-1}. \tag{12}$$

Therefore,

$$dP/d\tilde{T} = \tfrac{2}{3}C_n \int_0^\infty \epsilon^{3/2}(dF/d\tilde{T})\, d\epsilon. \tag{13}$$

Since

$$\frac{dF}{d\tilde{T}} = \frac{\exp[(\epsilon-\epsilon_f)/kT]\{(d\epsilon_f/d\tilde{T})+[(\epsilon-\epsilon_f)/T]\}}{kT\{1+\exp[(\epsilon-\epsilon_f)/kT]\}^2}, \tag{14}$$

and

$$\frac{\partial F}{\partial \epsilon} = \frac{-\exp[(\epsilon-\epsilon_f)/kT]}{kT\{1+\exp[(\epsilon-\epsilon_f)/kT]\}^2}, \tag{15}$$

then

$$dF/d\tilde{T} = -\{(d\epsilon_f/d\tilde{T})+[(\epsilon-\epsilon_f)/T]\}(dF/d\epsilon). \tag{16}$$

Substituting Eq. (16) into (13), we obtain

$$\frac{dP}{d\tilde{T}} = -\tfrac{2}{3}C_n \left\{ \left[\frac{d\epsilon_f}{d\tilde{T}} - \frac{\epsilon_f}{T}\right] \int_0^\infty \epsilon^{3/2}\left(\frac{\partial F}{\partial \epsilon}\right) d\epsilon + \frac{1}{T}\int_0^\infty \epsilon^{5/2}\left(\frac{\partial F}{\partial \epsilon}\right) d\epsilon \right\}. \tag{17}$$

Integrating each one of the two integrals by parts, we have

$$\frac{dP}{d\tilde{T}} = \left[\frac{d\epsilon_f}{d\tilde{T}} - \frac{\epsilon_f}{T}\right] C_n \int_0^\infty \epsilon^{1/2}F\, d\epsilon + \frac{5C_n}{3T}\int_0^\infty \epsilon^{3/2}F\, d\epsilon. \tag{18}$$

Recalling that

$$n = C_n \int_0^\infty \epsilon^{1/2}F\, d\epsilon, \tag{19}$$

we may divide then both sides of Eq. (18) by n, thereby getting

$$n^{-1}(dP/d\tilde{T}) = (d\epsilon_f/d\tilde{T}) - T^{-1}[\epsilon_f - \tfrac{5}{3}\langle\epsilon\rangle], \tag{20}$$

where $\langle\epsilon\rangle$ may be interpreted as the average thermal kinetic energy per electron. This quantity is given by

$$\langle\epsilon\rangle = \left[\int_0^\infty \epsilon^{3/2}F\, d\epsilon\right] \Big/ \left[\int_0^\infty \epsilon^{1/2}F\, d\epsilon\right]. \tag{21}$$

From Eqs. (9) and (20), it follows that

$$(d/d\tilde{T})\Pi_{AB} = q^{-1}[s - (d\epsilon_f/d\tilde{T}) + (1/T)(\epsilon_f - \tfrac{5}{3}\langle\epsilon\rangle)]_a^b. \tag{22}$$

Integrating with respect to $\tilde{T}$ between 0°K and T, we get

$$\Pi_{AB} = q^{-1}\left\{(\epsilon_{f0}-\epsilon_f) + \int_0^T [s+T^{-1}(\epsilon_f - \tfrac{5}{3}\langle\epsilon\rangle)]\, d\tilde{T}\right\}_a^b, \tag{23}$$

where ϵ_f and ϵ_{f0} are values of the Fermi energy at the upper temperature T

and at the absolute zero, respectively. The preceding equation involves an arbitrary constant which vanishes. For, the hyperspace boundary condition, expressed by Eq. (2), requires that, at $0°$K, $\Pi_{AB}=0$. At that temperature. it can be seen that the right-hand side of Eq. (23) vanishes for $T=0$.

It is of particular interest to observe that according to Eqs. (3) and (6), Π_{AB} consists of two distinct components, and may, therefore, be expressed as

$$\Pi_{AB} = \Pi_{ABd} + \Pi_{ABe}. \tag{24}$$

The first component is caused by diffusion, and hence will be

$$\Pi_{ABd} = q^{-1} \int_a^b \mathbf{f}_{da} \cdot d\mathbf{l}$$

$$= (q^{-1})[\epsilon_f(A) - \epsilon_f(B)]. \tag{25}$$

Clearly, Π_{ABd} is totally determinate from real-space considerations. The second component, Π_{ABe}, associated with the electrostatic field, is given by

$$\Pi_{ABe} = q^{-1} \int_a^b \mathbf{f}_{ea} \cdot d\mathbf{l}. \tag{26}$$

Now through hyperspace considerations, Eq. (23) has evolved. Consequently, Π_{ABe} has become completely determinate. Specifically,

$$\Pi_{ABe} = q^{-1}[\epsilon_{f0}(B) - \epsilon_{f0}(A)] + q^{-1} \left\{ \int_0^T [s + T^{-1}(\epsilon_f - \tfrac{5}{3}\langle\epsilon\rangle)] \, d\tilde{T} \right\}_a^b. \tag{27}$$

We shall see in Section 5 that, for metals, Π_{ABe} is negative when $n_a > n_b$. The implication, then, is that $\mathbf{f}_{ea}$ is a negative quantity, that is, opposite to $\mathbf{f}_{da}$ as illustrated in Fig. 1.

3. THE SEEBECK EFFECT IN GENERAL

3.1. *Solutions of the Hyperspace Equation and the Seebeck Voltage*

We shall next apply the hyperspace equation to derive an expression for the Seebeck voltage appearing between the terminal points of a thermocouple. The treatment in this section will be in general terms.

As we shall see, the hyperspace equation has two distinctly different solutions. The first expresses the conservation of net transport energy in the real space. This particular solution has been treated at length in Chapter 8. For the Seebeck effect, it is more appropriate to write this solution in the integral form; namely,

$$\oint (\mathbf{f}_{ta} - \mathbf{f}_{ts}) \cdot d\mathbf{l} = 0, \tag{28}$$

or

$$\oint \mathbf{f}_{ta} \cdot d\mathbf{l} = \oint \mathbf{f}_{ts} \cdot d\mathbf{l} = qV_s. \tag{29}$$

Here $d\mathbf{l}$ is an increment of length taken in the anticlockwise direction along the closed loop which includes the thermocouple and its resistive load, R, and V_s is the passive voltage across R. This resistance should be much higher than the internal resistance of the thermocouple. Consequently, passive fields within the thermocouple will be negligibly small.

We now observe that qV_s in Eq. (29) is equal to the closed-loop line integral of $\mathbf{f}_{ta}$. This integral is totally indeterminate from real-space relations. We shall see next that this integral will be completely determined from the *second solution* of the hyperspace equation.

To arrive at that solution for the Seebeck effect, consider the thermocouple illustrated in Fig. 2. Let the two junctions b and c be at two different temperatures T_1 and T_2, respectively. As observed in Fig. 2, the temperature T_1 is taken to be the ambient reference temperature.

Within the bulk of the isothermal segment ab, there are no electron intrinsic, active fields. As seen in the previous section, in the isothermal junctions b and c there are two types of intrinsic, active fields pertaining to electrons; a diffusion field $\mathbf{f}_{da}$ and an electrostatic force field $\mathbf{f}_{ea}$. Within the bulk of the nonisothermal segments bc and cd, there are more intrinsic, active force fields. Those are: a thermomotive field $\mathbf{f}_T$, supported by a temperature gradient: a diffusion field $\mathbf{f}_{da}$ induced by at least a temperature gradient; and an electrostatic force field $\mathbf{f}_{ea}$, supported by a space charge. The existence of $\mathbf{f}_{ea}$ is dictated by the conservation of transport energy in the thermodynamic hyperspace and its boundary conditions at the absolute zero. The space charge results from a departure in the distribution of conduction electrons from that of the fixed atoms within the two segments.

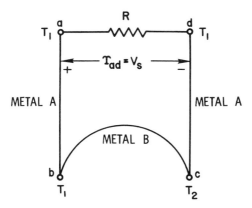

Fig. 2. Thermocouple consisting of two (different) metals A and B. Connected to the thermocouple is a sufficiently high resistance R, which draws a vanishingly small current.

Since the thermocouple, ideally, does not deliver any appreciable current, then passive fields will be negligibly small. Thus, at any point in the system, we may express generally the various force fields as follows:

$$\mathbf{f}_T = s \, \nabla T, \tag{30}$$

$$\mathbf{f}_{da} = -(\nabla \epsilon_f)_T - (d\epsilon_f/d\tilde{T}) \, \nabla T - (T^{-1}) \left[\tfrac{5}{3} \langle \epsilon \rangle - \epsilon_f \right] \nabla T, \tag{31}$$

$$\mathbf{f}_{ea} = -q\mathbf{E}_a. \tag{32}$$

Here, q is the magnitude of the electron charge and $\mathbf{E}_a$ is the intensity of the active electrostatic field at various points of the system. Equation (31) has been derived in about the same form in Chapter 6 [see Eq. (16) in that chapter].

At any point, if all the preceding force fields exist, their resultant

$$\mathbf{f}_{ta} = \mathbf{f}_T + \mathbf{f}_{da} + \mathbf{f}_{ea}. \tag{33}$$

The force field $\mathbf{f}_{ta}$ may now be split into two components. One component $\mathbf{f}_0$ has no dependence on ∇T. The other component does. Accordingly,

$$\mathbf{f}_{ta} = \mathbf{f}_0 + \zeta \, \nabla T, \tag{34}$$

where

$$\mathbf{f}_0 = -q\mathbf{E}_a - (\nabla \epsilon_f)_T, \tag{35}$$

$$\zeta = s - (d\epsilon_f/d\tilde{T}) - T^{-1} \left[\tfrac{5}{3} \langle \epsilon \rangle - \epsilon_f \right]. \tag{36}$$

The scalar function ζ, clearly, is dependent on temperature.

The Seebeck emf Υ_{ad} may now be defined in electron volts as

$$\Upsilon_{ad} = -q^{-1} \int_a^d \mathbf{f}_{ta} \cdot d\mathbf{l}, \tag{37}$$

where the path of integration must be through the system and points $abcd$ (Fig. 2).

We may now apply the hyperspace equation to evaluate Υ_{ad}. More specifically, we shall use the hyperspace equation to determine which components of the force field $\mathbf{f}_{ta}$ when inserted in the right-hand side of Eq. (37) give rise to a zero emf between points a and d. The rest of the components must, therefore, be the contributers to Υ_{ad}.

In the absence of passive fields, the hyperspace equation reduces to

$$\nabla \Theta = d\mathbf{f}_{ta}/d\tilde{T}, \tag{38}$$

where the scalar function Θ is dependent on the Cartesian position coordinates x, y, z and the hyperspace parameter τ. Specifically,

$$\Theta = s - n^{-1}(dP/d\tilde{T}) = \Theta[x, y, z, T(x, y, z, \tau)]. \tag{39}$$

From Eqs. (34) and (38), it follows that

$$\nabla\Theta = df_{ta}/d\tilde{T} = (d/d\tilde{T})[f_0 + \zeta\,\nabla T], \tag{40}$$

or that

$$\nabla\Theta = (df_0/d\tilde{T}) + (\nabla T)_\tau(d\zeta/d\tilde{T}) + (\zeta)_\tau[d(\nabla T)/d\tilde{T}]. \tag{41}$$

Before interpreting Eq. (41), it is particularly significant to know the meaning of the operation $d(\nabla T)/d\tilde{T}$. This operation can be performed by resorting to the basic definition of the thermodynamic hyperspace. We recall that

$$T(x, y, z, \tau) = T_0(x, y, z) + \tau, \qquad \text{for } \tau \geq -T_0, \tag{42}$$

and

$$T(x, y, z, \tau) = 0, \qquad \text{for } \tau \leq -T_0. \tag{43}$$

Furthermore,

$$d/d\tilde{T} = (d/dT)_{x,y,z} = \partial/\partial\tau. \tag{44}$$

Therefore,

$$d(\nabla T)/d\tilde{T} = d(\nabla T_0)/d\tilde{T} = 0. \tag{45}$$

In seeking the second solution of the hyperspace equation, it is essential to use the simple, but significant result expressed by Eq. (45), together with Eq. (41).

We now observe that, regardless of the value of $(\zeta\nabla T)$, the last term in Eq. (41) must vanish. The remaining two terms, designated by $(df_{taC}/d\tilde{T})$, will be

$$df_{taC}/d\tilde{T} = (df_0/d\tilde{T}) + (\nabla T)_\tau(d\zeta/d\tilde{T}) = \nabla\Theta. \tag{46}$$

We observe further that the component of Υ_{ad}, associated with f_{taC}, will be

$$\int_0^T \oint \left(\frac{df_{taC}}{d\tilde{T}}\right)\cdot d\mathbf{l}\; d\tilde{T} + \oint (f_{taC})_{T=0}\cdot d\mathbf{l} = 0. \tag{47}$$

The first term in Eq. (47) vanishes, because Eq. (46) requires $(df_{taC}/d\tilde{T})$ to be conservative. The second term, representing the boundary condition, vanishes, because at $T = 0°\text{K}$, there are no components of f_{ta} involving ∇T. Consequently, $f_{taC} = f_{ta}$. But f_{ta} must vanish at the absolute zero, as required by the boundary conditions of the hyperspace.

Therefore, it is concluded that the first two terms on the right-hand side of Eq. (41) are bound, by the powerful requirements of the hyperspace, to contribute to no Seebeck emf. However, the third term,

$$df_{taR}/d\tilde{T} = (\zeta)_\tau[d(\nabla T)/d\tilde{T}] = (d/d\tilde{T})[(\zeta)_\tau\nabla T]. \tag{48}$$

is not bound by the hyperspace equation to be conservative. In fact by its very mathematical nature, it is filtered out of the hyperspace equation through the differentiation along the temperature axis of the hyperspace. We shall call $\mathbf{f}_{taR}$ the total *residual* force field, which is the resultant of a few *residual* component fields. We shall also define $\mathbf{f}_0$ to be the total *non-residual* force field. From Eqs. (33), (34), (35), (36) and (46), it follows that the closed-loop line integral of $\mathbf{f}_0$ must vanish. Thus, *the nonresidual force fields cannot contribute to a Seebeck voltage.*

It can, therefore, be concluded that, in view of Eqs. (37) and (48), the Seebeck emf, Υ_{ad}, is given by

$$\Upsilon_{ad} = -\frac{1}{q} \oint \int_{T(x,y,z)=0}^{T(x,y,z,\tau)} \frac{d}{d\tilde{T}} [(\zeta)_\tau \nabla T] \, d\tilde{T} \cdot d\mathbf{l}, \qquad (49)$$

where the integration is carried in the anticlockwise direction (Fig. 2). Equation (49) involves an arbitrary function which is zero, and, therefore, omitted. For, if the entire system is at the absolute zero, then the integral will vanish, because its limits become equal, and $\zeta = 0$ at $0°K$, whether the system consists of fermions, or bosons. Furthermore, at $0°K$, the boundary conditions of the hyperspace require that $\Upsilon_{ad} = 0$.

That $\zeta = 0$ at $0°K$ will become apparent in Section 4 for conduction electrons in metals, representing fermions. The reader may verify this result for bosons.

Integrating Eq. (49) with respect to $\tilde{T}$, between the limits corresponding to $T(x, y, z) = 0$ and $T = T(x, y, z, \tau)$, we obtain

$$\Upsilon_{ad} = -q^{-1} \oint [(\zeta)_\tau \nabla T]_{\nabla T=0, \zeta=0}^{\nabla T, \zeta} \cdot d\mathbf{l}. \qquad (50)$$

Since the segment da of the thermocouple (Fig. 2) is invariably isothermal, then Eq. (50) reduces to

$$\Upsilon_{ad} = -q^{-1} \int_a^d (\zeta)_\tau \nabla T \cdot d\mathbf{l}. \qquad (51)$$

It should be noticed now that the integration in Eq. (51) is carried out in the real space, which means that the hyperspace parameter τ is kept constant.

From Eqs. (36) and (51), it follows that the Seebeck emf for our thermocouple will be given by

$$\Upsilon_{ad} = q^{-1} \int_a^d [(d\epsilon_f/d\tilde{T}) + T^{-1}(\tfrac{5}{3}\langle\epsilon\rangle - \epsilon_f) - s]_\tau \nabla T \cdot d\mathbf{l}. \qquad (52)$$

Equation (52) indicates that generally Υ_{ad} will not vanish whenever ∇T is nonvanishing. Furthermore, Υ_{ad} must vanish whenever the system is isothermal.

3.2. *Thermoelectric Power*

It is customary to measure what is generally known as the thermoelectric power, to be designated by S. In the framework of classical thermodynamics, with the absence of the concepts of thermomotive and diffusion fields, it has been thought that the true nature of the Seebeck emf inside the thermocouple is electrostatic. Accordingly, S has been defined to be the Seebeck *electrostatic field* divided by ∇T.

In the framework of the thermodynamic theory of generalized fields, we have seen that the true electrostatic field does not contribute to the Seebeck effect, for its effect is completely nullified by the components of the diffusion and thermomotive fields, which do not depend on the temperature gradient. The components of the last two fields, involving ∇T, do contribute to the Seebeck effect, as follows from Eq. (49).

Therefore, from the point of view of the thermodynamic theory of generalized fields, and to be consistent with the experimental meaning, we may define S to be the ratio of the '*gradient of the Seebeck (active) voltage*,' $\nabla \Upsilon$, divided by ∇T. Accordingly, from Eq. (52), it follows that

$$S = q^{-1}[(d\epsilon_f/d\tilde{T}) + T^{-1}(\tfrac{5}{3}\langle\epsilon\rangle - \epsilon_f) - s]. \qquad (53)$$

It can be shown that, for any system, as the temperature of the entire system approaches the absolute zero, S tends to zero.

4. FERMI ENERGY AND AVERAGE KINETIC ENERGY AND ENTROPY FOR ELECTRONS IN METALS

In the last two sections, general expressions have been obtained for the Peltier coefficient Π, and the Seebeck emf Υ. These expressions have been in terms of the Fermi energy ϵ_f, the average kinetic energy $\langle\epsilon\rangle$ per electron, and the entropy s per electron.

In order to develop a better appreciation of the general results obtained for the Peltier and Seebeck effects, one should evaluate Π and Υ for some specific materials. In this chapter, we have chosen to analyze metals for which the energy band is of a standard type. We begin in this section with determining ϵ_f, s, and $\langle\epsilon\rangle$ for conduction electrons in such metals.

4.1. *Temperature Dependence of the Fermi Energy in Metals*

For metals having a standard electron energy band [according to Eq. (69), Chapter 5], the electron concentration n is given at any temperature T by

$$n_T = C'\epsilon_f{}^{3/2}[1 + (\pi^2/8)(kT/\epsilon_f)^2]. \qquad (54)$$

Here C' is a constant which depends on Planck's constant and the electron effective mass in the metal; and ϵ_f is the Fermi energy at a temperature T.

It is customary in the literature to determine the temperature dependence of ϵ_f from Eq. (54) by assuming that n is temperature independent. We shall, however, see shortly that accounting for the lattice thermal expansion of metals introduces the most predominant effects.

Thermal Expansivity. The coefficient α_T of *linear thermal expansion*, or *linear thermal expansivity* may be defined as

$$\alpha_T = L^{-1}(dL/d\tilde{T}) = \tfrac{1}{3}(V^{-1})(dV/d\tilde{T}), \qquad (55)$$

where V is the volume of a cubic solid whose side length is L. The quantity $[V^{-1}(dV/dT)]$ may be defined as the volume thermal expansivity.

If the number of electrons in the volume V is N, then the electron concentration $n = N/V$. It is now possible to relate α_T to n as follows.

$$\alpha_T = \tfrac{1}{3}(N/V)[d(V/N)/d\tilde{T}] = \tfrac{1}{3}n[d(1/n)/d\tilde{T}], \qquad (56)$$

or

$$\alpha_T = -\tfrac{1}{3}n^{-1}(dn/d\tilde{T}) = -\tfrac{1}{3}(d/d\tilde{T})\ln(n/n_0), \qquad (57)$$

where n_0 is the electron concentration at $0°$K.

The coefficient α_T is by no means a constant. At temperatures sufficiently close to the absolute zero,

$$\alpha_T = a_0 T^3, \qquad \text{for } T < 50°T, \qquad (58)$$

where a_0 is a constant. Equation (58) follows from the Grüneisen relation[*] and Debye's theory of specific heat.[†] Figure 3 shows a plot of extensive experimental measurements of the linear thermal expansivity of copper, compiled by Hahn (1970).

Solving Eq. (57) for n, we get

$$n = n_0 \exp\left(-3\int_0^T \alpha_T \, d\tilde{T}\right). \qquad (59)$$

It may be observed in Fig. 3 that, even if $T = 800°$K, the exponent in Eq. (59) is less than 0.05. Therefore, Eq. (59) can be written to a good approximation as

$$n \simeq n_0\left[1 - 3\int_0^T \alpha_T \, d\tilde{T}\right]. \qquad (60)$$

The Fermi Energy. Equations (54) and (60) make it possible to solve for ϵ_f. Carrying out the steps, we obtain

$$\epsilon_f = \epsilon_{f0}\left[1 - 3\int_0^T \alpha_T \, d\tilde{T}\right]^{2/3} \Big/ \left[1 + \left(\frac{\pi^2}{8}\right)\left(\frac{kT}{\epsilon_f}\right)^2\right]^{2/3}, \qquad (61)$$

where ϵ_{f0} is the value of ϵ_f at $0°K$.

---

[*] See C. Kittel (1966), p. 183.
[†] See C. Kittel (1966), p. 178.

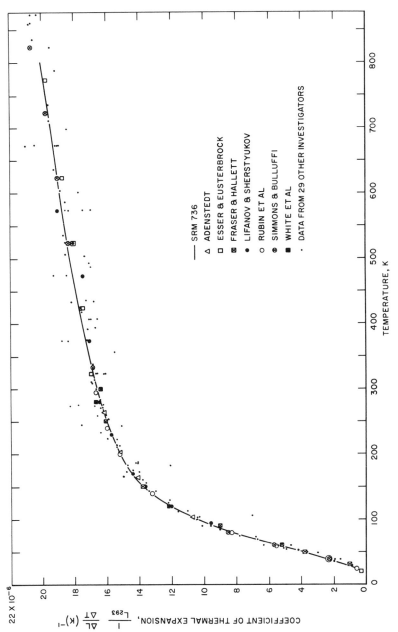

Fig. 3. Dependence on temperature of experimentally-measured coefficient of linear thermal expansivity α_T. The measurements have been conducted by thirty-seven investigators. After Hahn (1970).

For most metals $\epsilon_f > 1$ eV, while $kT \simeq 0.05$ eV at 600°K. As stated earlier, the numerator of Eq. (61) deviates from unity by less than 0.05. Therefore, Eq. (61) may be approximated to

$$\epsilon_f \simeq \epsilon_{f0} \left[1 - (\pi^2/12)(kT/\epsilon_{f0})^2 - 2 \int_0^T \alpha_T \, d\tilde{T} \right]. \tag{62}$$

For metals, in the temperature range of interest, the second term between the brackets in Eq. (62) is much smaller than the third term. For example, for copper, $\epsilon_{f0} = 7$ eV, and at 50°K the second term between the brackets is roughly 2.8×10^{-7}, whereas the third term is about 2×10^{-5}. At 300°K, however, the second term is about 10^{-5}, whereas the third term is approximately 6×10^{-3}.

4.2. *The Average Kinetic Energy per Electron*

We next calculate the average kinetic energy $\langle \epsilon \rangle$ per electron and the derivative of this quantity with respect to temperature.

According to Eq. (72) of Chapter 5,

$$\langle \epsilon \rangle \simeq \tfrac{3}{5} \epsilon_f [1 + \tfrac{1}{2} \pi^2 (kT/\epsilon_f)^2]. \tag{63}$$

Substituting Eq. (62) into (63), and ignoring the insignificant terms, we get

$$\langle \epsilon \rangle \simeq \tfrac{3}{5} \epsilon_{f0} \left[1 + (5\pi^2/12)(kT/\epsilon_{f0})^2 - 2 \int_0^T \alpha_T \, d\tilde{T} \right]. \tag{64}$$

To calculate $d\langle \epsilon \rangle/dT$, one can, of course, differentiate Eq. (64). However, this equation is not exact and differentiation would tend to reduce its accuracy. To calculate $d\langle \epsilon \rangle/dT$ with the same degree of accuracy as that of Eq. (64), consider the exact expression for $\langle \epsilon \rangle$, which is

$$\langle \epsilon \rangle = (C_n/n) \int_0^\infty \epsilon^{3/2} F \, d\epsilon. \tag{65}$$

Here C_n is a constant which depends on Planck's constant and the electron effective mass and F is the Fermi-Dirac distribution function. Therefore,

$$\frac{d\langle \epsilon \rangle}{d\tilde{T}} = -n^{-2}(dn/d\tilde{T})C_n \int_0^\infty \epsilon^{3/2} F \, d\epsilon + (C_n/n) \int_0^\infty \epsilon^{3/2}(dF/d\tilde{T}) \, d\epsilon. \tag{66}$$

From Eqs. (16), (57), and (65), Eq. (66) may be rewritten as

$$d\langle \epsilon \rangle/d\tilde{T} = 3\alpha_T \langle \epsilon \rangle - (C_n/n) \int_0^\infty \epsilon^{3/2}[(d\epsilon_f/d\tilde{T}) + T^{-1}(\epsilon - \epsilon_f)](\partial F/\partial \epsilon) \, d\epsilon. \tag{67}$$

Integrating by parts, Eq. (67) reduces to

$$d\langle\epsilon\rangle/d\tilde{T}=3\alpha_T\langle\epsilon\rangle+(C_n/n)[(d\epsilon_f/d\tilde{T})-(\epsilon_f/T)]\frac{3}{2}\int_0^\infty \epsilon^{1/2}F\,d\epsilon$$

$$+\tfrac{5}{2}(C_n/nT)\int_0^\infty \epsilon^{3/2}F\,d\epsilon. \quad (68)$$

Recalling that

$$n=C_n\int_0^\infty \epsilon^{1/2}F\,d\epsilon, \quad (69)$$

and in view of Eq. (65), Eq. (68) reduces further to

$$d\langle\epsilon\rangle/d\tilde{T}=3\alpha_T\langle\epsilon\rangle+\tfrac{3}{2}(d\epsilon_f/d\tilde{T})+\tfrac{5}{2}T^{-1}[\langle\epsilon\rangle-\tfrac{3}{5}\epsilon_f]. \quad (70)$$

Substituting Eqs. (62) and (63) into Eq. (70) and carrying out the algebraic steps, we get

$$d\langle\epsilon\rangle/d\tilde{T}\simeq-\tfrac{6}{5}\alpha_T\epsilon_{f0}\left[1-\tfrac{5}{8}\pi^2(kT/\epsilon_{f0})^2+3\int_0^T \alpha_T\,d\tilde{T}\right]+\tfrac{1}{2}\pi^2(k^2T/\epsilon_{f0})$$

$$\simeq-\tfrac{6}{5}\alpha_T\epsilon_{f0}\left[1+3\int_0^T \alpha_T\,d\tilde{T}\right]+\tfrac{1}{2}\pi^2(k^2T/\epsilon_{f0}). \quad (71)$$

4.3. *The Entropy per Electron*

Suppose that an amount of heat dQ is given reversibly to N particles occupying a volume V, and, in so doing, the volume and temperature of the particles have changed by dV and dT, respectively. The first law of thermodynamics, therefore, requires that the change in the internal energy dU of the particles will be

$$dU=dQ-P\,dV. \quad (72)$$

If the process just described has been performed quasistatically, then, according to the second law of thermodynamics, as interpreted in the theory of generalized fields,

$$dQ=T\,dS, \quad (73)$$

where dS is the change in the entropy of the N particles.

Solving the last two equations for dS, we get

$$dS=T^{-1}[dU+P\,dV]. \quad (74)$$

Dividing both sides of Eq. (74) by N, we obtain

$$ds=T^{-1}[du-(P/n^2)\,dn], \quad (75)$$

where $s = S/N$, $n = N/V$, and $u = U/N$. Accordingly, s may be defined as the entropy per particle, u the internal energy per particle (that is, $\langle \epsilon \rangle$), and n the concentration.

Recalling that, for electrons, P is two-thirds of the average kinetic energy per unit volume, we may write Eq. (75) as

$$ds = T^{-1}[(d\langle\epsilon\rangle/d\tilde{T}) - \tfrac{2}{3}\langle\epsilon\rangle(d/d\tilde{T})\ \ln(n/n_0)]\ d\tilde{T}. \tag{76}$$

Here, n_0 is the electron concentration at $0°$K.

Substituting Eqs. (59), (64), and (71) into Eq. (76), and neglecting higher-order terms, we get

$$ds \simeq \left\{ \tfrac{1}{2}\pi^2(k^2/\epsilon_{f0}) - 3\epsilon_{f0}(\alpha_T/T) \left[2\int_0^T \alpha_T\, d\tilde{T} - \tfrac{1}{6}\pi^2(kT/\epsilon_{f0})^2 \right] \right\} d\tilde{T}$$

$$\simeq \left[\tfrac{1}{2}\pi^2(k^2/\epsilon_{f0}) - 6\epsilon_{f0}(\alpha_T/T) \int_0^T \alpha_T\, d\tilde{T} \right] d\tilde{T}. \tag{77}$$

Equation (77) indicates that at sufficiently high temperatures, the entropy per electron will decrease in value below that at the absolute zero. This is caused by the lattice thermal expansion, which steadily decreases both the electron concentration and Fermi energy as the temperature is increased.

In no way should this result be construed as a violation of the second law of thermodynamics, since conduction electrons and the lattice collectively constitute an inseparable system. The entropy of one subsystem may decrease, but that of all components of a system must increase as the temperature is increased.

5. THE PELTIER COEFFICIENT FOR METALLIC JUNCTIONS

In Section 2, an expression has been derived in general terms for the Peltier coefficient Π_{AB} pertaining to the junction between any two metals A and B. In this section, we shall calculate Π_{AB} specifically for metallic junctions.

According to Eq. (23),

$$\Pi_{AB} = q^{-1} \left\{ [\epsilon_{f0} - \epsilon_f] + \int_0^T [s + T^{-1}(\epsilon_f - \tfrac{5}{3}\langle\epsilon\rangle)]\ d\tilde{T} \right\}_a^b. \tag{78}$$

Here, a and b are two points in metals A and B, respectively.

Using the results derived in the last section, we shall evaluate the various terms in Eq. (78). From Eq. (62), it follows that

$$\epsilon_{f0} - \epsilon_f \simeq \epsilon_{f0} \left[(\pi^2/12)(kT/\epsilon_{f0})^2 + 2\int_0^T \alpha_T\, d\tilde{T} \right]. \tag{79}$$

In view of Eq. (63), we may write

$$\int_0^T T^{-1}(\epsilon_f - \tfrac{5}{3}\langle\epsilon\rangle)\ d\tilde{T} \simeq -\int_0^T \tfrac{1}{2}\pi^2(k^2 T/\epsilon_f)\ d\tilde{T}$$

$$\simeq -\tfrac{1}{4}\pi^2[(kT)^2/\epsilon_{f0}]. \tag{80}$$

Integrating Eq. (77) between 0°K and T, the entropy s per particle will be expressed as

$$s = \epsilon_{f0}\left\{\tfrac{1}{2}\pi^2(k/\epsilon_{f0})^2 T - 6\int_0^T\left[(\alpha_T/T)\int_0^T \alpha_T\ d\tilde{T}\right] d\tilde{T}\right\}, \tag{81}$$

and

$$\int_0^T s\ d\tilde{T} = \epsilon_{f0}\left\{\tfrac{1}{4}\pi^2(kT/\epsilon_{f0})^2 - 6\int_0^T\int_0^T\left[(\alpha_T/T)\int_0^T \alpha_T\ d\tilde{T}\right] d\tilde{T}\ d\tilde{T}\right\}. \tag{82}$$

Substituting Eqs. (79), (80), and (82) into Eq. (78), we obtain

$$\Pi_{AB} \simeq \left\{(\epsilon_{f0}/q)\left[(\pi^2/12)(kT/\epsilon_{f0})^2 + 2\int_0^T \alpha_T\ d\tilde{T}\right]\right.$$

$$\left. -6(\epsilon_{f0}/q)\int_0^T\int_0^T\left[(\alpha_T/T)\int_0^T \alpha_T\ d\tilde{T}\right] d\tilde{T}\ d\tilde{T}\right\}_a^b. \tag{83}$$

Now let $\epsilon_{f0}(A)$ and $\alpha_T(A)$ be the Fermi energy at 0°K, and the linear thermal expansivity at a temperature T, respectively, for metal A; and $\epsilon_{f0}(B)$ and $\alpha_T(B)$ be the corresponding quantities for metal B. In terms of these four quantities, we may express the Peltier coefficient by

$$\Pi_{AB} \simeq 2\left[\frac{\epsilon_{f0}(B)}{q}\int_0^T \alpha_T(B)\ d\tilde{T} - \frac{\epsilon_{f0}(A)}{q}\int_0^T \alpha_T(A)\ d\tilde{T}\right]$$

$$-6\left\{\frac{\epsilon_{f0}(B)}{q}\int_0^T\int_0^T\left[\frac{\alpha_T(B)}{T}\int_0^T \alpha_T(B)\ d\tilde{T}\right] d\tilde{T}\ d\tilde{T}\right.$$

$$\left. -\frac{\epsilon_{f0}(A)}{q}\int_0^T\int_0^T\left[\frac{\alpha_T(A)}{T}\int_0^T \alpha_T(A)\ d\tilde{T}\right] d\tilde{T}\ d\tilde{T}\right\}$$

$$+\frac{\pi^2}{12}\left(\frac{kT}{q}\right)^2\left[\frac{q}{\epsilon_{f0}(B)} - \frac{q}{\epsilon_{f0}(A)}\right]. \tag{84}$$

From the manner in which α_T depends on T for metals—for example, see α_T for Cu in Fig. 3—it can be easily shown that

$$\int_0^T\int_0^T\left[\frac{\alpha_T(A)}{T}\int_0^T \alpha_T(A)\ d\tilde{T}\right] d\tilde{T}\ d\tilde{T} < \tfrac{1}{2}\alpha_T^2 T^2. \tag{85}$$

Consequently, the multiple-integral terms in Eq. (84) will be insignificantly small compared with the first two terms. Neglecting also the terms containing T^2, then Eq. (84) reduces to

$$\Pi_{AB} \simeq 2 \left[\frac{\epsilon_{f0}(B)}{q} \int_0^T \alpha_T(B) \ d\tilde{T} - \frac{\epsilon_{f0}(A)}{q} \int_0^T \alpha_T(A) \ d\tilde{T} \right]. \qquad (86)$$

Equation (86) should be accurate in a temperature range extending between $0°K$ and well above $1000°K$.

6. THE SEEBECK EFFECT IN METALS

In this section, we shall calculate the Seebeck voltage Υ_{ad} of the metallic thermocouple represented in Fig. 2. According to Eq. (52), the portion Υ_{bc} of Υ_{ad} generated by the nonconservative active force fields along the segment bc of the thermocouple may be expressed as

$$\Upsilon_{bc} = -q^{-1} \int_b^c \left[s - (d\epsilon_f/d\tilde{T}) - T^{-1}(\tfrac{5}{3}\langle\epsilon\rangle - \epsilon_f) \right]_\tau \nabla T \cdot d\mathbf{l}$$

$$= q^{-1} \int_{T_1}^{T_2} \left[(d\epsilon_f/d\tilde{T}) + T^{-1}(\tfrac{5}{3}\langle\epsilon\rangle - \epsilon_f) - s \right] dT. \qquad (87)$$

A similar expression may be written for Υ_{cd}. It should be noticed that the integration in Eq. (87) must be carried out in the real space, that is, with the parameter τ of the hyperspace kept constant. The right-hand side of Eq. (87) consists essentially of the algebraic sum of three integrals to be evaluated next.

From Eq. (62), it follows that

$$\int_b^c (d\epsilon_f/d\tilde{T}) \ \nabla T \cdot d\mathbf{l} = -\epsilon_{f0} \int_{T_1}^{T_2} \left[\tfrac{1}{6}\pi^2(k/\epsilon_{f0})^2 T + 2\alpha_T \right] dT$$

$$= -\epsilon_{f0} \left[(\pi^2/12)(k/\epsilon_{f0})^2(T_2{}^2 - T_1{}^2) + 2 \int_{T_1}^{T_2} \alpha_T \ dT \right]. \qquad (88)$$

Equations (62) and (63) make it possible to write

$$\int_b^c T^{-1}(\tfrac{5}{3}\langle\epsilon\rangle - \epsilon_f) \ \nabla T \cdot d\mathbf{l} \simeq \tfrac{1}{2}\pi^2(k/\epsilon_{f0})^2 \epsilon_{f0} \left\{ \int_{T_1}^{T_2} T \ dT + 2 \int_{T_1}^{T_2} \left[T \int_0^T \alpha_T \ d\tilde{T} \right] dT \right\}$$

$$= \tfrac{1}{4}\pi^2(k^2/\epsilon_{f0}) \left\{ (T_2{}^2 - T_1{}^2) + 4 \int_{T_1}^{T_2} T \left[\int_0^T \alpha_T \ d\tilde{T} \right] dT \right\}.$$

$$(89)$$

Using the value for s, expressed by Eq. (81), we have

$$\int_b^c s\nabla T \cdot d\mathbf{l} = \int_{T_1}^{T_2} s\, dT$$

$$\simeq \epsilon_{f0} \left\{ \tfrac{1}{4}\pi^2 (k/\epsilon_{f0})^2 (T_2{}^2 - T_1{}^2) - 6 \int_{T_1}^{T_2} \int_0^T \left[\frac{\alpha_T}{T} \int_0^T \alpha_T\, d\tilde{T} \right] d\tilde{T}\, dT \right\}.$$

$$(90)$$

Substituting Eqs. (88), (89) and (90) into Eq. (87), and neglecting the last term in Eq. (89), we get

$$\Upsilon_{bc} \simeq -q^{-1} \left\{ 2\epsilon_{f0}(B) \int_{T_1}^{T_2} \alpha_T(B)\, dT + \frac{\pi^2 k^2}{12\epsilon_{f0}(B)} (T_2{}^2 - T_1{}^2) \right.$$

$$\left. - 6\epsilon_{f0}(B) \int_{T_1}^{T_2} \int_0^T \left[\frac{\alpha_T(B)}{T} \int_0^T \alpha_T(B)\, d\tilde{T} \right] d\tilde{T}\, dT \right\}. \quad (91)$$

Here the letter (B) following ϵ_{f0} and α_T signifies pertinence to metal B, of which the segment bc of the thermocouple is made (Fig. 2).

Segment cd of the thermocouple is made of metal A. By comparison with Eq. (91), we may express the portion Υ_{cd} developed along this segment as

$$\Upsilon_{dc} = -q^{-1} \left\{ 2\epsilon_{f0}(A) \int_{T_1}^{T_2} \alpha_T(A)\, dT + \frac{\pi^2 k^2}{12\epsilon_{f0}(A)} (T_2{}^2 - T_1{}^2) \right.$$

$$\left. - 6\epsilon_{f0}(A) \int_{T_1}^{T_2} \int_0^T \left[\frac{\alpha_T(A)}{T} \int_0^T \alpha_T(A)\, d\tilde{T} \right] d\tilde{T}\, dT \right\}. \quad (92)$$

There will be no contribution to the Seebeck voltage by the segment ab of the thermocouple, or by the junctions b and c. For, in all these regions, $\nabla T = 0$, and the integration of Eq. (87) in the real space gives zero.

The overall Seebeck voltage Υ_{ad} for the thermocouple will be

$$\Upsilon_{ad} = \Upsilon_{ab} + \Upsilon_{bc} + \Upsilon_{cd} = \Upsilon_{bc} - \Upsilon_{dc}. \quad (93)$$

In view of Eqs. (91)–(93), Υ_{ad} may be expressed as

$$\Upsilon_{ad} \simeq 2 \left[\frac{\epsilon_{f0}(A)}{q} \int_{T_1}^{T_2} \alpha_T(A)\, dT - \frac{\epsilon_{f0}(B)}{q} \int_{T_1}^{T_2} \alpha_T(B)\, dT \right]$$

$$- 6 \left\{ \frac{\epsilon_{f0}(A)}{q} \int_{T_1}^{T_2} \int_0^T \left[\frac{\alpha_T(A)}{T} \int_0^T \alpha_T(A)\, d\tilde{T} \right] d\tilde{T}\, dT - \frac{\epsilon_{f0}(B)}{q} \right.$$

$$\left. \times \int_{T_1}^{T_2} \int_0^T \left[\frac{\alpha_T(B)}{T} \int_0^T \alpha_T(B)\, d\tilde{T} \right] d\tilde{T}\, dT \right\} + (\pi^2/12)(k/q)^2 (T_2{}^2 - T_1{}^2)$$

$$\times \{ [q/\epsilon_{f0}(A)] - [q/\epsilon_{f0}(B)] \}. \quad (94)$$

Since α_T is a monotonically increasing function of T (see Fig. 3), it can be shown that

$$\int_{T_1}^{T_2} \int_0^T \left[\frac{\alpha_T(A)}{T} \int_0^T \alpha_T(A) \, d\tilde{T} \right] d\tilde{T} \, dT < \tfrac{1}{2}\alpha_T^2(T_2^2 - T_1^2). \qquad (95)$$

Therefore, the multiple integral terms in Eq. (94) will be much smaller than the first two terms. This statement holds for a temperature range extending from $0°K$ up to about $1000°K$. In that range, it can be easily seen that, in Eq. (94), the two terms which depend on T^2 are also insignificantly small compared with the first two terms. Consequently, Eq. (94) reduces to

$$\Upsilon_{ad} \simeq 2 \left[\frac{\epsilon_{f0}(A)}{q} \int_{T_1}^{T_2} \alpha_T(A) \, dT - \frac{\epsilon_{f0}(B)}{q} \int_{T_1}^{T_2} \alpha_T(B) \, dT \right]. \qquad (96)$$

If we now differentiate Υ_{ad} with respect to temperature, one gets the relative thermoelectric power S_{AB} between two metals A and B. This quantity will be

$$S_{AB} \simeq (2/q) [\epsilon_{f0}(A)\alpha_T(A) - \epsilon_{f0}(B)\alpha_T(B)]. \qquad (97)$$

Using the methods of classical thermodynamics, it can be shown* (Blatt 1968) that

$$S_{AB} = \pi^2(k/q)^2 \{[q/\epsilon_f(A)] - [q/\epsilon_f(B)]\} T, \qquad \text{high-temperature limit,} \quad (98)$$

$$S_{AB} = \tfrac{1}{3}\pi^2(k/q)^2 \{[q/\epsilon_f(A)] - [q/\epsilon_f(B)]\} T, \qquad \text{low-temperature limit.} \quad (99)$$

Multiplying Eqs. (98) and (99) by (∇T) and integrating in the real space from a point at T_1 to a point at T_2, we get the Seebeck voltage, which may be written as

$$\Upsilon_{ad} \simeq \tfrac{1}{2}\pi^2(k/q)^2 \{[q/\epsilon_f(A)] - [q/\epsilon_f(B)]\} (T_2^2 - T_1^2),$$

$$\text{high-temperature limit,} \quad (100)$$

$$\Upsilon_{ad} \simeq \tfrac{1}{6}\pi^2(k/q)^2 \{[q/\epsilon_f(A)] - [q/\epsilon_f(B)]\} (T_2^2 - T_1^2),$$

$$\text{low-temperature limit.} \quad (101)$$

The derivations of S_{AB}, based on the methods of classical thermodynamics, necessarily involve dependence on the electron mean free path, for which models have been assumed. By contrast, using the thermodynamic theory of generalized fields has made it possible to determine the Seebeck voltage, thermoelectric power and the Peltier coefficient in terms of the Fermi energy, thermal expansivity and *no other* than the universal constants. No hypotheses *ad hoc* have been deemed necessary to use.

---

* The reference cited above derives the absolute thermoelectric power, from which the relative one S_{AB} follows at once.

It is interesting to notice that for many metals, results obtained for Υ and S by the thermodynamic theory of generalized fields, and by classical thermodynamics, have different algebraic signs. This is because ϵ_f occurs in the numerator in Eqs. (96) and (97); whereas ϵ_f is in the denominator in Eqs. (98)–(101).

For many metals, the discrepancy, in both sign and magnitude, is well known to occur between the classical theories for S and Υ and experiment. Concerning the thermoelectric power for metals, expressed by Eqs. (98) and (99), Blatt (1968, p. 211), for example, states:

"Comparison of the above (classical) theory with experiment allows only one conclusion: The theory is woefully inadequate in explaining the observed thermopowers (thermoelectric powers) of even the monovalent metals. These frequently prove to be positive, rather than negative as [Eqs. (98) and (99)]* would predict."

7. THEORY AND EXPERIMENT

On the basis of the theory of generalized fields, we have derived expressions for the Peltier coefficient Π, the Seebeck voltage Υ, and the relative thermoelectric power S. Expressions have actually been derived in general terms, and for metals with a standard electron energy band.

The Seebeck voltage of a thermocouple, and the Peltier coefficient for each one of the thermocouple junctions, can be measured by direct experimental means. However, Υ has the significant advantage over Π of lending itself to accurate and totally electrical measurements. In many instances, one finds data for Π, determined from Υ by classical theoretical relations, rather than by direct experiment. Such data for Π cannot, of course, be used as a basis to check predictions consequential to the thermodynamic theory of generalized fields.

From Eqs. (96) and (97), it is apparent that Υ and S can be calculated theoretically, if one has accurate data on the linear thermal expansivity, α_T, of the metals.

Figure 3 represents an extensive set of data for copper compiled and studied by Hahn (1970). The measurements, represented in Fig. 3, were conducted by thirty-seven investigators. The figure shows an appreciable departure from the average values. The scattering is generally within 10% of the average curve, with the exception of a few points. This author tends to think that the scattering in the α_T data is not totally caused by observational errors. In fact, the different mechanical, chemical, and metallurgical methods of preparation of different samples may be equally to blame, if not the primary cause of the scattering.

As seen in Eqs. (96) and (97), a small error in the measurement of α_T will cause the errors in the calculated values of Υ and S to be magnified

* These equations are (7.48) and (7.49), respectively, in the quoted reference.

many times, since, usually, $\epsilon_{f0} \gg 1$ eV. For example, $\epsilon_{f0} = 7$ eV for copper, and $\epsilon_{f0} = 5.5$ eV for gold. A list of the Fermi energies for other metals with a standard electron energy band may be found in Appendix C, p. 247.

Precautions for Future Experiments. It is strongly suggested that in future experiments, *not only* that samples used for measuring α_T and S should have the same chemical composition, but also they should be prepared in identical ways metallurgically and mechanically. Quite preferably, the same sample, somehow, should be used for both the thermal expansivity and the thermoelectric power experiments. Unfortunately, experimental data taken with such precautions do not exist at present. Consequently, comparison of theory and experiment cannot be significant.

8. SUMMARY

8.1. *The Peltier and Seebeck Effects and the Hyperspace Equation*

On the basis of the hyperspace equation, we have derived general expressions for the Peltier coefficient Π, and the Seebeck voltage Υ, between any two solids. More specific answers have been obtained for metals with electron energy bands of a standard type.

Determining Π has been accomplished by integrating the hyperspace equation over a four-dimensional segment, involving the independent temperature axis $\tilde{T}$ of the hyperspace, and the width of the junction between two different media. To evaluate the resulting arbitrary function, the hyperspace boundary conditions have been invoked.

To determine Υ, two fundamental solutions of the hyperspace equation have been used. The first solution prescribes that active and passive voltages around the closed loop are equal. The second solution makes it possible to evaluate the active Seebeck voltage, Υ, around the loop.

8.2. *Residual and Nonresidual Force Fields*

The Seebeck voltage, Υ, has been shown to be equal to the real-space, closed-loop line integral of what has been defined as the total residual, active force field, $\mathbf{f}_{taR}$. The components of $\mathbf{f}_{taR}$ are all force fields which involve ∇T. Specifically, in the case of a thermocouple, these components are: the thermomotive field,

$$\mathbf{f}_T = s\,\nabla T, \tag{102}$$

and only a portion of the diffusion field, given by

$$\mathrm{Res}\,(\mathbf{f}_d) = -n^{-1}(dP/d\tilde{T})\,\nabla T. \tag{103}$$

The nonresidual force fields, which do not contribute to the Seebeck voltage, are the electrostatic force field,

$$\mathbf{f}_e = -q\mathbf{E}, \tag{104}$$

and the nonresidual component of the diffusion field, expressed as

$$\text{Nonres}(f_d) = -n^{-1}(\nabla P)_T.$$ (105)

For metals with electron energy bands of a standard type, it has been shown that Eqs. (103) and (105) reduce to

$$\text{Res}(f_d) = -(d\epsilon_f/d\tilde{T})\,\nabla T - T^{-1}[\tfrac{5}{3}\langle\epsilon\rangle - \epsilon_f]\,\nabla T,$$ (106)

$$\text{Nonres}(f_d) = -(\nabla\epsilon_f)_T.$$ (107)

Equations (106) and (107) follow at once from Eq. (31).

9. DISCUSSION

The object in this section is to compare briefly between results obtained for the Seebeck effect on the basis of classical methods and the thermodynamic theory of generalized fields. It will be further explained how the most significant components of the Seebeck voltage cannot possibly be derived by classical thermodynamics and/or equivalent methods.

In the framework of the theory of generalized fields, as summarized above, the Seebeck voltage is contributed only by: (1) f_T, and (2) $\text{Res}(f_d)$. The other nonresidual force fields, consisting of (1) f_e, and (2) $\text{Nonres}(f_d)$, have jointly a vanishing closed-loop line integral through the thermocouple, and, therefore, contribute to no Seebeck voltage. There are no requirements whatever that, above 0°K, the summation of f_e and $\text{Nonres}(f_d)$ is to be zero at every point. At 0°K, however, $f_{ta}=0$, $\text{Res}\,f_{ta}=0$, and $\text{Nonres}\,f_{ta}=0$.

In analyzing the Seebeck voltage Υ, for metals, we have seen that the most significant component of Υ is contributed by $(d\epsilon_f/d\tilde{T})$. This conclusion can be arrived at by inspecting Eqs. (87)–(90) and (96). Evidently, $(d\epsilon_f/d\tilde{T})$ is only a part of the residual force field, $\text{Res}(f_d)$, which, in turn, is a part of f_d. In total

$$f_d = -\nabla\epsilon_f - T^{-1}[\tfrac{5}{3}\langle\epsilon\rangle - \epsilon_f]\,\nabla T.$$ (108)

Now let us turn to the results obtained for Υ by classical methods. By comparing Eqs. (89) and (90) with Eqs. (100) and (101), one can observe that the classical values of Υ are of the same character as some terms obtained by the theory of generalized fields. Unfortunately, the classical terms mispredict the experimental values, not only in magnitude but, in most cases, in voltage polarity sign as well.

Are the terms, appearing in the expressions for Υ [Eqs. (100) and (101)], the only ones obtainable by classical thermodynamics and/or equivalent methods? Actually, an additional term usually comes out (Blatt 1957) to be $(-\nabla\epsilon_f)$. However, it is mathematically impossible for this term to contribute to the Seebeck voltage. For around any closed-loop in any system, the line integral

$$\oint \nabla \epsilon_f \cdot d\mathbf{l} = 0. \tag{109}$$

Thus, the term $(-\nabla \epsilon_f)$ is dropped out in the classical theories, as it should from a mathematical point of view.

It is interesting to state that in the framework of the theory of generalized fields, the nature of $(-\nabla \epsilon_f)$ is *not* at all electrostatic, as it is in the framework of the classical theories. As seen in Eq. (108), $(-\nabla \epsilon_f)$ is a component of $\mathbf{f}_d$, the nature of which is a force in the Newtonian sense, strictly associated with an internal pressure gradient.

How the term $(-\nabla \epsilon_f)$ in Eq. (108) leads to the most significant contribution pertinent to the Seebeck voltage, is already discussed earlier in this section and the preceding one.

It has been shown in this chapter that the temperature variation of the Fermi energy in metals is most predominantly contributed by the lattice thermal expansion. In the theory of the Seebeck and Peltier effects, based on the thermodynamic theory of generalized fields, the thermal expansivity proved to be fundamentally important. For, the theoretical results depend on both the Fermi energy and the thermal expansivity of the metals.

If one accounts for the thermal expansivity in the classical theories, however, the answers will be modified only by negligible amounts, as may be observed in Eqs. (62), and (98)–(101).

PROBLEMS

1. Verify Eqs. (14), (15), and (16).

2. Accounting for thermal expansivity α_T, show that, for conduction electrons in metals, ζ [as expressed by Eq. (36)] vanishes at $0°K$. Assume that, sufficiently close to $0°K$, $\alpha_T = a_0 T^3$, where a_0 is a constant.

3. For a fermion system, having a constant number of particles and a constant volume at all temperatures, show by inspection (on the basis of the answer to Prob. 2) that ζ vanishes at $0°K$.

4. For a boson system, derive an expression for ζ. The expression should be of the same general form as that of Eq. (36).

5. For a boson system, having a constant number of particles and a constant volume at all temperatures, show that ζ vanishes at $0°K$.

6. Derive Eq. (64) from Eq. (63).

7. Accounting for the thermal expansivity, derive, for electrons in metals with a standard energy band, the diffusion component Π_{ABd} and the electrostatic component Π_{ABe} of the Peltier coefficient Π_{AB} between two metals

A and B. Verify that the summation of the two components equals Π_{AB}, as expressed by Eq. (86).

8. Show that if the thermocouple of Fig. 2 has points a and d at a temperature T_0, and points b and c at T_1 and T_2, respectively, then the Seebeck voltage Υ_{ad} will still be the same as expressed by Eq. (94).

9. For metals with a standard electron energy band, using Eq. (84), derive an expression for the Peltier coefficient Π_{AB} applicable only near the absolute zero. Assume in that temperature range that $\alpha_T \simeq a_0 T^3$, where a_0 is a constant.

10. Under the same assumptions stated for Prob. 9, derive an expression for the Seebeck voltage Υ_{ad} for the thermocouple shown in Fig. 2. Use Eq. (94) as a starting point.

11. Verify inequality (85).

12. Verify inequality (95).

13. Explain why in an electron system, such as in metals, the existence of *passive* force fields, other than $\mathbf{f}_{es}$, constitutes a violation of the conditions underlying the derivation of the hyperspace equation and its two fundamental solutions. Explain why no such restrictions exist for active fields.

14. Show generally that, under the conditions for which the hyperspace equation is derived, the total active nonresidual force field is conservative.

REFERENCES

Blatt, F. J. 1957, Solid State Physics, vol. 4, p. 199, Academic Press.
—— 1968, Physics of Electronic Conduction in Solids, McGraw-Hill.
Bridgeman, P. W. 1934, The Thermodynamics of Electrical Phenomena in Metals, Macmillan.
Egli, P. H. 1958, Thermoelectricity, John Wiley.
Frederikse, H. P. R. 1953, Phys. Rev. **91**, 491.
Goldsmid, H. J. 1960, Applications of Thermoelectricity, John Wiley.
Hahn, T. A. 1970, J. Appl. Phys. **41**, 5096.
Herring, C. 1953, Phys. Rev. **92**, 857; **92**, 248; **92**, 857.
—— 1954, *Ibid.*, **96**, 1163.
Ioffe, A. F. 1957, Semiconductor, Thermoelements and Thermoelectric Cooling, Infosearch, London.
Kittel, C. 1966, Introduction to Solid-State Physics, John Wiley.
—— 1971, Introduction to Solid-State Physics, John Wiley (4th ed.).
Peltier, J. C. 1834, Ann. Chim. et Phys. **56**, 371.
Seebeck, T. J. 1826, Ann. Physik Pogg. **6**, 1, 133, 253.
Thomson, W. (Lord Kelvin) 1882, Mathematical and Physical Papers, Vol. 1, p. 316, Cambridge University Press, Cambridge.
Ziman, J. M. 1960, Electrons and Phonons, Oxford University Press.

Chapter 10

SUPERCONDUCTIVITY AND SUPERFLUIDITY AND THE TEMPERATURE-POSITION HYPERSPACE

1. INTRODUCTION

In Chapter 8, we defined the temperature-position hyperspace. We have further derived a fundamental differential equation expressing the conservation of transport energy in that hyperspace. Systems considered have been those for which each identifiable particle flux density is solenoidal.

It has also been explained in Chapter 8, and demonstrated by examples in Chapter 9, that complete solutions of the hyperspace equation require specifying its boundary conditions. From fundamental considerations, these conditions have been determined for any system generally at the absolute zero. At that temperature, specifically, passive fields vanish individually and intrinsic, active fields vanish collectively.

In this chapter, we shall briefly investigate the possibility that the phenomena of superconductivity and superfluidity are fundamental consequences of the conservation of transport energy in the temperature-position hyperspace and its boundary conditions at the absolute zero. To do so, we shall first determine a generalized relationship which, if satisfied at every temperature T in the interval $0 \leq T \leq T_0$, will then have the boundary conditions of the hyperspace remaining fixed in value at any temperature in the said interval. We shall then show that the individual vanishing of passive force fields and collective vanishing of intrinsic active force fields underlie several of the experimentally observed phenomena of superconductivity and superfluidity. Specifically, for systems consisting of electrically charged particles, we shall see that it is *forbidden* to have any one of the following: (1) heat dissipation, that is, a nonvanishing electrical resistivity; (2) thermoelectric phenomena of any kind; (3) electric currents in the interior of the system; and (4) a magnetic flux inside the system. It is *allowable*, however, for charged particles to have surface conduction.

The preceding five properties are characteristic of superconductors (Shoenberg 1960).

For electrically neutral fluids, if the boundary conditions of the hyperspace are satisfied above the absolute zero, then it is *forbidden* to have heat dissipation (nonvanishing viscosity). On the other hand, it is *allowable* to have both surface and bulk flow.

The properties just described are characteristic of superfluids (Atkins 1959, Donnelly 1967).

On the basis of the condition which requires preserving the hyperspace boundary conditions above the absolute zero, we shall further show that fermion assemblies cannot be superconductors, or superfluids.

2. PRESERVATION OF THE HYPERSPACE BOUNDARY CONDITIONS ABOVE THE ABSOLUTE ZERO

Without loss of generality, consider a one-constituent system. Let the particle flux density be solenoidal at all points of that system. Under such conditions, as shown in Chapter 8, the conservation of transport energy in the temperature-position hyperspace may be expressed by

$$d(\mathbf{f}_{ta}-\mathbf{f}_{ts})/d\tilde{T} = \nabla[s-(1/n)(dP/d\tilde{T})], \tag{1}$$

provided that the particle flux density is solenoidal, even when the independent temperature axis of the hyperspace is being swept. Here $\mathbf{f}_{ta}$ and $\mathbf{f}_{ts}$ are the resultants of all intrinsic active, and passive force fields, respectively; s the entropy per particle, n the particle concentration, and P the internal pressure.

As arrived at in Chapter 8, at the absolute zero in any system generally, even under nonequilibrium conditions

$$\mathbf{f}_{ta}=0, \tag{2}$$

$$\mathbf{f}_{1s}=0, \quad \mathbf{f}_{2s}=0, \quad \mathbf{f}_{3s}=0, \quad \cdots, \quad \mathbf{f}_{is}=0, \tag{3}$$

$$\mathbf{f}_{ts}=0. \tag{4}$$

The force fields $\mathbf{f}_{is}$, $i=1, 2, \cdots$, are the components of $\mathbf{f}_{ts}$. The last three equations must be satisfied for each constituent in a multicomponent system at $0°$K.

Let us now determine the condition requiring Eqs. (2) and (3) to remain satisfied, as the temperature at various points of a system departs from the absolute zero. The system in its final state does not have to be isothermal. Generation of the temperature profile of the system must proceed, of course, as described by Eqs. (5) and (6) in Chapter 8.

Suppose for the moment that

$$\nabla[s-(1/n)(dP/d\tilde{T})]=0, \qquad \text{for } 0\leq T\leq T_0, \tag{5}$$

then from Eq. (1), we get

$$d(\mathbf{f}_{ta}-\mathbf{f}_{ts})/d\tilde{T}=0, \qquad \text{for } 0\leq T\leq T_0, \tag{6}$$

or

$$d\mathbf{f}_{ta}/d\tilde{T}=d\mathbf{f}_{ts}/d\tilde{T}, \qquad \text{for } 0\leq T\leq T_0. \tag{7}$$

Recalling that, except for the relation expressing the conservation of transport energy around closed, real and hyperspatial loops, $\mathbf{f}_{ta}$ and $\mathbf{f}_{ts}$ have no point relationship. For example, in a battery connected to a resistor, the electron active force field in the first element and the electron passive force field in the second are not at all equal at any point of the system, and more generally have no point relationship. The reader may consider for himself other cases such as p-n junctions, and metal interfaces.

Consequently, for Eq. (7) to be generally satisfied, despite that f_{ta} and f_{ts} are generally unrelated, we must have

$$f_{ta} = K_1, \quad f_{ts} = K_2, \qquad \text{for } 0 \leq T \leq T_0, \tag{8}$$

where K_1 and K_2 are two arbitrary constants which are independent of temperature. Equation (8) will require that each one of the two force fields f_{ta} and f_{ts} retain its hyperspace boundary value. Accordingly,

$$f_{ta} = 0, \qquad \text{for } 0 \leq T \leq T_0, \tag{9}$$

and

$$f_{ts} = 0, \qquad \text{for } 0 \leq T \leq T_0. \tag{10}$$

Now if Eq. (10) is to be satisfied, it is necessary and sufficient that

$$f_{1s} = 0, \quad f_{2s} = 0, \quad f_{3s} = 0, \quad \cdots, \quad f_{is} = 0. \tag{11}$$

For, if any of the components of f_{ts} is nonvanishing, regardless of direction, positive heat dissipation necessarily results. Yet there can be no heat dissipation anywhere in the system, since $f_{ta} = 0$, and $f_{ts} = 0$, and consequently the line integral of $(f_{ta} - f_{ts})$ between any two points in the system must vanish.

We, therefore, conclude that active and passive force fields in any system will retain their absolute-zero values at any temperature T lying in the range extending between $0°$K and T_0, if Eq. (5) is satisfied in that range. Let us see next how Eq. (5) can be satisfied.

In that equation, the operand,

$$s - (1/n)(dP/d\tilde{T}) = \Theta, \tag{12}$$

in general, can be made a function of the position coordinates x, y, z. For example, for a system of electrons, the entropy s per particle is a function of the absolute-zero value ϵ_{f0} of the Fermi energy [see Eq. (81), Chapter 9] and T. But ϵ_{f0} is generally a function of position, and so is T.

Accordingly,

$$\Theta = \Theta(x, y, z). \tag{13}$$

Now for

$$\nabla\Theta = 0, \qquad 0 \leq T \leq T_0, \tag{14}$$

$$\Theta = K, \qquad 0 \leq T \leq T_0, \tag{15}$$

where K is a constant, which does not depend on position. Since K does not depend on temperature either, its value is the same as that at $0°K$. We now observe that, for any system, by definition,

$$s = 0, \quad \text{at } T = 0. \quad (16)$$

Furthermore, it is a consequence of the third law of thermodynamics that

$$dP/d\tilde{T} = 0, \quad \text{at } T = 0. \quad (17)$$

Thus, from Eqs. (12), and (15)–(17), we get

$$\Theta = 0, \quad \text{for } 0 \leq T \leq T_0. \quad (18)$$

Equation (18) represents the only possible general solution of Eq. (14), subject, of course, to the requirements of the third law of thermodynamics.

We may, therefore, conclude that in order to keep the absolute-zero hyperspace boundary conditions unchanged in our system up to a temperature T_0, we must have

$$s = (1/n) (dP/d\tilde{T}), \quad \text{for } 0 \leq T \leq T_0. \quad (19)$$

As stated earlier, Eq. (19) is automatically satisfied at the absolute zero in any system.

3. PREDICTABILITY OF SOME OBSERVED PHENOMENA OF SUPERCONDUCTIVITY AND SUPERFLUIDITY

In the last section, we have explored the possibility of keeping unchanged the boundary values of the hyperspace at temperatures above the absolute zero. These boundary values are expressed by Eqs. (9) and (11). In this section we shall investigate some fundamental properties possessed by electrically neutral and charged fluids (electrons) for which Eqs. (9) and (11) are satisfied.

Property I: Forbidden Dissipation. The disappearance of all passive force fields under nonequilibrium conditions means that it is impossible to have heat generated at any point in any system when there is a nonvanishing particle flux density everywhere in the system. Disappearance of dissipation is a well-known phenomenon observable both in superfluids and superconductors. These two phenomena were first discovered by Onnes in 1908 and 1911, respectively (Onnes 1908, 1911, 1912).

Property II: Disappearance of Thermoelectric Phenomena. We have seen in Chapter 9 that the Peltier coefficient Π for a junction equals the line integral of (f_{ta}/q) through the junction. Therefore, $\Pi = 0$, whenever $f_{ta} = 0$. This will be the case, even if there is a temperature gradient at various points of the junction leading to a finite temperature difference between both sides of the junction.

We have further seen in Chapter 9 that the Seeback voltage Υ of a thermocouple, whose two junctions are at different temperatures, is related to the total active residual force field $\mathbf{f}_{taR}$ in the system by

$$\Upsilon = q^{-1} \oint \mathbf{f}_{taR} \cdot d\mathbf{l}, \qquad (20)$$

where

$$\mathbf{f}_{taR} = s \, \nabla T + \text{Res}(\mathbf{f}_d), \qquad (21)$$

$$\mathbf{f}_{da} = -(1/n) \, \nabla P. \qquad (22)$$

Identification of the polarity of Υ has been ignored in Eq. (20), for it is irrelevant to our present discussion.

The nonresidual force fields, however, are bound by the hyperspace equation to make no contribution whatsoever to Υ. The resultant of these force fields is given by

$$\mathbf{f}_0 = \mathbf{f}_e + \text{Nonres}(\mathbf{f}_d). \qquad (23)$$

The electron internal pressure P may be considered to be a function of the absolute-zero value of the Fermi energy ϵ_{f0}, and temperature. In turn, ϵ_{f0} is a function of the Cartesian position coordinates x, y, z. Hence,

$$P = P[T, x, y, z]. \qquad (24)$$

We may, therefore, write

$$\nabla P = (\nabla P)_T + (dP/d\tilde{T}) \, \nabla T. \qquad (25)$$

From Eqs. (22) and (25), it follows that

$$\mathbf{f}_{da} = -(1/n)(\nabla P)_T - (1/n)(dP/d\tilde{T}) \, \nabla T. \qquad (26)$$

The force fields $\mathbf{f}_{taR}$ and $\mathbf{f}_0$ may now be expressed more specifically as follows:

$$\mathbf{f}_{taR} = [s - (1/n)(dP/d\tilde{T})] \, \nabla T, \qquad (27)$$

$$\mathbf{f}_0 = [f_e - (1/n)(\nabla P)_T]. \qquad (28)$$

Suppose that we have in a system the hyperspace boundary conditions satisfied above the absolute zero, that is, Eq. (19) is satisfied, then at once we can see that $\mathbf{f}_{taR} = 0$, even when $\nabla T \neq 0$. Equation (20), then, requires that

$$\Upsilon = 0, \qquad \text{for } 0 \leq T \leq T_0, \qquad (29)$$

even when the two junctions of the thermocouple are at different temperatures.

We conclude that the Peltier and Seebeck effects must continue to disappear, above the absolute zero up to a temperature T_0 in any thermo-

couple, if the hyperspace boundary conditions are satisfied at any temperature T, for which $0 \leq T \leq T_0$. Such properties are well known to be characteristics of superconductors (Cusack 1958).

It is interesting to observe that since $\mathbf{f}_{ta} = 0$, $\mathbf{f}_{taR} = 0$, and $\mathbf{f}_{ta} = \mathbf{f}_0 + \mathbf{f}_{taR}$,
then $\mathbf{f}_0 = 0$. Thus, whenever the hyperspace boundary conditions are
frozen in a system above the absolute zero, the total residual force field
vanishes and likewise the total nonresidual force field vanishes. This statement does not, in any way, mean that the individual components of these
fields should vanish.

*Property III: Forbidden Electrical Conduction in the Interior of Charged
Fluids.* If the total active force field $\mathbf{f}_{ta}$ vanishes everywhere in a system,
clearly then, no single finite force field can exist by itself. For, if the number
of distinguishable force fields is not zero, then it must be two, or more.
This matter has been discussed in Chapter 8 [Section 5].

Suppose now that it were possible to pass a steady-state electric current,
with a density $\mathbf{J}$ through the interior of a medium in which $\mathbf{f}_{ta} = 0$, and
$\mathbf{f}_{is} = 0$, $i = 1, 2, 3, \cdots$. In this case the current carriers—electrons, for
example—will have a nonvanishing flow velocity $\mathbf{v}$ throughout the medium.
The existence of a current density $\mathbf{J}$ produces within the bulk a magnetic
field intensity $\mathbf{H}$ such that

$$\mathbf{J} = \nabla \times \mathbf{H}. \tag{30}$$

But $\mathbf{H}$ will be associated with a magnetic flux density $\mathbf{B}$, given by

$$\mathbf{B} = \mu \mathbf{H}, \tag{31}$$

where μ is the magnetic permeability. Therefore, in the electron stream,
each electron will statistically be subject to a Lorentz force, $\mathbf{f}_{la}$, which is
intrinsic and active. This force field

$$\mathbf{f}_{la} = -q\mathbf{v} \times \mathbf{B}. \tag{32}$$

If there were no force fields in the interior of the system, other than
possibly $\mathbf{f}_{la}$, then satisfying the boundary conditions of the hyperspace
requires simply that

$$\mathbf{f}_{la} = 0. \tag{33}$$

Since $\mathbf{B}$ would be induced by $\mathbf{J}$, then $\mathbf{B}$ should vanish whenever $\mathbf{J}$ vanishes,
and conversely. But at any one point in the interior of the system, $\mathbf{v}$ is
proportional to $\mathbf{J}$. Therefore, $\mathbf{v}$ and $\mathbf{B}$, if they vanish, they must do so
simultaneously. In view of Eqs. (32) and (33), it is evident, then, that
inside the system under consideration

$$\mathbf{v} = 0, \tag{34}$$

that is

$$\mathbf{J} = 0. \tag{35}$$

Thus, for a charged fluid, whenever the hyperspace boundary conditions are satisfied in a continuous temperature range extending down to the absolute zero, it is forbidden in that temperature range to have electrical conduction in the interior of the fluid. This property is a well known phenomenon observed in superconductors (Kittel 1971).

Property IV: Allowable Surface Electrical Conduction. The surface of a medium, such as that of a metal, may be regarded as an interface between the system and air, vacuum, or whatever surroundings there may be. In that interface, the current carriers—in this case electrons—have a concentration gradient, and consequently an internal pressure gradient. The latter supports an active electron diffusion field f_{da}.

Now if for our electrons the hyperspace boundary values are satisfied, then f_{da} cannot be the only force field. An active electrostatic force field f_{ea} has to be established in the interface such that

$$f_{da} + f_{ea} = 0. \tag{36}$$

The force field f_{ea} requires, of course, that there will be a space charge in the interface.

Let us now see if a surface current is allowable. If there is such a current, it will induce a magnetic field **H** and a magnetic flux density **B**. At various points within the surface, **B** and **H** will be parallel to this surface and perpendicular to the current. In turn, **B** and the current will generate an active Lorentz force field f_{la}, as described by Eq. (32). Clearly, f_{la} is perpendicular to the surface. Thus, f_{la} is in the same direction as f_{da} and f_{ea}. To satisfy the hyperspace boundary conditions, then

$$f_{da} + f_{ea} + f_{la} = 0. \tag{37}$$

Accordingly, surface electrical conduction is allowable. By a similar argument, this conclusion holds for any electrically charged fluid, provided that the hyperspace boundary conditions are satisfied.

Surface conduction is well known to occur in superconductors (Shoenberg 1952).

Property V: Forbidden Magnetic Flux and Magnetic Field in the Interior of Charged Fluids. Consider a charged fluid bounded by a closed surface. Let the boundary conditions of the hyperspace be satisfied for that system. Suppose that the system is in thermal equilibrium, although placed in a magnetic field.

If it were possible for the magnetic flux to exist within the system, it must then penetrate through the surface where electrical conduction is allowable. We could then pass a current through the interfacial surface of the body. Hence, a Lorentz force field would be generated peripherally through the interfacial surface. But a single finite force field cannot exist while the hyperspace conditions are satisfied. Hence, the component of **B** normal to the outer boundary of the body must vanish at every point of this interface.

As explained in Chapter 3, the magnetic flux lines are invariably continuous in any medium and even at the boundary between two different media. It follows then that **B** must vanish throughout the interior of the body under consideration.

We conclude then that the existence of magnetic flux lines is forbidden in the interior of a charged fluid, for which the hyperspace boundary conditions are satisfied. This property is a well known phenomenon, first discovered in superconductors by Meissner and Ochsenfeld (1933).

It should be pointed out here that in the literature, it has been generally recognized that $B = 0$ inside a superconductor. This result is directly observable by experiment. However, it has been generally assumed that **H** does not necessarily vanish. To resolve between the two results with the relation: $B = \mu H$, it has been concluded that $\mu = 0$ in the bulk of the superconductor.

Our theory, however, suggests that, in the bulk of a superconductor, both **H** and **B** vanish simultaneously. For, if $\mu = 0$ inside the system, then **v** in Eq. (32) does not have to vanish to make $f_{la} = 0$. Unfortunately, direct experimental observation of **H** inside a superconductor is believed to be difficult, if not impossible. However, observing the configuration of both the **B** and **H** lines in the close neighborhood of a superconductor is, of course, possible. Such observation suggests that, like **B** lines, the **H** lines would not penetrate a superconductor.

Property VI: Allowable Bulk and Surface Flow in Electrically Neutral Fluids. In a neutral fluid, such as superfluid helium, a Lorentz force field does not exist. Accordingly, under isothermal conditions, which is necessarily the case as observed by experiment, there are no active fields whatever in the bulk. Thus, there are no restrictions on flow in the interior of the fluid.

Within the interface constituting the surface, above the absolute zero, there must be a diffusion field f_d. This field will therefore require the existence of another active electrostatic field. For the latter to be established in the interfacial space, the particles have to be electrically polarized. Electrons in the atoms of the fluid lying within the interface have to shift positions.

Accordingly, we conclude that the bulk and surface flow for an electrically-neutral fluid are both allowable with the hyperspace boundary conditions satisfied for the fluid. These properties are observable in superfluid helium (Allen 1966).

4. NONSUPERCONDUCTING PROPERTY OF ELECTRONS OBEYING THE FERMI–DIRAC STATISTICS AND HAVING A STANDARD ENERGY BAND

In a number of metals, conduction electrons have a standard band. The object of this section is to investigate for such electrons whether the boundary conditions of the hyperspace can be satisfied above the absolute zero. Specifically, we shall determine whether

$$s = (1/n)\,(dP/d\tilde{T}), \tag{38}$$

can be satisfied for $T > 0$.

For electrons with a standard band, we have derived in Chapter 9 a number of results of relevance here. These results are as follows:

$$s = \epsilon_{f0}\left\{\tfrac{1}{2}\pi^2\left(\frac{k}{\epsilon_{f0}}\right)^2 T - 6\int_0^T\left[\frac{\alpha_T}{T}\int_0^T \alpha_T\,d\tilde{T}\right]d\tilde{T}\right\}, \tag{39}$$

$$(1/n)\,(dP/d\tilde{T}) = (d\epsilon_f/d\tilde{T}) - (1/T)\,(\epsilon_f - \tfrac{5}{3}\langle\epsilon\rangle), \tag{40}$$

$$\epsilon_f \simeq \epsilon_{f0}\left[1 - \tfrac{1}{12}\pi^2\left(\frac{kT}{\epsilon_{f0}}\right)^2 - 2\int_0^T \alpha_T\,d\tilde{T}\right], \tag{41}$$

$$\langle\epsilon\rangle = \tfrac{3}{5}\epsilon_{f0}\left[1 + \tfrac{1}{12}(5\pi^2)\left(\frac{kT}{\epsilon_{f0}}\right)^2 - 2\int_0^T \alpha_T\,d\tilde{T}\right]. \tag{42}$$

Equations (39)–(42) have, in Chapter 9, the following numbers: (81), (20), (62) and (64), respectively.

Sufficiently near the absolute zero, the thermal expansivity α_T may be expressed as

$$\alpha_T = a_0 T^3, \tag{43}$$

where a_0 is a constant which depends on the metal.

In view of Eqs. (39)–(42), we have

$$s = \epsilon_{f0}\left[\tfrac{1}{2}\pi^2(k/\epsilon_{f0})^2 T - \tfrac{3}{14}\alpha_T^2 T\right], \tag{44}$$

$$(1/n)\,(dP/d\tilde{T}) = \pi^2 k^2 T/3\epsilon_{f0} - 2\alpha_T\epsilon_{f0}. \tag{45}$$

Clearly,

$$s \neq (1/n)\,(dP/d\tilde{T}), \qquad \text{for } T > 0, \tag{46}$$

although

$$s = (1/n)\,(dP/d\tilde{T}) = 0, \qquad \text{at } T = 0. \tag{47}$$

We may conclude that, except at the absolute zero, it is not possible for electrons obeying the Fermi–Dirac statistics and having a standard band to be superconducting. Such statistics and energy band characterize conduction electrons in metals which include the following: lithium, sodium, potassium, copper, silver, gold, and cesium.

It is interesting to state that no evidence of superconductivity was experimentally found, in almost all the metals just mentioned, down to the lowest temperatures studied (Matthias, Geballe, Compton 1963). Specifically, lithium, sodium and potassium were still normal conductors down to 0.08°, 0.09°, and 0.08°K, respectively. Also copper, silver, and gold behaved still as normal conductors down to 0.05°, 0.35°, and 0.05°K, respectively.

The preceding experimental results have been obtained at atmospheric pressure. It has been found, however, that cesium becomes a superconductor below the critical temperature of 1.5°K at a pressure of 110 kilobars, after several phase transformations. Under such extreme conditions one cannot possibly expect that the electron energy band in the metal will remain simply parabolic. Thus, for such severe pressures, the treatment and conclusions arrived at in this section would not hold.

5. SUMMARY AND CONCLUSION

In this chapter, we have deduced a new general thermodynamic relation requiring that the hyperspace boundary conditions be preserved above the absolute zero. Systems considered have been those containing no other than solenoidal particle flux densities, even when the $\tilde{T}$-axis is being swept. We have further shown that fluids, for which the hyperspace boundary conditions are satisfied in a continuous temperature range beginning at 0°K, necessarily exhibit the observable phenomena of superconductivity or superfluidity, depending on whether the particles are electrically charged, or neutral, respectively.

That in a superconductor a temperature gradient is allowable, can be reasoned readily on the basis that the total residual force field, f_{taR}, in a system vanishes [Eqs. (19) and (27)], only because the coefficient of (∇T) vanishes. Furthermore, the collapse of the total nonresidual force field f_0, on the other hand, has no relevance to a temperature gradient.

We have shown that metals, with a standard electron energy band, cannot be superconducting, except at the absolute zero. This result has been arrived at on the basis of the thermodynamic relation which requires preserving the hyperspace boundary conditions above the absolute zero. By similar arguments, it can be concluded at once that fermion assemblies generally, with a standard energy band, cannot be superconductors, or superfluids, above the absolute zero. *At the absolute zero, however, any fluid whatever must possess either superconductivity, or superfluidity.*

Therefore, in the framework of the thermodynamic theory of generalized fields, superconductivity and superfluidity are essentially normal phenomena, revealing the existence of the hyperspace boundary conditions above the absolute zero.

REFERENCES

Allen, J. F. 1966, Superfluid Helium, Academic Press.

Atkins, K. R. 1959, Liquid Helium, Cambridge University Press, Cambridge.

Cusack, N. 1958, The Electrical and Magnetic Properties of Solids, Longmans.

Donnelly, R. J. 1967, Experimental Superfluidity, University of Chicago Press, Chicago.

Kittel, C. 1971, Introduction to Solid-State Physics. John Wiley.

Matthias, B. T., Geballe, T. H., and Compton, V. B. 1963, Rev. Mod. Phys. **35**, 1–22.

Meissner, W. and Ochsenfeld, R. 1933, Naturwiss. **21, 787**.

Onnes, H. 1908, Akad. van Wetenschappen (Amsterdam), Proc. **11, 168**.

—— 1911, Akad. van Wetenschappen (Amsterdam), Proc. **14, 113**.

—— 1912, *ibid*. **14, 818**.

Shoenberg, D. 1960, Superconductivity, Cambridge University Press, Cambridge.

Appendix A

FURTHER MATHEMATICAL ASPECTS RELEVANT TO THE INTERNAL ENERGY EQUATIONS

In Chapter 4, we have discussed two different forms of the internal energy equation for a one-component system of particles which occupy an appropriately small volume V, and which may be transported while subject generally to electric, magnetic, and gravitational fields. The object here is to discuss in some detail a few mathematical points relevant to the two internal energy equations.

In its classical form, the internal energy equation is usually written as

$$dU = T\, d\eta - p\, dV + \tilde{\mu}_t\, dN, \tag{1}$$

where all the symbols are as defined in Chapter 4 (see also the List of Symbols).

As may be recalled, $\tilde{\mu}_t$ is the generalized potential which is supposed to be the sum of the chemical potential $\tilde{\mu}$, and a potential function ϕ associated with all other force fields. These fields may be electric, magnetic, and gravitational. By definition, therefore,

$$\tilde{\mu}_t = \tilde{\mu} + \phi. \tag{2}$$

If the system is nonisothermal and is further nonuniform in the sense that it has concentration and pressure gradients, then choosing an appropriately small (cubic) volume V within the system makes it possible to consider all such parameters to be (to a first approximation) uniform within V. Mathematically, uniformity of these parameters is exactly attained in the limit as V tends to zero. In no way does this statement imply that any of the gradients of these parameters or any of their other derivatives will necessarily vanish within V. In fact, all possible derivatives of each parameter will additionally be (to a first approximation) uniform within V. Again exact uniformity is attained by these derivatives in the limit as V tends to zero.

The properties of approximate and exact uniformity, just described, can be shown by using Taylor's series expansions.

A.1. EULER'S THEOREM

A thorough understanding of Euler's mathematical theorem largely depends on making a careful distinction between two fundamental properties which are characteristic of almost all thermodynamic quantities. These prop-

239

erties may be precisely defined and identified by considering the following situation.

Suppose that we have a volume V containing a system of particles. Let the particle concentration, temperature, pressure and other such thermodynamic parameters be exactly uniform throughout V. Imagine further that V is divided into any number l of, say, equal volumes, each of which is designated by v. Clearly then

$$v = V/l. \qquad (3)$$

It is evident that uniformity throughout V implies that the parameters (with subscripts v) pertinent to v are related to those of V as follows:

$$U_v = U/l, \qquad \eta_v = \eta/l, \qquad N_v = N/l, \qquad (4)$$

or

$$U_v = v(U/V), \qquad \eta_v = v(\eta/V), \qquad N_v = v(N/V), \qquad (5)$$

whereas,

$$T_v = T, \qquad p_v = p, \qquad \tilde{\mu}_{tv} = \tilde{\mu}_t. \qquad (6)$$

We now observe that each one of the parameters U_v, η_v, and N_v are proportional to the volume v. On the other hand, T_v, p_v and $\tilde{\mu}_{tv}$ are entirely independent of v. We may, therefore, distinguish between the first and second sets of quantities by the two important definitions to follow.

Extensive and Intensive Quantities

If a system, or part thereof, is uniform throughout some volume V, and if v is any part of V, then the quantities which are proportional to v are called *extensive*. However, those quantities which do not depend on v are called *intensive*.

A Mathematical Consequence of the Internal Energy Equation

Consider once more the classical internal energy equation as described by Eq. (1). It will be recalled that this equation expresses the infinitesimal change in the internal energy for a one-component subsystem of particles which are within an appropriately small volume V. In a nonuniform system, still the subsystem can be considered uniform throughout V, as discussed earlier.

We now observe in Eq. (1) that each differential quantity is extensive and each coefficient of a differential is intensive, or constant in the mathematical sense. This particular distribution of extensive and intensive variables endows Eq. (1) with a fundamental consequence to be arrived at next.

Suppose that we wish to calculate from Eq. (1) the amount of internal energy U within V. To do so, consider an infinitesimal part dV of the volume V. The extensive quantities corresponding to dV will be: dU, $d\eta$, and dN. We may now calculate U by simply integrating both sides of Eq. (1) as follows:

$$\int_0^U dU = \int_0^\eta T\, d\eta - \int_0^V p\, dV + \int_0^N \tilde{\mu}_t\, dN. \tag{7}$$

But the intensive quantities: T, p and $\tilde{\mu}_t$ are all constants throughout V. Therefore, Eq. (7) reduces to

$$U = T \int_0^\eta d\eta - p \int_0^V dV - \tilde{\mu}_t \int_0^N dN, \tag{8}$$

or

$$U = T\eta - pV + \tilde{\mu}_t N. \tag{9}$$

The preceding relation represents what we termed in Chapter 4, the Euler equation corresponding to Eq. (1).

A.2. THE DIFFERENTIAL GENERALIZED POTENTIAL

From Eq. (9), it follows that

$$dU = T\, d\eta + \eta\, dT - p\, dV - V\, dp + \tilde{\mu}_t\, dN + N\, d\tilde{\mu}_t. \tag{10}$$

Subtracting Eq. (1) from Eq. (10) and solving for $\tilde{\mu}_t$, we get

$$d\tilde{\mu}_t = (V/N)\, dp - (\eta/N)\, dT. \tag{11}$$

Equation (11) is identical with Eq. (9) [Chapter 4] which is stated there without proof.

A.3. UNIQUENESS OF THE DIFFERENTIAL GENERALIZED POTENTIAL

In Chapter 4, we have seen that the result obtained above for $d\tilde{\mu}_t$ would not be compatible with the fundamental criterion of thermal equilibrium as expressed in the framework of classical thermodynamics for systems subject to, or containing electric, magnetic and gravitational fields. For such systems, $\tilde{\mu}_t$ is assumed to be constant everywhere at thermal equilibrium so that $\nabla\tilde{\mu}_t = 0$. Under such conditions, of course, $\nabla T = 0$. But at least in some systems $\nabla p \neq 0$. Examples include an atmosphere of a planet when it is (hypothetically) in thermal equilibrium.

The inconsistency between Eq. (11) and the classical condition for thermal equilibrium that $\nabla\tilde{\mu}_t = 0$ has not, however, been generally recognized in the literature. For, from Eq. (1) a different answer is derived for $d\tilde{\mu}_t$; namely

$$d\tilde{\mu}_t = (V/N)\, dp - (\eta/N)\, dT + d\phi, \tag{12}$$

where ϕ is as defined earlier.

We shall next discuss how Eq. (12) is derived in the literature, and investigate its derivation from a mathematical point of view.

Let the intensive variables T, p, and ϕ be functions of some independent variables such as the position coordinates x, y, and z, and time t. It is customary to consider a (sufficiently) small volume in the system during a (sufficiently) small interval of time. Throughout this *space-time* increment, it is assumed that ϕ and all its (space and time) derivatives vanish so that

$$d\phi = 0. \tag{13}$$

Consequently, if we consider a large part of the system at one instant, the potential function ϕ, if linear, may be represented one-dimensionally as shown in Fig. 1(a). In this case χ represents the coordinate of one position such as x.

If, however, we consider only a fixed point in the system during a long period of time, we may represent the variation of ϕ in time, again, as shown in Fig. 1(a). In this case, χ represents time t.

Now within any one of these *space-time increments*, the generalized potential will be given by

$$\tilde{\mu}_t = \tilde{\mu} + \phi_i, \tag{14}$$

where ϕ_i is the potential function in the ith space-time increment. Notice here that while ϕ_i is considered exactly constant, $\tilde{\mu}$ is not considered so. For, all the derivatives of $\tilde{\mu}$ are assumed to be generally nonvanishing. As we shall see shortly, such considerations for $\tilde{\mu}$ and ϕ_i involve some mathematical incombatibility.

On the basis that ϕ_i is constant but not $\tilde{\mu}$, however, when Eq. (14) is substituted into Eq. (9), we get

$$dU = T\,d\eta + \eta\,dT - p\,dV - V\,dp + (\tilde{\mu} + \phi_i)\,dN + N\,d\tilde{\mu}. \tag{15}$$

Substituting Eq. (14) into Eq. (1), and subtracting the latter from Eq. (15) makes it possible to solve for $d\tilde{\mu}$ which may be written as

$$d\tilde{\mu} = (V/N)\,dp - (\eta/N)\,dT. \tag{16}$$

It is then concluded in the literature that from Eq. (2) and (16), Eq. (12) follows at once.

The preceding derivation of Eq. (12) involves serious mathematical shortcomings of which we discuss two fundamental aspects.

1. The function ϕ for any physical system is continuous and differentiable at every instant t and at every point in the space occupied by the system. Replacing ϕ by another discontinuous function whose shape is illustrated in Fig. 1(a) implies that

$$d\phi/d\chi = 0, \qquad \text{for } \chi \neq \chi_i, \tag{17}$$

and

$$d\phi/d\chi = \infty, \qquad \text{or undefined for } \chi = \chi_i. \tag{18}$$

Here i is an integer, and the χ_i's represent the discrete points of discontinuity in space, or in time.

If χ represents, for example, a position coordinate, then $(d\phi/d\chi)$ represents a mechanical force. From Eq. (17) and (18), it follows that this force will vanish at all points of the system except at the boundary points (or surfaces in three dimensions) of the space intervals [Fig. 1(a)]. At the latter points (or surfaces), the force is *infinite*! If χ, however, represents time, then correspondingly there will be discontinuities on the time axis. The distribution of $(d\phi/d\chi)$ is illustrated one-dimensionally in Fig. 1(b).

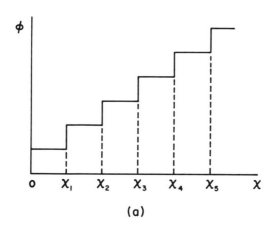

(a)

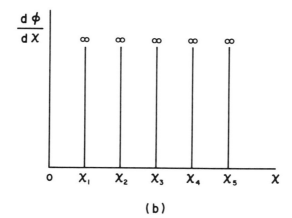

(b)

Fig. 1

2. The assumption that within any space interval [Fig. 1(a)], $\tilde{\mu}$ may have a gradient, but not ϕ, imposes severe adverse restrictions on the distribution of pressure and concentration of particles in the system. For we recall that in the framework of classical thermodynamics, at thermal equilibrium,

$$\nabla \tilde{\mu}_t = \nabla \tilde{\mu} + \nabla \phi = 0, \tag{19}$$

at every point in the system.

If within some space intervals $\nabla \phi = 0$, then necessarily within those intervals

$$\nabla \tilde{\mu} = 0. \tag{20}$$

Therefore, at thermal equilibrium, since $\nabla T = 0$, then in view of Eq. (16),

$$\nabla p = 0, \quad \text{and hence} \quad \nabla n = 0, \quad \text{wherever} \quad \nabla \phi = 0. \tag{21}$$

It is also evident that at thermal equilibrium, Eq. (19) leads to

$$\nabla \tilde{\mu} = -\infty, \quad \text{and hence} \quad \nabla n = -\infty, \quad \text{wherever} \quad \nabla \phi = \infty. \tag{22}$$

From a mathematical point of view, introducing discontinuities for the function ϕ, and consequently for $\tilde{\mu}$, p, n, etc... means that all the derivatives of these quantities with respect to the independent variables will be nonexistent at all the points of discontinuity. Thus, Eq. (12), derived on the basis of the scheme described above, *would not be* a consequence—through correct mathematical steps—of Eq. (1) and Euler's theorem.

It is interesting and significant to observe the following result. All the discontinuities, pointed out above, in ϕ, $\tilde{\mu}$, p, etc. ..., will be nonexistent only in case ϕ is truly constant throughout the system at all times. In this special case, $d\phi = 0$, everywhere in the system, and Eq. (12) agrees with Eq. (11). The latter equation has been derived by virtue of Euler's theorem and without introducing discontinuities at any point.

A.4. ON THE MODIFIED INTERNAL ENERGY EQUATION

Although Eq. (12) does not follow from the classical internal energy equation through correct mathematical steps, one can see, at least by intuition, that Eq. (12) is basically sound. A question can now be immediately posed: what is the internal energy equation which is relevant to our problem and which leads through rigorous mathematical steps to Eq. (12)? Arriving at a satisfactory answer to this question is *particularly important*, since it is through the internal energy equation that some fundamental thermodynamic quantities are defined together with the manner in which the first and second laws are interpreted.

Attempting to answer the question just stated has occupied a considerable part of chapter 4. In that chapter, we have arrived at an internal energy equation applicable for equilibrium and nonequilibrium [see Eq. (99), Chapter 4]. Our concern, however, in this rather limited space is to discuss some points relevant to Eq. (99).

If we account for the energy stored in the electric and magnetic fields in our appropriately small volume V, then the internal energy equation should be modified to

$$dU = T \, dS - P \, dV + \zeta \, dN + dW_e + dW_m + r \, (\mathbf{f}_{ta} - \mathbf{f}_{ts}) \cdot d\mathbf{l}, \qquad (23)$$

where

$$W_e = \tfrac{1}{2}\kappa E^2 V, \qquad W_m = \tfrac{1}{2}\mu H^2 V. \qquad (24)$$

Equations (24) have been derived in Section 4, Chapter 3. It is evident that W_e and W_m are extensive quantities. For E and H are uniform throughout V and hence each one of W_e and W_m is proportional to V.

It is, however, somewhat less obvious why $[r \, (\mathbf{f}_{ta} - \mathbf{f}_{ts}) \cdot d\mathbf{l}]$ represents an extensive differential. To show this point imagine that $d\mathbf{l}$ is one specific dimension of our sufficiently small cubic volume V—which in the limit is supposed to be a differential quantity. Let the particle flux density, which is uniform throughout V, be along $d\mathbf{l}$. Notice now that: (1) within V, $\mathbf{f}_{ta}$ and $\mathbf{f}_{ts}$ are uniform; and (2) r, representing the number of particles crossing V in a given time, must be proportional to the cross-sectional area of V. This area is perpendicular to $d\mathbf{l}$.

Therefore, $(r \, dl)$ is proportional to V, while $(\mathbf{f}_{ta} - \mathbf{f}_{ts})$ is constant throughout V. This will mean at once that $[r \, (\mathbf{f}_{ta} - \mathbf{f}_{ts}) \cdot d\mathbf{l}]$ is extensive and we may write

$$r \, (\mathbf{f}_{ta} - \mathbf{f}_{ts}) \cdot d\mathbf{l} = r \, d\nu_t. \qquad (25)$$

Since r does not depend on $d\mathbf{l}$, then it is evident that $r \, d\nu_t = d \, (r\nu_t)$. Substituting this result into Eq. (23), we get

$$dU = T \, dS - P \, dV + \zeta \, dN + dW_e + dW_m + d \, (r\nu_t). \qquad (26)$$

Since each differential in Eq. (26) is extensive and each coefficient of a differential is intensive, or constant, then from Euler's theorem it follows that

$$U = TS - PV + \zeta N + W_e + W_m + r\nu_t. \qquad (27)$$

Thus, subtracting dU, as expressed by Eq. (26), from that determined from Eq. (27), makes it possible to solve for $d\zeta$. Carrying out the steps, we have

$$d\zeta = -s \, dT + (1/n) \, dP. \qquad (28)$$

Equation (28) represents a fundamental result derived in chapter (4) from a less general internal energy equation for which the energy stored in the electric and magnetic fields was, for simplicity, neglected.

Appendix B

VALUES OF ENERGY GAPS IN SOME COMMON SEMICONDUCTORS

Crystal	ϵ_g (0°K), eV	ϵ_g (300°K), eV
InSb	0.25	0.175
Ge	0.75	0.66
Si	1.14	1.09
GaAs	1.53	1.45
SiC		2.86*

* This value has been reported by Choyke, W. J. and Patrick, L. 1957, Phys. Rev. **105,** 1721. All other values, together with their respective references may be found in Hanney, N. B. 1959, Semiconductors, Reinhold.

Appendix C

ELECTRON CONCENTRATION AND FERMI ENERGY IN THE MONOVALENT METALS

	n (cm^{-3})	ϵ_f (eV)
Ag	5.84×10^{22}	5.48
Au	5.9	5.51
Cs	0.91	1.58
Cu	8.41	7.0
K	1.4	2.1
Li	4.7	4.7
Na	2.65	3.23
Rb	1.15	1.85

Appendix D

UNIVERSAL CONSTANTS

Avogadro's number

$$N_{av} = 6.0222 \times 10^{26} \text{ molecules per kg M.W.}$$

Boltzmann's constant

$$k = 1.3806 \times 10^{-23} \text{ joule/deg K}$$

Planck's constant

$$h = 6.6262 \times 10^{-34} \text{ joule-sec}$$

Electron charge

$$q = 1.6022 \times 10^{-19} \text{ coulomb}$$

Electron (rest) mass

$$m = 9.1096 \times 10^{-31} \text{ kg}$$

Energy per Kelvin degree

$$k/q = 8.616 \times 10^{-5} \text{ eV/deg}$$

Dielectric constant in free space

$$\kappa_0 = (1/36\pi) \times 10^{-9} = 8.854 \times 10^{-12} \text{ farad/m}$$

Magnetic permeability in free space

$$\mu_0 = 4\pi \times 10^{-7} \text{ henry/m}$$

Velocity of light in free space

$$c = 2.99793 \times 10^8 \text{ m/sec}$$

Wavelength of photon, with $h\nu = 1$ eV

$$hc/q = 1.23981 \times 10^{-6} \text{ m}$$
$$= 1.23981 \text{ micron}$$

Source: Taylor, B. N., Parker, W. H., Langenberg, D. N. 1969, Rev. Mod. Phys. **41**, 375.

AUTHOR INDEX

249

SUBJECT INDEX

A

Acceptor, atoms, 102
  (energy) level, 102
  (*See also* impurity deionization)
Active force fields, allowable number at
  0°K, 198–199
  definition of, 77, 129–130
  examples of, 131–133
  (*See also* Interactions of active and
    passive force fields)
Ampère's law, 37
Atmospheric thermal equilibrium, 139–140
Average kinetic energy per particle, 105
  classical gases, 107
  degenerate electrons, 115–116
  electrons in metals, 216

B

Band theory of solids, 97–102
  metals, 98
  semiconductors and insulators, 99–102
Boltzmann's distribution function, 95
Bose–Einstein distribution function, 96
Bose energy, definition of, 96
  dependence of diffusion field on, 126
Bosons, definition of, 96

C

Characteristics of:
  a heterojunction, 178
  p–n junctions, 168–177
  Schottky diodes, 180–183
Chemical potential, 55–56
Circuit theory, in TTGF framework, 84–
  86, 77–81, 145–146
Classical gases, 103–104
Conduction band, definition of, 98–100
Conduction electrons, 98–100
Conduction zones of junction diodes,
  171–173
Conductivity types (*see* n-type semicon-
  ductors; p-type semiconductors)
Conservative vector fields (*see* Irrotational
  vectors)
Continuity equation for minority carriers,
  153–156
  a solution of, 156–157

Corollaries of TTGF propositions:
  I, 128–129
  II, 129
  III, 129
  IV, 129
  V, 129
  VI, 130
  VII, 130
  VIII, 198
  (*See also* Propositions of TTGF)
Coulomb's law, 29–30
Cross product (*see* Vectors, multiplica-
  tion of)
Curl of a vector, 18–19
  cylindrical coordinates, 26
  physical interpretation of, 19–21
  spherical coordinates, 27
Cylindrical coordinates, definition of,
  24–25
  del operations in, 26

D

Degeneracy-nondegeneracy   borderline,
  104–105
Degenerate gases, definition of, 91
  Sommerfeld–Bethe approximation, 112–
  114
Del operator, definition of, 14
Dependence on Fermi energy of,
  average particle kinetic energy, 115–116
  electron concentration, 108, 115, 118
  diffusion field, 125–127
  diffusion–mobility relationship, 135–136
  hole concentration, 108
  internal pressure, 115–116
Detailed balancing, 57–59
Detailed *self*-balancing, 74, 121, 143,
  181–182
  and hyperspace, 186–187
  and third law, 200–201
  (*See also* Thermal equilibrium)
Dielectric constant, 29–30
Diffusion field, definition of, 71, 121–122
  statistical-mechanical interpretation of,
  126
    isothermal relativistic electrons, 127